gargoyle

editors
Richard Peabody
Lucinda Ebersole
Maja Prausnitz *(UK)*

UK staff
Sean Rabin
Sandra Tharumalingam

US staff
Casey Kane
Kris Kane

g a r g ⊙ y l e

41

— In Memoriam —

Kathy Acker
Luther Allison
Mel Bay
William S. Burroughs
Randy California
Nancy Compton
Patty Donahue
William Eastlake
Gabrielle Edgcomb
Sam Fuller
Martha Gellhorn
Allen Ginsberg
Stephane Grappelli
Pamela Harriman
Ed Hogan
Simon Jeffes
Ernst Juenger
James Laughlin
William Matthews
Judith Merril
Jack Micheline
Toshiro Mifune
Walter Miller, Jr.
Robert Mitchum
Betty Parry
Robb Rauth
William F. Ryan
Red Skelton
Jimmy Stewart
Roland Topor
Amos Tutuola
Oscar Williams
Tony Williams
Robert Winson

gargoyle magazine is published irregularly
by Paycock Press
c/o Atticus Books & Music
1508 U Street, NW
Washington, DC 2009
email atticus@atticusbooks.com
http://www.atticusbooks.com

In London:
152 Harringay Road
London N15 3HL
United Kingdom
email maja@ursarum.demon.co.uk

Price per single issue varies.
Subscriptions are $20 / £14 for two issues to individuals;
$25 / £18 for institutions.

ISBN 0-931181-05-4
ISSN 0162-1149

Special Thanks to John Bailey, Nicole Blackman, Jodi Bloom, Ann Burrola, Junior Bridge, Andrew Coffey, Georgia de Chamberet, John Elsberg, Francesca Ford, Elena Goodinson, Michael Horovitz, Gilbert Lee, Paul Lyalls, Steven Moore, Martin Norris, Simon Pettifar, Andrea Prausnitz, Liana Sperow, and Patrick Tedd.

Jamika Ajalon's poem is reproduced by kind permission of the author, care of BookBlast Ltd. Copyright © by Jamika Ajalon 1995. Nicole Blackman's "27 List Poems I Should Write" first appeared on the *Indie Rock Blueprint* CD produced by Go! Discs. Stokes Howell's story first appeared in the California magazine *Tales of the Heart*. Dorothy Porter's poems are reprinted from her new book, *Crete* published in Australia by Hyland House, 1996. Ifigenija Simonovic's poems are reprinted with her permission from *Striking Root: Fifty Poems* published by the Menard Press in 1996.

Cover image © 1998 Andi Olsen   Cover design by Maja Prausnitz and Kris Kane. Interior design and layout by Kris Kane. Batteries not included.
Printed by McNaughton and Gunn, Inc., Saline, Michigan.

gargoyle is distributed by

US	UK and Europe	Australia
Bernhard DeBoer, Inc.	Airlift Book Company	Peribo Distribution
113 E. Centre Street	8 the Arena	58 Beaumont Road
Nutley, NJ 07110	Mollison Avenue	Mount Kuring-Gai
(201) 667-9300	Enfield, Mddx EN3 7NJ	NSW 2080 Australia
	Phone 0181-804-0400	Phone 02 457-0011
	Fax 0181-804-0044	Fax 02 457-0022

"An artist is now much more seen as a connector of things, a person who scans the enormous field of possible places for artistic attention, and says, 'What I am going to do is draw your attention to this sequence of things ...' You have made what seems to you a meaningful pattern in this field of possibilities ... This is why the curator, the editor, the compiler, and the anthropologist have become such big figures. They are all people whose job it is to digest things, and to connect them together."

— *Brian Eno*

Doggie   Leave   my   baby
             alone.
He is not a bone
and I don't want him burying,
                      thanks.

Contents

Cover
Andi Olsen

Drawing/Poem
John Hegley 6

Nonfiction
Jennifer Egan   Rowing: a(n Anti-)Memoir 10
Amy Halloran   The Talking Writer 17
Anne LeBaron   Ode to the Golden Toad 23
Steven Moore   Sheri Martinelli: A Modernist Muse 29
David Ulin   Kerouac's Ghost 55

Photography
Cynthia Connolly   Black Canyon, Arizona 1-19-97 62

Poetry
Jamika Ajalon   Blackability (where da revolution at—revisited) 67
Elizabeth W. Andrews   The Swimming Lesson 70
Joe Asser   Graffiti Artist 71
Steve Aylett   Bestiary 72
Francesca Beard   The Poem That Was Really a List 74
Elisa Biagini   Morgue 76
Paul Birtill   Best Seller 81
Eugénie Bisulco   Bodies 82
Nicole Blackman   Black Box 83
    27 List Poems I Should Write 85
Claire Calman   Love is Blind 86
Glenn Carmichael   And 87
John Cooper Clarke   Eat Lead Clown 88
Robert O. Costa   Tango 89
Virginia Crawford   Drowning 90
    Someone Else's 91
Tim Cumming   Landscape with Valve 92
Blair Ewing   Just Another Byte out of Time 94
Brenda Frazer   Animated Midnight Dream 95

Tina Fulker   Untitled 96
Karen Garthe   The Soutine 98
Regan Good   The War Horse 99
John Greaves   Untitled 101
Janet Hamill   Nocturne 5 102
Elizabeth Hamilton   It Is Easter Week 103
Brian Hinton   Love Poem 106
Bruce A. Jacobs   Blood Dance 107
Valerie Jean   Again 109
    22nd Revelation 110
Halvard Johnson   White Lies 111
Martha Johnson   Losing Jane 112
LuAnn Keener   Wild Dogs 113
Mimi Khalvati   Terrapin 115
Ronald Koertge   Q and A 117
    Myths 118
Wayne Koestenbaum   History of Boys 119
Avra Kouffman   Lush 122
Elizabeth Mary Larson   Ditch Digging 124
Sara Elizabeth Levy   Nocturne 125
    Rise 126
Lyn Lifshin   The Mad Girl Finds It Excruciatingly Painful... 128
Julie Liu   The Patron Saint of Pests and Mosquitoes 130
Roger McGough   Whoops! 132
Gwyn McVay   You Have Nothing Left to Disbelieve But This ... 133
    Quipu 134
Miriam Morsel Nathan   The Absurd Messiah 135
Dorothy Porter   Hot Date 136
    My At-last-lover 139
    Crete 140
Minnie Bruce Pratt   The Ferry 141
Jeremy Reed   Poe's Marriage Night 144
    Leader of the Pack 145
    Female Singers 146
    Novels 147
Elizabeth Rees   Home Movie 149
Kim Roberts   St. Anthony Preaching to the Fish 150
Natasha Sajé   Fruit 152
Leslie Scalapino   from *Deer Night* 153
Maureen Seaton/Denise Duhamel   The Scarlet Letter 156
    The Scarlet Letter 2 157
Edgar Silex   Distances 158
Ifigenija Simonovic   Love Poem 160
    I Used to Be a Girl 161
Bob Slaymaker   Yearning 163
W. Loran Smith   The Playboys 164

Andrew Sofer   Aunt Winnie 165
Virgil Suarez   Milagros *La Flaca* 167
        Auto Erotica 169
Peter Tatlin   Made Rich 171
        Paris Revisited 172
Alexander Theroux   Dropping Fleas into a Glass of Water 173
        To Mickey Hood Who Travels the World… 174
Mike Topp   French Style 176
Tim Turnbull   Raw Horse 177
Christopher Twigg   Gorillas 180
Ruth Vaughn   Castle Rock 182
ruth weiss   One Night 184
Tim Wells   Cinnamon Girl 185
        Biscuits Ain't Biscuits 'til They're Baked 186
Terence Winch   Pegleg 187
Rose Zaeske   Pink 188

Photography
Connie Imboden   Three Photographs 189

Fiction
Kim Addonizio   Reading Sontag 196
Roberta Allen   The Wrong One 200
R.R. Angell   Greyhound 201
Mary Caponegro   Whoever is Never Born with the Most Toys Wins 210
Billy Childish   The Medway Bog Man 231
Julia Duncan   Ghost in a Glass House 237
Mary Halnon   How It Seems in September 244
Ken Hollings   I Am Singing 247
Stokes Howell   Just Drive 252
Kevin Jackson   Zembla 255
Shelley Jackson   Sperm 261
R.A. Kapler   King 266
Gregory Maguire   The Hurricane Lamp 276
James Mathews   Devil's Rain 284
Jeff Minerd   The Humpty Dumpty Game 300
Pedro Ponce   Stories of the Unexplained 308
Lou Robinson   Havoc Wreaked by the Bean of Doubt 312
Elizabeth Roca   Final Curtain 320
Helen Schulman   I Heart Dan Jansen 323
Marilyn Stablein   The Rat Caterer 333
Eugene Stein   The Barn Fire 335
Carolyn Weaver   Celia's Bridegroom 342
Curtis White   from *America's Magic Mountain* 348

Jennifer Egan

Rowing: a(n Anti-)Memoir

Eleven years ago, my mother and I spent Christmas together in Paris. She had come from San Francisco, our home town, and I from Cambridge, England, where I was a graduate student. Her then-boyfriend, who joined us soon after Christmas, was something of a shutterbug, and there are lots of pictures from that holiday: my mother and me with the lights of the Champs Elysee flung out behind us like comet tails, or smiling outside shop windows, thick scarves swaddling our necks. In every picture, I'm wearing the same pair of yellow pants—a bold, primary yellow, like traffic signs. They were baggy cotton with an elasticized waist, and they were the only pants I could fit into, having gained some fifteen pounds in the previous three weeks. They were summer pants, and I had to wear thick tights underneath to stay warm. It was one of the coldest winters on record.

By the time I reached Paris, I had weathered a bad luck streak of such operatic dimensions that I could only imagine it concluding with my own death. I was twenty-three. There is a sort of young woman who conceals a precarious inner life with a loud voice and a brightly colored wardrobe—that was me. My college years, which I'd spent in varying states of melancholy and panic, had paid off in the form of a two year scholarship to study English literature at St. John's College, in Cambridge. The startled joy I took in my new surroundings acted upon me like a mild hallucinogenic—a Medieval city, where I rode my bicycle past cows! Weekly meals in a hall, where we sat at long tables and wore gowns! I was seized with euphoric hope that as my new self, in this new life, I no longer would be sad or anxious. From the 'backs,' a range of phosphorescent green lawn behind the colleges, St. John's looked like a sandcastle of yellow stone. I lay sprawled for hours in its crenelated shadow, working furiously on the novel I'd made the goal of my stay in England. The graduate house where I lived was a lopsided Tudor (not Tudor Style, *Tudor*) with slanty floors and a sharp, peaty smell that I was certain dated back to Elizabethan times. The room facing mine from the opposite end of the hall belonged to an Englishman, an engineering student named Rick. By my fifth day in England, we were having a torrid and (for reasons I can't fully recall) clandestine affair.

My romance with Rick was one of those in which the attraction is augmented, at least briefly, by the lack of a single common interest. His primary passion was rowing, and he was captain of the St. John's Boat Club, a title every bit as crucial in the context of St. John's College as it is irrelevant anywhere else. He was mystified by my constant writing; once, when I stepped away from my computer, he sat down and rendered on the screen an image of a rowboat. I returned as he was completing the oars, looked at them over his shoulder and decided I had better learn to row. I tried the following day, but experienced shooting pains in my back. Surely my scoliosis can't be the problem, I mused, and consulted an orthopedist, who took one look at my zigzagging spine on an X-ray and forbade me to row again. Shortly thereafter, about five weeks into term, I lost track of Rick at a party. I waited nonchalantly, filled with an advancing sense of doom, but he never reappeared. I went home alone. The next morning I heard he'd left the party with an undergraduate member of the Ladies Boat Club.

I had never imagined a future with Rick, yet the moment our relationship ended, I began to feel very strange. The English, I noticed, were not really friendly—almost no one said hello in the street. Something about me seemed to make them wince; was it my tendency to bellow when I spoke? My conversational technique: a fusillade of questions aimed at dislodging as much information as possible in the shortest amount of time? Because the English were so reserved, I turned the hose of my curiosity more fully upon them, hoping to jolt them out of their shyness through sheer force. This prompted squirming discomfort at best, and occasionally outright hostility. My personality felt like a wallet full of radically devalued currency, and I was yanking out wads of cash in a prolonged, surreal discovery that it had the power to buy almost nothing. A day or so after dumping me, Rick installed his rower girlfriend at the end of my hallway, and I was treated to sounds of their giggly return from the college bar at night, the chilling sight of his closed door during lazy weekend hours after they'd returned from their morning rows.

I tried at first to read and work on my novel, but I found myself leaping to the window each time I heard footsteps on the gravel outside, tracking Rick's comings and goings. Unless I knew exactly where he was, I felt unmoored, panicky, as if my own existence were in doubt; a glimpse of him had the power to calm me. Within a week I'd abandoned the pretense of living my own life and begun shadowing him in earnest. I would position myself near his cafeteria table and eye him ruefully over plates of roast beef and broiled potatoes and bowls of fruit "crumble" drenched in cream, all of which I consumed briskly and without thought, like someone eating in her sleep. Later, in the St. John's Bar, I would wedge myself in some nook near Rick and his cavorting fellow rowers, and eat Cadbury Eggs full of gooey sugar yolks and whites, washed down with half-pints of hard cider. Having once been anorexic, I knew what it was to passionately starve while adoring boys from afar, but this was different—I was going to get him back! The power of my desperation felt sufficient to bend forks and upend furniture; surely it would immolate whatever bond he felt to his rower girlfriend. After a week of surveillance, with my thighs bursting out of my jeans, I began taking long runs beside the Cam—a narrow, tortuous river that gives Cambridge its name and the site, not coincidentally, of rowing practice. I would run until I reached Rick's boat, and then I would run alongside it, fixing upon him a frantic, wild-eyed, longing stare. He looked back at me sometimes, his face set in what I would have to call, in retrospect, a glare. But these moments electrified me: he'd seen me, acknowledged the brutal urgency of our reunion. Sometimes I passed his girlfriend pedaling along the river on her bike, but more often she about-faced and zoomed the opposite way before our paths could cross. She told a mutual friend that she and Rick were afraid of me.

Rick managed to resist the siren song of my stalking, staring, spying, eating and weeping, and my campaign was halted by the arrival of Christmas break. I'd had the good sense to cram this five-week interlude with ambitious travel: first to Southern Spain with two friends; then to Paris for Christmas with my mother; finally to the Soviet Union, where I had splurged with my scholarship money on a week-long package tour. But I was instantly taught the meaning of that old chestnut, "trouble comes in clusters": on the train from Madrid to Cordoba, Paige's purse was stolen with her Nikon camera in it. I began carrying her valuables with my own in my treasured calfskin bag, which was yanked from my shoulder in Seville by a motorcyclist thief. We lost everything: wallets, passports, all of the notes for my novel. My new passport, issued in Spain, rendered my Soviet visa invalid, and I was forced to withdraw from my package tour with only dubious prospects of a refund. Spain in winter was stunningly cold. We slept fully dressed in cheap, unheated pensions. Once, after going to bed with my hair wet, I awoke to find it partly frozen.

I rolled into Paris on an overnight train from Madrid a few days before Christmas. My mother was to have arrived earlier that day from San Francisco, and I went straight to the Relais Christine, a small, quiet hotel tucked inside a former nunnery on the Left Bank. Bloated and weary, snuffling under my backpack in my yellow pants, I must have cut quite a figure in the opulent lobby, and the concierge took a long, close look at me before parting with the number of my mother's room. As I crept toward her door, I dreaded her reaction to my weight. My mother and I have always looked virtually identical, a fact that heightens the vanity I suppose most mothers take in their daughters' appearances. But nothing could have prepared me for the stricken face I met in the doorway. "My God, Jen," she said. "Where have you been?"

I'd gotten the date wrong, and was twenty-four hours late. With no means of reaching me, my mother had naturally been frantic, the more so, she explained, because the week before, a childhood friend of mine who was backpacking in Italy had been asphyxiated in her pension bed by a faulty heating system. My childhood friend was also a runner, and during visits home from college I had occasionally seen her jogging from the Marina Green to the base of Golden Gate Bridge, a favorite route of mine. Nowadays, I still think of her when I take that run—what an arbitrary thing it is that she, not I, exists only in memory.

When my mother was satisfied that I was fully alive, her attention drifted to my person. "Those pants look a little gamy," she remarked, and within the hour had dispatched them, along with the other contents of my backpack, to the hotel laundry.

My mother's new boyfriend, Sandy Walker, joined us in Paris shortly after Christmas. I didn't know him well. Sandy was an architect, red haired and a little shy, with a cheerful, easy disposition that made his sharp wit come as a surprise. He was always impeccably dressed, tweedy by day for sightseeing, blue blazered and shiny buttoned at night. My mother was anxious that we become friends, but my social skills had abandoned me. I drifted beside the two of them through Notre Dame and the new Picasso Museum; I stumped over bridges and slouched in silence down quaint streets where Sandy would stop occasionally to sketch some sconce or railing in his small architect's notebook. Meals enlivened me somewhat. I ate *foie gras* and *moules muniere*, I scarfed down *tartes tatin* and roast chicken, tureens of soup, herb omelettes and pork loin. I sawed my way through vegetable pates and slabs of duck as thick and red as steak; I swilled heavy Bordeaux, and steaming basins of bouillabaisse. My mother and Sandy, both conscientious eaters and very thin, looked on in wonderment as I slurped and devoured and waved for more baguette to mop up sauces. The chocolate mousse! The *crème brule*! Each night I would resolve, aloud, to begin a diet, but those plans were scrapped at the sight of my first fresh croissant the following day.

In a feverish attempt to become more English, I spoke in a near whisper and had ceased asking questions, despite the obvious damper this put on conversation. The subject of Rick, however, induced violent logorrhea, and I would enumerate in endless, painstaking detail my stratagems for getting him back, conscious of the glazed look in my mother's and Sandy's eyes but unable to stop myself. I was obsessed with the question of what had gone wrong: Would it have made a difference if I'd rowed? Should I have rowed despite the doctor's orders? I cried at the dinner table, startling waiters, fellow diners, and most of all, Sandy Walker, whose WASP reserve, not to mention the fact that he barely knew me, must have made my outbursts excruciating for him. He would give me a gruff pat, then look away discreetly while my mother comforted me.

"Maybe you should try writing a little, dear," she gently suggested, but I'd lost my notes. I would never write again.

"Or try running," Sandy volunteered.

I tried. Though I hadn't brought running clothes, I knew my mother's shoes would do in a pinch. But her sweatpants were so tight I could barely move, and I was ashamed to be seen in them. "You can't fit into my sweatpants ?" she said, alarmed. She suggested we shop for bigger ones, so I could run along the Seine. She offered to buy me a warmer outfit, partly to combat the withering cold; partly, I'm sure, to give us all some relief from the yellow pants. But I refused, afraid that by accommodating this version of myself, I would raise my chances of staying this way forever.

"Oh Sweetheart," my mother said, and took my hot, sweating hands in both of hers, which were cool as leaves. "You'll look back on this and you honestly won't believe it ever happened—that's how dreamlike it's going to seem." She had reason to know, after a terrible divorce from my stepfather four years before. She'd thought her life was over. "I know it's hard to believe," she said. I didn't believe her.

The Relais Christine was fully booked for the holidays, and I would be forced to relinquish my room on the date I'd planned to leave for the Soviet Union. This was fine by me; even I could see that I was the worst company imaginable, and I wanted my mother and Sandy to have their romantic vacation. I'd settled on a murky notion of going to Germany, but the day before my departure, Sandy seemed troubled at breakfast. "Now wait a minute," he said, peering at me over his bifocals. "Where exactly are you headed?" I said I wasn't sure. Sandy pulled a giant, cracking map of Europe from inside his architect's bag, and spread it open on the floor. "Take a look," he said.

I stared at the map, waiting for a plan to form. "There's no rush," Sandy said. "We'll find you another room."

He negotiated with the concierge, and managed to eke out a single night in a different room. Further negotiations the following day led to a second extra night in yet another room. Each time I mentioned Germany, Sandy would flap at his pockets for the bifocals and unfetter the map, and shortly thereafter would make another visit to his new friend, the concierge. I changed rooms nearly every night, but I stayed in Paris. One afternoon, when I was between rooms, the three of us returned from sightseeing exhausted. With nowhere else to go, I lay down on my mother's and Sandy's bed and fell asleep. When I woke, they were napping on either side of me, Sandy still wearing his tweed jacket, though I noticed he had removed his tie.

A number of San Franciscans had come to Paris that holiday season, and we joined their group one evening in the velvety pied-à-terre of a prominent Bay Area interior designer. Accustomed as I was to the cocoon of my mother's and Sandy's attention, I felt cowed at first by these exotic strangers: a Brazilian plastic surgeon and his raven-haired wife, who wore a skin-tight sequined gown; a real estate tycoon whose jacket had giant zebra-skin lapels. There were young girls—daughters, mostly, who wore small black cocktail dresses laughed loudly. I felt ludicrous in their midst, sipping wine in my yellow pants and unraveling Benneton Christmas sweater, but if anyone shared my view, they hid it gracefully. As we left the designer's home that night, I took my first notice of the cold winter beauty of Paris, the trees like cracked glass, the halos of pale yellow streetlight.

The next night we joined an even larger party at La Coupole, whose name I recognized, with a thrill, from the novels of Jean-Paul Sartre. I was seated apart from my mother and Sandy, and as the atmosphere progressed from festive to celebratory, I learned from the woman beside me that she earned her living as a psychic. "Really?" I cried. "Can you tell me my future?" Meaning, of course, the single question that seemed to define it: would I get Rick back?

She was a blond, portly woman whose face I can't remember. She ignored my proffered palm, looked into my eyes for a moment and said, "You might go home."

"Home?" I said. What do you mean 'home'? Home where?" But she'd turned the other way. I sat quietly, awaiting the chance to press her for more details, but soon she moved to another table and was out of reach. Home, I thought. Home from this restaurant? Home from Paris to Cambridge? Home to San Francisco, without completing even one year of my scholarship? This last seemed inconceivable, yet when I thought back on the despair and lunacy of my first months in England, I grew certain that it was this possibility—my giving up—that the psychic had meant. It haunted me. Go home, I thought. Would I actually have to go home?

In retrospect, "You might go home" strikes me as a fortune cookie phrase, one that a self-proclaimed psychic can rest assured will mean something to just about anyone.

15

As the merriment at La Coupole began to ebb, I moved to sit with my mother and Sandy. They leaned against a banquette, looking red cheeked and very relaxed. "We've missed you," Sandy said, and I realized this was the first time since his arrival in Paris that we had dined apart. He added, "I think I've finally figured out what went wrong with you and Rick."

"You did?" I said, dumbfounded. "What was it?"

"Well," he said, "you told him you *wrote*, and he thought you said that you *rowed*."

My own laughter sounded strange, an old contraption wheezing to life after weeks of idleness. I laughed and laughed, and so did my mother and Sandy—that helpless, silly laughter that always reminds me of childhood.

I returned to Cambridge shortly after the New Year, arriving late at night. The St. John's porter was dozing in his lodge. I woke him to let me in through the college gate, then walked alone through the silent, stone-smelling halls toward the dreaded Tudor house. The entrance to the backs had been left open, despite the late hour, and I stopped and peered into the darkness splayed at my feet, wide and black, deep as a lake. The sky swarmed with stars, and there was a bright, narrow moon, like a wink. I heard nothing but silence. And I knew that my mother was right; this was the dream. I wanted it.

That week, I moved out of the Tudor house, and Rick and I never spoke again. At the rare times when I think of him now, I imagine him living with his rower wife and their several rower children, all of them rowing together in one long boat (with oars of varying lengths) in whatever river is nearby, the way so many English people do. I have no idea if any of this is true. But so keen is my affection for that time that even Rick is suffused with its marmalade glow.

I was reminded of Cambridge last month, when mother and Sandy were married in a small ceremony at their home, and Sandy teasingly asked if I planned to join them on their honeymoon. As the wedding lunch was served, I strained to remember how I'd felt, living in England: reading Shakespeare at the University Library, where the cafeteria baked fresh scones three times each day; the tangy smell of woodsmoke on clear, cold nights. And something else: the dazzling uncertainty of knowing I had yet to begin my real life. The yellow pants are long gone, of course—cast aside in triumph the moment I could fit into anything else. Now I wish I'd kept them. Without artifacts, there is so little to separate memory from imagination.

Amy Halloran

The Talking Writer

I used to work at a lodge in Vermont. My life was propped as a tv set, with famous people popping up to say witty lines. When I first started my job, I was always trying to tag the stars, but after a few months the fame became familiar and I stopped trying to match the names.

I ran the front desk until after the early dusk, and when I was done I visited friends who worked at inns that looked just like mine.

I had a boyfriend but we didn't see each other much so I was often seen alone, appearing available to all but the locals. I learned to dodge dates from tourists in need of a fling. The shy ones were hardest to shake. Older men, who thought they were still adorable, and maybe actually were, would follow me. First with their eyes, and then, from the first bar to the second. I would will them to leave town before they found the courage to approach me, but sometimes I wasn't so lucky.

One of these men is the object of this story. I noticed him following me for a few days. He tracked my path so I made it irregular to lead him astray. Still, he would find me, and, open his notebook and take notes, as if I were a creature in the wild.

I am used to writer-types. I have known and admired them all my life, and am, in fact, one of them. I found this man's attention both flattering and invasive. When he had been trailing me for a week, my friend Mark stopped cutting limes and leaned toward my glass of beer.

"Do you know who that is?"

"Who?" I said, playing dense.

"That guy who's been following you and writing things down."

I shook my head, no.

"That," he said, pointing with his paring knife, "is Spalding Gray."

"Spalding Gray!" I whispered. It couldn't have been worse. All my writerly life I'd been baffled and bothered by his success. How come he could milk his life dry and get people pay to listen to him moan about it? How could he keep using relationships as raw materials for his very public product? How come I wasn't getting paid for the same thing? All day long I scribbled in my own composition books, character sketches and bombs of dialogue dropped in my ear as I eavesdropped on guests' conversations. At night I typed the results into stories that started as buds, and bloomed before my invisible audiences' eyes. I dreamt my efforts met success, but in the morning I always had submissions for the mailman, and he always had returns.

Mark knew this. If his bar wasn't crowded, I read him short pieces, and he'd buy me a beer for encouragement. He never asked if I got anything accepted. He knew if I did I would tell him.

"I think you should sleep with him," he said, in spite of my grimace.

"Mark!" I said. It wasn't like he didn't know about Lloyd. I got worried. Did he have evidence of *his* infidelity? No, I knew Lloyd better than that. We'd been together for years, forever. Our relationship wasn't dull or distant. We just knew the economy of time and what portions we could spend together.

"Do you want to get published?" he asked, scraping the limes into a bowl. "Or would you rather keep wasting your money on postage?"

I fiddled with my almost empty glass. I didn't like those kind of choices or the people who asked me to make them.

"See you later," I told Mark. I didn't want to talk about it. I didn't want to think about it, either, but I knew I would, or I wouldn't be able to sleep. As I walked outside I felt the famous eyes bore through me. I felt him fold his notebook and follow.

"Hi," he said, accosting me before I could figure out how I felt. Before I could talk myself into being less than disgusted. Opportunity infrequently knocks on my door. If I slept with him I could become a part of his repertoire. Lloyd be damned, if I wanted to get forward I would have to climb the ladder. There just aren't that many routes for a gal. I didn't plan to spend the rest of my early career on my knees, a la Marilyn Monroe, but, maybe a short affair would get me national coverage and those envelopes would start to come back skinnier, full of checks. Boy! I didn't need much persuasion. The advantages were clear. But so was my guilt. Thinking of being unfaithful to Lloyd was almost as bad as doing it. If I even dreamt of desires that were aimed not at him I confessed them, wanting his forgiveness.

"Hi," I said, my squeaking voice a bad mask for my confusion.

"I'm Spalding Gray," he said, trying to get me to look at him, tilting his head into mine. I was leading us into the dark, off the sidewalk. There was still a path, but it would be harder to read his face. I wanted my reactions to be blind, based on what I felt, not what I saw.

"What's your name?" he said.

"Amy."

I gave him my first. I spared him my last. He wouldn't know me from a bunch of bananas.

"You're very pretty," he said.

"I know," I snapped, like it was a bullet instead of a compliment. I stopped walking. He stopped too, closing the small gap between our heavy coats, touching the toe of his boot near my own. "I have a boyfriend. And you have a girlfriend, or maybe a wife, or both. I can't keep up with your details."

"Neither can I," he said, his voice really slow, like he was sad. "That's why I write them down, and repeat them."

"Oh," I said, as if that explained things. He took off his glove and put a warm hand on my cold cheek, which I turned, against him. He pinched my nose. I pushed his hand down. "Put your glove on. It's cold. Don't try to kiss me."

18

"Okay," he obeyed. "But I'm not giving up. I'm learning how to ski. I'm going to be here for a while."

"I'm too old to be the other woman," I told him. "I mean too much. And besides, I'm not up for grabs. I'm in love."

"This isn't about love, Amy," he said.

"Well, I don't want to talk about lust."

I had already gone too far. Everything I said was public domain. He would tell our story to audiences so ready to laugh they'd explode over the slightest change in tone. Would he use my name? I wanted to be a star for a small moment in his boring but loudly lived life.

I walked away. He said good-bye. So this, I thought to myself, is what it feels like to almost be a resource. I felt as valuable as uranium, and noted that I'd feel strip mined when my story became a part of his. Will my victimization be vilified by his broadcast of our liaison? Will this yield what I need?

I decided to talk to Lloyd. We weren't supposed to see each other for another day, but in emergencies the separations could be shortened. I walked to his house, liking my life a little more than I had in the morning. Then I had just been flattered, in a bored, anonymous way, that someone was attracted to me. Now I felt special.

Lloyd lives with his sister. The lights were on in the living room. He was watching television. He smiled when he saw it was my key that had turned the lock, and he turned off the set.

"Hi Amy," he said. "What's wrong?"

I took off my coat and boots and sat on the section of sofa he patted. He poised his lips for a kiss I wouldn't give.

"Spalding Gray wants to sleep with me," I said.

"Really?" He thought it was a joke, and leaned into my face for a kiss.

"Really. He does. He's been following me. I didn't know who he was, and tonight, he left the bar when I did and he wants me to have an affair."

"How do you know?"

"He told me!"

"Wow," he said, cowed by jealousy and awe. "Did you kiss him?"

"No!" I yelled.

"Don't shout. I can't tell what you'll do."

"Neither can I!" I said as quiet as I could, which was still too loud.

Carol was washing dishes. She ignored our fracases. This was why we all got along.

We sat there for a while, looking at our hands.

"Do you want to fuck him?" he asked.

"I want to get published," I said, as if the two were equal.

"You want my permission, don't you," my boyfriend said. I nodded my head, my eyes on my jeans.

"Couldn't we just break up for a month?" I tried.

"You'll get an affair that might further your career and when it's over, you'll come back to me? You think I can ignore you for a month?"

19

"I don't know, it's only a guess. What if somebody extremely famous and influential were interested in you? Wouldn't you think of abandoning me, if only temporarily?"

I could have, I realized then, just fucked Spalding Gray. Why did I have to consult Lloyd? As if he could feel comfortable with the situation. I could have just had a tiny affair and cut it off, like my hair, and wait to see if I would be discovered or revealed. The whole point of affairs is that they're secrets, but that's too obvious for me.

Lloyd was quiet, thinking. I was sorry, and I said so. He let me touch his shoulder. We went to his room and made love.

"Is this," he asked, "what you want to do with him?"

"No," I said, and I meant it. How could I explain to him that the sex would have nothing to do with sex. I am a woman in a man's world. I don't want to be a housewife. I have to use my wiles, once in a while, to get things done.

I stayed at Lloyd's and left him before the sun even thought about doing it's winter version of rising. I was tied to my job. I tried not to stay away too often. There were other staff who lived there, but it was better if we were around, in case of problems.

I lay down on my made bed and tried to think of the talking writer beside me. His hair was the color of his name. I'd once slept with a man that old before, when I was much younger. It was okay. Spalding Gray. I couldn't say his first name without his second. It made me think of tennis balls, and why anyone would name their son after such a bouncy sport. Maybe the brand wasn't invented when he was born. My God, I suddenly felt young! Most days I feel time's trial like a another gravity. I am almost thirty, and worried.

Could I still have sex without my heart? I had been good at it when I was younger, sampling the crowd. But Lloyd and I had been each other's for so long, it was hard to imagine risking him for something that meant nothing. What did I want, a boyfriend or an audience? Both. What the heck, I thought, I couldn't be forever damning my luck. There was already, in the hall of lost opportunities, the time I met Mikail Barishnikov. I was wearing a lace gown that hid my body like lingerie a mannequin. He held my hand too long, and stared at me. My best friend almost killed me for ignoring that lead. I guessed it was time for me to fuck someone famous.

I took my stance at the desk and answered the phones and ordered breakfast and sent towels to rooms that needed them. The morning passed quickly. Before I knew it, it was ten o'clock, and Spalding Gray was in front of me.

"Hi Amy," he said.

"Hi yourself," I said back, and smiled. He must have read my mind. "I thought you were learning to ski?"

"I wanted another challenge," he said.

"That would be me, right?"

"Right."

I was blushing on the clock, getting paid for getting flushed. This was kind of fun, kind of like high school.

"What time do you get off?"

"Four o'clock," I told him.

"Can I come for you then?"

I nodded. I was taken but I could be coerced into giving. How did he know this? He must play these games in every town he visits. I hoped my name would make it onstage.

The rest of the day dripped slow. I didn't eat lunch. My stomach was too fluttery. At two Lloyd came in the door, with an animal he cut from a fork of branches. He is an arborist, and makes things from pieces he cut from trees.

"What is it?" I said, by way of greeting.

"A camel. You're going to sleep with him, aren't you?"

I nodded, staring at the papers on the desk. I couldn't look in his eyes, see what shade of blue they were. His eyes changed colors with his mood. I didn't want to read him.

He left. I didn't know if this meant the end. We had stopped talking about our end a year ago, fearing that foreboding would will it so. I wouldn't know if he would be mine again until after I did the deed. I regretted having consulted him, and then making love, as if our sex had made my mind. I wanted to tell him that last night had not influenced me at all, that we were as great as ever and it wasn't excitement I was seeking. But he wouldn't hear me anyway. He was too hurt.

At four Spalding Gray came for me. I felt so warm, I didn't want to wear my coat. I wondered how I hadn't recognized him at first. I guessed it was like hearing. You know how it's hard to hear what people say if you don't know what's coming? I never expected to have Spalding Gray behind me, watching.

But here he was, at my side, wanting to put his arm around me. He had a car. We drove to the next town over, as if that would afford us privacy. Everyone knew everyone for miles around. I couldn't let myself think of what others might think. They would have their thoughts and I would have my affair, and maybe, some success.

We didn't talk in the car. I looked at the scenery, my blessedly familiar territory, and felt insulated by the snow. If I looked at him, I felt incredibly vulnerable. What I was doing could change my life. I couldn't think about my realities, the past I had with Lloyd and the vague future I had relied on. I could only think about my dreams, about my driver sitting at a desk in front of a rapt audience, musing on this relation that was about to start.

We went to another anonymous lodge and sat in swallowing chairs in front of the fire. We drank scotch, the kind that tastes like bacon. We kept not talking. This was not about our worlds. This collision was meant to divide us from our experiences. I didn't want to know about his life on the road or at home. I didn't want to know about the women he loved. I knew enough from what I remembered of his monologues. He didn't need my details. If he wanted to talk about me he could, but it would all be invented information, except for one fact. I didn't know when I should tell him I was a writer. I didn't want to seem an opportunist, even though he was the one who sought me.

Finally he put his hand over mine. I was relieved it was beginning.

"I'm a writer," I told him, like it was a disease I was obliged to disclose prior to disrobing.

He nodded, and put his hand on the back of my head, very paternal. I took this gesture to mean he would provide.

21

He had already arranged for a room, and discretely gained the key. When we had had enough scotch, we went up there. I felt very wrong, and warm between my legs. I tried to like being bad. I felt so amateur. My youth was dissolved as a dream.

We stacked our coats in a fluffy pile tall as the dresser. He unlaced my boots and kissed my toes when they were free. I put my hands on his face and kissed him. The first kiss felt like nothing, because I didn't know him. We switched places and I helped him out of his boots. It would have been obvious, from that position, for me to take his cock, but I wouldn't go that far. I wouldn't turn this into a simple blow.

"You know," I said, when he was pulling my turtleneck over my head, "I'm only doing this for my career."

"That's all right, Amy," he said. He kept repeating my name, as if he wanted me to use his. "I'm only doing this for mine."

We had sex. It was driven. There was a lot of lust between us. This went on for weeks. Four of them, exactly, and then, he thought he knew how to ski and he said good-bye. I didn't want his address. I crumpled up the piece of paper he had written it on and threw it in the blazing fire in the lobby. I wouldn't write him any letters. I had given him enough evidence for his projects, and he had my last name. My words would remain my own, regardless of the thrust of our intersection.

Lloyd broke up with me. I don't blame him, and I'm just beginning to feel my broken heart. I left Vermont. There wasn't enough room in that state for me to start fresh. I am waiting for my rewards: my writing still gets rejected. Spalding Gray is booked to tour here next spring. I'll get a ticket, and sit up front. I wonder if I'll be a part of the script, or if he'll have to improvise when he sees me. I don't feel as empty as I thought. I miss Lloyd, but there was always the risk that we would fail. I feel better having invested in my future. I will have that always.

Anne LeBaron

Ode to the Golden Toad

Croak or The Last Frog is a music/theater piece that depicts, in the form of a myth, the destruction of life forms and of the fragile relationship between animals (including *human* animals) and their habitats. The play opens on the last day of the last frog on earth. Anne LeBaron composed this musical work during her residency at George Washington University. The work was performed at George Washington University's Marvin Center on April 10-13, 1997.

Ode to the Golden Toad

Anne LeBaron

24

4

M.

Whit...h become of them? What
will ...me of me? Only one
Bufo ...glenes left.

Is he the last of his kind?
When he dies, will we ever
know another golden toad?

And does it

Piano

*replaces m. 1 of
" Does it Matter?"*

Steven Moore

Sheri Martinelli: A Modernist Muse

No notice was taken by the press of artist-writer Sheri Martinelli's death in November 1996, unfairly ignoring the significant role she played in the literary history of our time. A brief overview of her career indicates her range of roles: she was a protégée of Anaïs Nin and is described at length in her infamous *Diary*; she was the basis for a major character in William Gaddis's novel *The Recognitions* and then became the muse and (some say) mistress of Ezra Pound (she appears in various guises in the later *Cantos*); Charlie Parker and the members of the Modern Jazz Quartet hung out at her Greenwich Village apartment; Marlon Brando was an admirer and Rod Steiger collected her art, as did E. E. Cummings; she knew and was admired by all the Beats—Ginsberg was an especially close friend and mentions her in one of his poems—and was herself known in San Francisco in the late 1950s as the Queen of the Beats; H. D. identified with her and wrote about her in *End to Torment*; Pound wrote the introduction to a book of her paintings, and her art is now in collections throughout the world. She wrote unusual prose and poetry, much of it published in her own 'zine. She was a regular correspondent with Charles Bukowski and was one of the first to publish his work. More recently, she appeared under a pseudonym in Anatole Broyard's posthumous memoir *Kafka Was the Rage*, under her own name in David Markson's novel *Reader's Block*, and she was anthologized in Richard Peabody's *A Different Beat*. When younger, she even modeled for *Vogue* and acted in one of Maya Deren's experimental films. And yet not a single obituary marked the passing of this remarkable woman—whom it was my honor and pleasure to have known the last dozen years of her life—and no account of her life exists anywhere.

So, for the record: Sheri Martinelli was born on 17 January 1918 in Philadelphia—on Ben Franklin's birthday and in his city—with the given name Shirley Burns Brennan. Her father, Alphonse Brennan, was the son of a fisherman, and in later years Sheri liked to refer to herself as "The Fisherman's Granddaughter." Her mother was Mae Trindell, who was from New Orleans. Sheri's grandmother claimed descent from Scottish poet Robert Burns. Shirley Burns Brennan was later told that her first name had the wrong numerological value, so to rectify that she dropped two letters and moved the others around to form Sheri. (All her life she had a weakness for occult and metaphysical notions.) She was the oldest of three girls and a brother and was largely responsible for raising them. At some point her family moved to Atlantic City, New Jersey, but in the late 1930s Sheri moved back to Philadelphia to study art, specifically ceramics under John Butler at the Philadelphia School of Industrial Arts.

In Philadelphia she met Ezio Martinelli, a painter and sculptor who was studying at the Barnes Foundation in nearby Merion, Pennsylvania. Born in 1913, he was five years older than Sheri. They got married at the beginning of World War II, and in 1943 Sheri gave birth to a daughter, Shelley (named after the poet). The family moved to New York City, but by the end of the war they had grown apart. Sheri and Ezio separated; she kept his surname, and he kept the daughter. (It's been said that Sheri left her husband because she felt she was a better painter, though by conventional standards Ezio Martinelli went on to achieve considerably more success in his field than she did: his abstract paintings were regularly exhibited at the Willard Gallery in New York City and respectfully reviewed; several sculptures of his are on display at the United Nations complex; from 1947 to 1975 he taught at Sarah Lawrence College, he won many grants and awards, and so on. A photograph of him receiving one such award appears in *Art Digest*, 15 September 1947, p. 21.)

Sheri stayed in Greenwich Village, moving into an apartment at 23 Jones Street in the West Village. Talented, beautiful, and intriguingly eccentric, she made a striking impression on all who met her, evident from the writings of those who knew her. In her diary entry for December 1945, Anaïs Nin recounts how she learned that a "romantic-looking girl" was reading her short-story collection *Under a Glass Bell* and had told her publishing partner Gonzalo Moré that she wanted to meet Nin but was too shy to approach the older woman. Nin suggested that she attend a lecture of hers at Mills College. When Sheri approached her at the end of the lecture, Nin writes, "I recognized her. She was like a ghost of a younger me, a dreaming woman, with very soft, burning eyes, long hair streaming over her shoulders." At first, Sheri didn't say a word: "She merely stared at me, and then handed me a music box mechanism, without its box. She finally told me in a whisper that she always carries it in her pocket and listens to it in the street. She wound it up for me, and placed it against my ear, as if we were alone and not in a busy hall, filled with bustling students and professors waiting for me. A strand of her long hair had caught in the mechanism and it seemed as if the music came from it."

"She came to see me," Nin goes on, "blue eyes dissolved in moisture, slender, orphaned child of poverty, speaking softly and exaltedly. Pleading, hurt, vulnerable, breathless. Her voice touches the heart. . . . She looks mischievous and fragile. She wears rough, ugly clothes, like an orphan. She is part Jewish, part Irish. Her voice sings, changes: low, gay, sad, heavy, trailing, dreaming" (107-8). Journalist Anatole Broyard, forty years later, remembered her in much the same way: "She had a high, domelike forehead, the long silky brown hair of women in portraits, wide pale blue eyes with something roiling in their surface. Her nose was aquiline, her mouth thin and disconsolate, her chin small and pointed. It was the kind of bleak or wan beauty Village people liked to call quattrocento. Her body seemed both meager and voluptuous. Her waist was so small, it cut her in two, like a split personality, or two schools of thought. Though her legs and hips were sturdy and richly curved, her upper body was dramatically thin. When she was naked it appeared that her top half was trying to climb up out of the bottom, like a woman stepping out of a heavy garment" (3-4). Nin observed the same dichotomy: "Half of her body is heavy and animal, and the upper half is childlike and fragile" (144).

Sheri approached Nin for the same reason she would approach Pound a few years later: "She came because she felt lost," Nin writes. "I had found the words which made her life clearer." She goes on to quote Sheri: "Oh God, all the books one reads which don't bring you near the truth. Only yours, Anaïs" (108). As ingenuous as it may sound, it was this quest for truth, rather than celebrity-worship, that led Sheri to apprentice herself to writers like Nin and Pound.

Sheri joined Nin's entourage, a group mostly made up of young male admirers, with whom Nin felt more comfortable than with people of her own age (she was in her mid forties). "The presence of the young lightens the world and changes it from an oppressive, definitive, solidified one to a fluid, potentially marvelous, malleable, variable, as-yet-to-be-created world. I call them the transparent children" (95). At twenty-seven Sheri was a bit older than the young men who surrounded Nin, but she began accompanying them to parties and outings. In the spring of 1946 she joined Nin and the others to act in Maya Deren's film *Ritual in Transfigured Time*; she appears in the party scene in the middle of the short film and in the park scene at the end. At this time Sheri was still starstruck; Nin quotes her as gushing, "You're a legendary character. I keep thinking that in the future I will look back and say: 'I was here in Yonkers Park with the legendary Anaïs!'" (145).

One of the young men dancing attendance on Nin was a French surrealist poet named Charles Duits (1925-91), who had come to the U.S. in 1941 to attend Harvard, but left it a year or two later to live *la vie bohème* in New York. He is mentioned frequently in volumes three and four of Nin's *Diary*, always singled out as the most brilliant and talented of her "transparent children." He seems to have been quite taken with Sheri, for he gave her a poem entitled "La Naissance de Sherry Martinelli" (like Nin and some others, he misspelled her first name). Written in French, which Sheri couldn't read, it was apparently never published; it follows as an appendix to this essay in a translation made by Sheri's and my mutual acquaintance George Kearns (a Pound scholar (and revised by writer-artist Rikki Ducornet). It is a surrealist birth myth in which no sooner is Sheri born than she is "preyed upon by starving men." Sheri came across the poem in her papers in 1985; when I sent her Kearns's translation she commented, "One regrets that it has one's name on it. Charles Duits was forsooth writing this to his own dream female 'twin soul' born into t/mind of t/male that he ever cherishes/nourishes/seeks/desires & possesses in every female he meets outside his mind. His perfect opposite/his extreme norm/his action polarity." Duits was the first of many "starving men" to mythologize Sheri, an act her strange beauty and endearing eccentricity encouraged. It is the inverse of her own exaltation of wise teachers like Nin and Pound.

In the same diary entry for December 1945 quoted earlier, Nin reports that Sheri was then living with a Chilean-American painter named Enrique Zanarte; Anatole Broyard gives his first name as Nemecio. But she seems to have been living alone in 1946 when she met Broyard, who says he moved in with her and was her lover for about three months. Their affair is recounted at length in his memoir *Kafka Was the Rage*, written in 1988 but not published until 1993, three years after his death. It is an engaging account of life in Greenwich Village

31

immediately after the war and of the "sentimental education" he received from Sheri (he changed her surname to Donatti to protect her privacy), but its reliability is in doubt. When I sent Sheri a copy of the book in 1993 she insisted Broyard had never spent a single night with her and dismissed the book as "a voyeur's wet dream." It's difficult to know whom to believe. Sheri sometimes misrepresented her past, glossing over some of its scandalous aspects, not so much out of vanity as (she said) to avoid giving young people any encouragement to emulate bad behavior. But Broyard himself was duplicitous; as Henry Louis Gates, Jr., shows in his recent memoir of him, Broyard's entire life can be said to be a lie. (He hid his black heritage and passed for white, keeping his secret from his friends and family until near the end of his life.) The Sheri Donatti of *Kafka Was the Rage* certainly has much in common with Sheri Martinelli: Broyard's physical descriptions of her are accurate and he captures her unique way of talking and her oblique intelligence, but Sheri told me many of his details are wrong: her apartment was clean and comfortable, not dirty and crowded as he says, and she most often wore cloth pants, not the clinging dresses and no underwear that Broyard obsesses over. (He constantly worried that she would inadvertently expose herself, most comically the time she accidentally knocked W. H. Auden over and on top of herself.) In some ways Broyard's portrait of Sheri is as fanciful as Charles Duits's surrealistic one and springs from the same male tendency to project desired qualities onto the unsuspecting female. Taken with a huge grain of salt, however, Broyard's book provides yet another testimony to Sheri's appeal. For Broyard, she was literally unforgettable; on his deathbed forty years later, Sheri was one of the people he spoke of (Gates 80).

Broyard notes that Sheri was still an abstract painter at the time (like her former husband) and describes a few of her works. She continued to take classes during this time, studying engraving under Stanley William Hayter at the Atelier de Sept. She was in one class with Spanish painter Joan Miró, who ogled her shamelessly; as she later wrote me, "his round blue eyes 'ate' all of t/ black net off my chorus girl stockings." One of her projects was described by Josephine Gibbs in the 15 December 1946 issue of *Art Digest*:

> Three young up-and-coming modernists have contributed five original prints each to an unusual portfolio of etchings and serigraphs which may be seen at the Joseph Luyber Gallery. . . . Sheri Martinelli's velvety, soft ground-etchings are technically fascinating. They are as deeply bitten as can be imagined to produce raised areas and lines under pressure, and imaginatively manipulated to produce a variety of textures in abstract compositions which may have had their inspiration in the accidental forms of nature.

(Sheri would continue to find "inspiration in the accidental forms of nature" in her later artwork.) This portfolio was limited to 100 copies, priced at $40.00 each; I've never seen a copy. In fact, little if any of her art from this period survives. Sheri also kept an ungainly printing press in her apartment at this time— no doubt in emulation of Nin, who owned one and typeset her own books— which she used for her etchings.

During the late 1940s Sheri supported herself by modeling, principally for *Vogue*. Such noted photographers as Karl Bissinger, Cliff Wolfe, Tommy Yee, and Dick Rutledge took hundreds of shots of her. I haven't been able to identify any of them in the pages of *Vogue*, though Sheri's second husband has folders full of these photos. Like many a *Vogue* model today, Sheri also experimented with heroin during this time, though not so often as to become addicted.

One thing Broyard got right is that Sheri had many suitors. He describes an amusing episode when critic Richard Gilman came over one night and presented an elaborate argument why he would be a more suitable partner for her than Broyard. He also describes a similar visit from Zanarte; if they had indeed lived together earlier, perhaps he was there to win her back. But Broyard doesn't mention another rival for Sheri's attention, novelist William Gaddis, whose portrayal of a thinly disguised Sheri in his novel *The Recognitions* is the most extensive and memorable of her various appearances in literature.

Leaving Harvard (without a degree) in 1945, Gaddis had moved to Manhattan and been hired as a fact-checker at the *New Yorker*. He lived on Horatio Street in the West Village and frequented the same places Sheri did, such as the San Remo bar on the corner of Bleecker and Macdougal. He was twenty-five when he met her, five years her junior. In her first letter to me Sheri remembered attending an opening at the Museum of Modern Art with Gaddis; he had borrowed someone's shoes for the occasion, which were too big and flapped noisily the entire time. He was quite smitten with her by all accounts, but she apparently didn't reciprocate his interest, regarding him as something of a "mama's boy" (which he was, literally, having been raised by his mother because his father left her when Gaddis was three). I don't know how long they were involved, or how deeply; if *The Recognitions* is any indication, it was a case of unrequited love that lasted only a few months. Polite and gentlemanly, Gaddis was no match for more practiced skirt-chasers like Broyard, but he would rout all his rivals when it came to immortalizing Sheri in a book.

Broyard writes that Sheri "looked more like a work of art than a pretty woman" (3). She is introduced in *The Recognitions* in the same way: Otto (Gaddis's self-deprecating self-portrait) is attending a Greenwich Village party given by Max (Broyard, more or less) when he briefly glimpses "the face of a girl who was sitting alone on the couch, . . . Then she was gone, with the silent consciousness of a painting obscured by a group of nattering human beings" (183). A little later, having taken down a volume of Browning and pretending to read it while spying on her, Otto reads the following lines from "A Likeness" just as he realizes she is watching him:

He never saw, never before today,
What was able to take his breath away,
A face to lose youth for, to occupy age
With the dream of, meet death with... (193)

Her name is Esme, and in almost every respect she is Sheri Martinelli: she lives on Jones Street, has a four-year-old daughter somewhere, owns a printing press, and speaks in a curious way. (Broyard: "Like everything else about her, her style of talking took some getting used to. She gave each syllable an equal stress and cooed or chanted her vowels. Her sentences had no intonation, no rise and fall, so that they came across as disembodied, parceled out, yet oracular too" [5].) Otto introduces himself and even manages to sleep with her that night, but his relationship to her throughout the rest of the novel is one of frustration. Otto has a rival in the unsavory person of Chaby Sinisterra (based on a jazz musician Sheri knew named Eddie Shu [1918-86]; *The Recognitions* is very much a *roman à clef*), but Esme is hopelessly in love with the painter for whom she models, the enigmatic Wyatt Gwyon.

A romantic quadrangle links Wyatt and Otto with the novel's two principal female characters, Esme and Wyatt's wife Esther (based on a woman Gaddis knew named Helen Parker), both of whom tolerate Otto only because of Wyatt's chilly indifference to them. Both women have additional lovers, making Otto even more superfluous, and many of the other male characters seem to have slept with Esme or Esther. But the promiscuity of Greenwich Village women is hardly Gaddis's chief concern. Esther and Esme represent the two traditional forms of female salvation open to the mythic hero, and their inadequacies as suitable anima figures dramatize Gaddis's critique of that very tradition. Though both women share initials and an avocation for writing, they are diametrically opposed: Esther is rational, big-boned, ambitious, and writes prose, while Esme is mystical, delicate, aimless, and writes poetry. Gaddis's prose sharpens the contrast further: his character analysis of Esther (78-80) is written in the well-balanced, logically ordered style of Henry James—an author Esther admires—while Esme's equivalent analysis is fractured into two sections (276-77, 298-302), presaging her incipient schizophrenia, and written with the illogic of an interior monologue, punctuated with solipsistic questions and fragments of poems, fictions, and esoteric trivia. They are united, however, in their unrequited love for Wyatt and, after losing him, in their despair.

Gretchen to Wyatt's Faust, Esme has been sent to him by the novel's Mephistopheles, Recktall Brown. A promiscuous manic-depressive schizophrenic junkie, she nevertheless models as the Virgin Mary in Wyatt's religious forgeries ("No needle marks on your Annunciation's arm, now," Brown reminds him [259]). Although Esme is associated with a wide variety of other female figures of salvation in addition to Mary and Faust's Gretchen—Dante's Beatrice, Saint Rose of Lima, the Egyptian goddess Isis, the Flying Dutchman's Senta, Peer Gynt's Solveig (like other modernist masterpieces, *The Recognitions* is thickly allusive to other texts)—she is elsewhere associated with succubae and sirens, and when Wyatt deigns to think of her at all, it is unfortunately in her role as temptress. Rebelling from Brown in his role as the Troll King, Wyatt comes to view Esme more as Ibsen's Green-clad One than as the maternal Solveig and at that point rejects her offer of intimacy to return to his father and take up the priesthood. In her face Wyatt had found the lines necessary to complete his childhood portrait of his dead mother Camilla, but this only adds unconscious fears of incest to his relationship with Esme. After he spurns her, she attempts suicide, and though she is rescued she drifts through the rest of the novel in a state of acute schizophrenia, referring to herself in the third person. Wyatt eventually comes to his senses and realizes that Esme is the one woman capable of offering him selfless love, but by that time she has disappeared, a stowaway on a ship taking Stanley, a neurotic Catholic organist also in love with Esme, to Italy. By day Stanley tries to convert her to Catholicism, but by night her "simulacra" assail him "immodest in dress and licentious in nakedness, many-limbed as some wild avatar of the Hindu cosmology . . . full-breasted and vaunting the belly, limbs indistinguishable until he was brought down between them and stifled in moist collapse" (828). Ever the victim of male projections, Esme slips deeper into madness and religious mania as the long novel nears its conclusion, her unrequited love for Wyatt causing her to waste away, "so quickly as though she . . . she had no will to live," as Stanley mournfully confesses, reporting her Firbankian death (a "staphylococcic infection . . . from kissing Saint-Peter-in-the-Boat" [953]).

On the one hand, all this sounds like an elaborate revenge fantasy contrived by Gaddis because of Sheri's indifference to him, but on the other, it shows that he learned from her how ridiculous some of his preconceived notions about her had been. One of the strangest yet memorable heroines in contemporary literature, Esme betrays the absurdities of the role of romantic redemptress forced upon so many female characters by males who prefer virgins and whores to any more complex woman in between. As with Broyard, Sheri provided Gaddis with an invaluable "sentimental education."

Gaddis sent a copy of *The Recognitions* to Sheri upon publication in 1955, but she never read it. At that time she was visiting Ezra Pound regularly at St. Elizabeths Hospital in Washington, DC. She showed the novel to Pound, but he wasn't interested in such "verbiage." "I'll help your friends any way I can," he told her, "but I won't read their books." The jacket carried a blurb by Stuart Gilbert favorably comparing *The Recognitions* to *Ulysses*, so Pound added: "Tell your friend Joyce was an ending, not a beginning." (It should be remembered that Pound didn't care for *Ulysses*, and regarded *Finnegans Wake* as unreadable.)

In addition to inspiring Esme, Sheri made a literal contribution to *The Recognitions*: a long letter of hers to Gaddis is reproduced verbatim on pages 471-73. (Gaddis didn't ask Sheri's permission to do so, and since she never read the novel she was unaware of the letter until I pointed it out to her, after Gaddis told me the letter was hers.) The thousand-word letter is too long to reproduce here, but it's a remarkable piece of writing and valuable both as a statement of her aesthetics at the time and as the earliest surviving example of her prose style. Written under Nin's obvious influence—just as Sheri would adopt Pound's idiosyncratic way of writing in later years—the letter discusses "the demands of painting," principally the psychological demands made on the painter. A short extract follows, concluding with a striking image of the sort Nin is known for:

> The painter concerned for his mortal safety, indifferent because he fears to scrutinize, paradoxically sacrifices that very safety, for he will not be allowed to escape painting.
>
> He will make paintings or they will revolt and make him, unhappy being in the grasp of them. He compulsively must, then, live them cold as they are, static, perversely with warmth and movement he cannot know but feel painfully, a bird with broken eggs inside. (472)

In the context of the novel, the letter is a suicide note Esme leaves for Wyatt; Broyard too describes a suicide attempt by Sheri (65-66), but she told me she never attempted suicide. Perhaps she meant she never *seriously* attempted suicide, because the attempts described in both *The Recognitions* and *Kafka Was the Rage* are half-hearted, more theatrical than suicidal.

Gaddis left for Europe in 1948 to write his novel. Anaïs Nin seems to have drifted away by then too; a year earlier Sheri had found a doctor to perform an abortion for Nin (Bair 328), and in later years Nin would send Sheri inscribed copies of her books, but she was no longer part of her entourage. (When Nin died in 1977, Sheri wrote a poem entitled "Goodbye Anaïs," which was eventually published in the journal *Anaïs*.) Sheri was popular with jazz musicians at that time, who would hang out at her Jones Street apartment and sometimes give her shirts that they had worn too often on the bandstand. Charlie Parker was a frequent visitor, as were the members of the Modern Jazz Quartet. Sheri painted a splendid abstract portrait of MJQ bassist Percy Heath entitled *Daw oo* that was later included in her book. At some point she became friends with Leonard Bernstein's fiancée, Felicia Montealegre (she lived a few blocks from Sheri), who was to become something of a patron to her. It was the heady beginning of the Beat era, and Sheri was leading a hedonistic but (as she later admitted) empty life. In the early 1950s she was living with a musician named Joseph Castaldo, who was studying at Juilliard; aware of her ennui, Castaldo suggested that she go down to Washington, DC, and visit Ezra Pound, then incarcerated at St. Elizabeths Hospital. There she met the man who would dominate the second half of her life.

Writing in 1973 to one of Pound's biographers, Sheri gave this lively, freely punctuated account of her state of mind in 1952 when she first met Pound:

> I was going around t/world with the/clouds and t/air like Chief of All The Chiricahuas Apache: Cochise—when Ezra Pound (known to us as: "E.P.") "spoke to my Thoughts." I, too, "carried My Life on My Finger-Nails" and they were each & all a different colour because I was a working painter—a Fighter in The Ethical Arena wherein you KNOW what's Really Wrong because you did that yourself and you found out by The Way of Be-ing There. Artist. Maestro.
>
> Was There Ever Such A Man, Dear Goddess. A Man who found me Lost in Hellishness but FIRST I had been Made Trusting & Loving & Innocent & Ignorant "Love One Another Children" . . . so as not To Even Know for a split second that I was Lost. I was having a Ball. All Those Sweet-faced Indians! T/guiltless sex of animal desire; pure, simple & uncomplicated by The Falsities of Any Other Facts! Freedom of Diet & No Two Days Running The Same....
>
> Today I remembered: His great Faith in Art when he said: "PAINT me out of here, Cara." So Painted E.P. in Paradise as he had sung me from Purgatory. . . . This is The Power of Art Work. With Out A Picture of It inside your mind— how can you Find It? (Heymann 226; his ellipses)

Pound was in his own form of Purgatory at the time. Detained by the U.S. Army in 1945 for making allegedly treasonous broadcasts over the Italian radio network during the war, Pound had, on the advice of his lawyers, pleaded insanity rather than risk being tried for treason (and if convicted, executed), and had been confined since the end of 1945 to St. Elizabeths Federal Hospital for the Insane. (The government's plan was to keep Pound there rather than risk an acquittal after a trial, so the fiction of his insanity was maintained by sympathetic psychiatrists.) During his first few years there he was allowed very few visitors, but by 1951 his visiting privileges had been extended, as they would continue to be over the years. Surrounded by madmen and with the threat of being tried for treason hanging over his head should he "recover" from his insanity, Pound was understandably miserable and his creative drive at a standstill. *The Pisan Cantos*, written in 1945 while Pound was incarcerated in Italy, had been published in 1948, and he had written nothing since. In 1949 Pound won the Bollingen Prize for *The Pisan Cantos*, and the controversy surrounding the award attracted the attention of a new generation of readers, many of whom began making pilgrimages to St. Elizabeths in the 1950s to study under the master at his "Ezuversity" and do his bidding.

Sheri wrote to Pound's supervisor Dr. Overholser on 26 December 1951 to ask permission to visit him; her request was granted, and though there's no record of their first meeting, the mutual attraction must have been immediate. Pound encouraged her to move down there and informally adopted her. She got a job working in the admissions office of George Washington University, which didn't last long, and then worked in a waffle shop on K Street, but Pound made her quit so that she could concentrate on her painting. He paid the rent on her apartment and gave her a dollar a day for expenses. Aged sixty-six and thirty-three, respectively, there was a father-daughter relationship at first (or older: she called him "Grampaw"). Pound was still married to Dorothy Shakespear, who had taken a small apartment near the hospital and visited him daily, but the older woman was apparently not jealous of the younger one; she even approved of Pound's financial assistance to Sheri. In the summer of 1954, Dr. E. Fuller Torrey notes in *The Roots of Treason*, "Dorothy wrote to Dr. Overholser requesting that Sheri Martinelli be allowed to take her place as [Pound's] guardian while out on the lawn because she had to go away for a week; Dorothy reassured Dr. Overholser that Ezra thought of Sheri as his own daughter" (242). The following year Pound asked Dr. Overholser whether Sheri could move onto the grounds of St. Elizabeths and work as an art therapist; both requests were denied (Torrey 241). Dorothy too seems to have looked upon Sheri as a daughter; spotting Sheri walking up toward Pound and her, Dorothy once commented, "Here comes 'family.'" Sheri proudly accompanied Dorothy on various outings in Washington, DC, dazzled by the older woman's Edwardian elegance. In her letters and phone conversations Sheri told me she loved Dorothy, and often sang her praises.

Sheri lived in a variety of small apartments in and around Washington, DC, for the next seven years—once sharing a basement apartment with another Pound disciple named David Horton—and visited Pound almost daily. (She did, however, maintain a studio apartment on New York's Lower East Side for occasional visits; after another disciple, John Kasper, moved to New York and opened his Make It

New bookshop on Bleecker Street, Sheri used it as a mailing address. She received more than a hundred letters from Pound during her periods away from St. Elizabeths.) She joined the growing number of young acolytes who visited Pound, listening to his pronunciamentos and undertaking various projects at his suggestion. Sheri could always be seen with sketchpad in hand, doing studies of the Maestro, and occasionally of Dorothy. Virtually everyone who has written about Pound's life at St. Elizabeths mentions Sheri, in terms ranging from praise to bemusement to condemnation. Noel Stock, one of Pound's earliest biographers, calls her "a strange, rather scatterbrained young woman" (439) and a later biographer dismisses her as a manipulative, troublesome "odd-ball" (Wilhelm 287, 308). On the other hand, one visitor at the time said of her, "so far as I could tell the only visitor of those years who had any perception at all of what Pound was doing then was a young woman painter from one of those 'passionate religious traditions conscious of its roots in European paganism'" (McNaughton 323), and critic Wendy Stallard Flory goes so far as to suggest that Sheri practically saved Pound's life, at least his creative life: "the poet sees her as more than an individual; she comes to represent for him the very idea of love as inspiration. Set against the bleak and stultifying reality of the asylum ward, her youth, enthusiasm, and spontaneity must seem to provide a contact with all those things in the outside world that he most minds being shut away from" (246).

Pound playfully called her "La" Martinelli, adding the mock title *la* more often used in reference to actresses and divas, which Sheri adopted as her professional name thereafter. Pound obviously enjoyed her company: "Seeing Sheri approach across the lawn," another vistor recalls, "he jumps out of his chair and hurries to greet La Martinelli with his most affectionate and energetic bear hug" (Booth 383). It's been said she and Pound became lovers, as Sheri herself claimed in a letter to Archibald MacLeish (Torrey 241), though a later biographer doubts the couple would have had much opportunity to do so (Carpenter 803). Allen Ginsberg called Sheri Pound's "girlfriend," and one of her musician friends teased her with "I guess you're Ezra's pound cake now." In Timothy Findley's play *The Trials of Ezra Pound*, Sheri is portrayed as a concubine, there merely to satisfy Pound's sexual needs. As late as 1957, they acted like lovers: when David Rattray visited Pound that fall he recorded for the *Nation* another example of Pound's greeting Sheri upon her arrival: "Pound embraced her and ran his hands through her hair, and they talked excitedly, each interrupting the other." "Grandpa loves me," she told Rattray. "It's because I symbolize the spirit of Love to him, I guess." She also boasted, "Grandpa says I know intuitively what it takes a great genius years of study to learn." When she left, "Pound threw his arms around her, hugged her, and kissed her goodbye." To Rattray's critical eye, "Her appearance suggested a frayed and faded survivor of the early bobby-sox days. She had huge eyes like a cat. They bulged in a flushed face that tapered down from an enormous forehead to a tiny chin and tinier double chin. Her lips were tight and pale, but sometimes relaxed and parted into a naive smile. I assumed that she was a patient from another ward." Sheri was infuriated by Rattray's article and wanted to sue for slander, but Dorothy talked her out of it.

Pound was attentive to her emotional needs as well. On 23 September 1954 her only brother, Walter Albert Brennan (Buddy to his sister), committed suicide, the result of a decade of misery ever since being wounded in World War II. So great was Sheri's grief that Pound wrote a "Prayer for a Dead Brother" for her, which was eventually published in 1972. When Charlie Parker died the following year, Pound again attempted to assuage her grief with a poem, which remains unpublished. He also fed her during these years, passing along items from the hospital cafeteria. However, by 1956 he began tiring of her, and "turned her over" (as her second husband put it) to Gilbert Lee, ten years her junior, whom she had met shortly after coming to St. Elizabeths. Sheri moved in with Gilbert at his mother's gallery on Mount Vernon Avenue across the Potomac in Alexandria, Virginia. Gilbert drove her into Washington frequently, though, so she could continue her studies at the Ezuversity.

Ostensibly Sheri was at St. Elizabeths to study "the classic arts and letters" (as she would later put it in her résumé), and her art did undergo a change under Pound's tutelage. "Stay between Giotto and Botticelli," he advised her, so she supplemented her abstract style with an older, more representational style. She painted portraits almost exclusively, and mostly self-portraits. The paintings are small, 12" by 14" at the largest, and are richly colored. As with Sheri herself, her art elicited contradictory reactions from Pound's visitors: his U.S. publisher James Laughlin has said "Her drawings were not very good, in fact, quite bad" (24), but Eustace Mullins, a photographer and sculptor among other things, wrote: "She had perfected a jewel-like tone in her painting, much like the ancient Persian painting, which was very effective" (307; a shadowy photograph of Sheri and Mullins is reproduced on p. 292 of his book). Art historian Max Wykes-Joyce paid her splendid tribute by writing, "La Martinelli, Italo-American, brings to painting a sense of hieratic splendour lost since Byzantium. The *Testa Invocatrice*, the terra-cotta head of a Madonna, no higher than a man's thumb, is a manifestation of religious art in the direct tradition of Giotto and Crivelli" (249).

Pound himself was delighted with the development of Sheri's painting under his direction and actively sought to promote her career. His rooms were decorated with her paintings and he proudly talked them up to his visitors. (On p. 339 of the winter 1974 issue of *Paideuma* there is a photograph from the 1950s of Pound seated at a desk displaying her painting *Giotto*.) His letters of 1955 are full of exhortations to correspondents like MacLeish and Laughlin to do something for Sheri: grants, foundation support, publication, museum showings, anything, but nothing came of his efforts (*Pound/Laughlin* 236-42). As late as 1958 he was still trying to get some sort of subsidy for her from a European admirer (Stummvoll 75-78), again without results.

He did, however, arrange for publication in book form of a small selection of her paintings. He suggested the project to Vanni Scheiwiller, the son of Pound's Italian publisher, and offered to write an introduction for it. David Gordon, a photographer who later became a leading Pound scholar, photographed the paintings he thought should be included—Sheri wasn't consulted and later was irritated at his selection—and in February of 1956 Scheiwiller published *La Martinelli*, a miniature booklet (2 3/4" x 4") limited to 500 copies. It reproduces nine paintings: *St. Elizabeth's Madonna* (also reproduced on the cover), *Giotto, Patria, Cleofe Santa, Isis of the Two Kingdoms, Daw oo* (the portrait of Percy Heath mentioned earlier), *Ch'iang* (Fortuna), *E.P.*, and *Leucothoe, Daughter of Orchamus*, and two ceramic works, the *Testa Invocatrice* admired by Wykes-Joyce and a *Ra Set*. In his introduction, Pound notes that several of Sheri's paintings were works in progress (indeed, she would continue working on some of them up until her death) and states: "The unstillness that delayed my recognition till quite a while after that of my less restless contemporaries [e.g., Joyce and Eliot] runs parallel in the work of la Martinelli, who is the first to show a capacity to manifest in paint, or in la ceramica what is most to be prized in my writing" (11). (Pound's introduction was reprinted later in 1956 in Noel Stock's magazine *Edge* with the title "Total War on 'Contemplatio'"—a phrase from Canto 85—and has been reprinted a few times since.)

Pound mentions two of Sheri's paintings not included in *La Martinelli* but that are mentioned in *The Cantos*: *Lux in Diafana* and *Ursula Benedetta*, both dating from 1954. By that time Pound had resumed work on his epic poem, and the next two installments he would publish, *Section: Rock-Drill* (1956) and *Thrones* (1959) are, at a basic level, a record of what he was reading and, in Sheri's case, seeing at St. Elizabeths. Through the thicket of Pound's dense, allusive poetry, Sheri can be glimpsed in various guises.

Sheri's presence in these cantos takes two forms: references to her person and/or her role in Pound's life at the time, and references to her art. As in *The Recognitions*, she is mythologized in *The Cantos* as a romantic figure of redemption, and like Gaddis, Pound associates Sheri with a wide range of women in myth and literature. The first half of *Rock-Drill* (cantos 85-89) continues the manner and matter of the pre-Pisan cantos in their concern with history and ethics. But Canto 90 makes a sudden shift to the lyrical mode, recalling the love poetry of the troubadours Pound had studied nearly a half-century earlier. "In fact," writes Italian scholar Massimo Bacigalupo, "the forty pages of [cantos] 90-95 may be taken as a single new *Canzone d'amore*, modelled upon Cavalcanti's (and Dante's) *poesis docta* and on Provençal *trobar clus*" (259). (One of Pound's earliest books had been a translation of the sonnets and ballads of the medieval Italian poet Guido Cavalcanti; Pound gave his personal copy of the book to Sheri, who filled the margins with drawings and love poems to Pound.) Pound later told Sheri that cantos 90-95 were "her" cantos, for like the troubadour's Lady, she personified love as a creative force. On the second page of Canto 90 the poet cries out to Cythera (Aphrodite), and then addresses a prayer to "Sibylla," the all-seeing sibyl of the Delphic oracle in ancient Greece. Most critics agree with Carroll F. Terrell's annotation: "Sheri Martinelli is understood to be the real-life sibyl at St. Elizabeths" (542). Chanting in liturgical refrain the phrase "m'elevasti" ("you lifted me up," from Dante's praise of Beatrice in the *Paradiso*), Pound registers his gratitude to Sheri for lifting him up out of his personal hell and reanimating him with the spirit of love:

                                    Sibylla,
from under the rubble heap
                        m'elevasti
from the dulled edge beyond pain,
                        m'elevasti
out of Erebus, the deep-lying
              from the wind under the earth,
                        m'elevasti
from the dulled air and the dust,
                        m'elevasti
by the great flight,
                          m'elevasti,
                                    Isis Kuanon
from the cusp of the moon,
                        m'elevasti (90/626)

Isis Kuanon conflates the Egyptian goddess with the Chinese goddess of mercy. Next Sheri is referred to as the mermaid Undine, a nickname Pound gave her ("Thus Undine came to the rock" [91/630]; "Yes, my Ondine, it is so god-damned dry on these rocks" [93/643]). Although this could be a reflection on her dangerous, sirenlike persona—Sheri was, after all, tempting Pound away from his wife and practicing what Laughlin learnedly calls "*concitatio senectutis* (the arousing of desire in old men)" (25)—the undine is another redemptress, especially when Pound further conflates her with the sea-nymph Leucothea (from book 5 of Homer's *Odyssey*). In the second half of *Rock-Drill* Pound resumes the persona of wandering Odysseus, and Leucothea makes her smashing entrance in Canto 91. Appearing in the form of a seagull to Odysseus, who is adrift on a raft in wet clothes, Leucothea coos, "my bikini is worth your raft" (91/636), a flippant paraphrase of her offer to give him her magic veil in exchange for his wet clothes. The flirty line is repeated in Canto 95 (665), and even J. J. Wilhelm, who goes out of his way to deny Sheri's role in *The Cantos*, grudgingly admits that Leucothea "may well have been a tribute to Sheri Martinelli at this time" (302) for rescuing Pound just as the sea-nymph rescued Odysseus. When Sheri left St. Elizabeths in 1958, among the paintings and drawings she left with Norman Holmes Pearson for safekeeping was a photograph she had taken of herself in a mirror, wearing a bikini (H. D. 52).

In Canto 92, Pound writes:

"And if I see her not,
            no sight is worth the beauty of my thought."
Then knelt with the sphere of crystal
That she should touch with her hands,
                        Coeli Regina
The four altars at the four coigns of that place,
But in the great love, bewildered
            farfalla in tempesta (92/639)

41

"This passage is surely a tribute to Sherri [*sic*] Martinelli," Wendy Flory feels, "and the 'sphere of crystal' that the poet holds out to her is perhaps the poetry which she has inspired him to write" (253). Flory goes on to suggest that in Canto 93 Sheri is evoked as Flora Castalia (650), goddess of flowers (256), and Terrell sees another reference to Sheri in Canto 94 as Pound's "Blue jay, my blue jay" (570). In Canto 97 there are two intriguing descriptions of Sheri's hair and eyes. Brooding on the Homeric epithet "wine-dark," Pound again refers to Sheri as "Sibilla" and tries to describe the color of her hair, settling on "russet-gold" (97/695). Sheri had been a brunette earlier, but at St. Elizabeths she sported "splendid red hair" (Laughlin 24), which she later explained in this wise: "It was a spectacular crimson & it came about because E.P. had placed his hand on one's head and where E.P. put his hand on one's hair (a bit later on not instantly) that hair turned crimson. . . . E.P.'s touch (a 'laying on of hands'??) also deep'n'd t/eye colour into a lavender which E.P. is also noting in C/97 indicating that E.P. was aware of t/ changes" ("Pound as Wuz"). Sheri's second reference is to the lines:

> with eyes pervanche [violet-blue]
>   three generations, San Vio
> darker than pervanche?
>   Pale sea-green, I saw eyes once (97/696; cf. 97/698)

A little later in Canto 97 there is a line that some have knowingly said refers to Sheri, but which she disavowed:

> mid dope-dolls an' duchesses
>   tho' orften I roam
> some gals is better,
>   some wusser
>   than some. (97/700-701)

Sheri told me this was merely the chorus of a bawdy song Pound had composed; she was no longer a "dope-doll," having given up heroin by then. But it's true that during her first few years at St. Elizabeths she was still using heroin and marijuana. As early as March 1952 Pound was asking an acquaintance "have you any angles on keeping dope pushers away from young people of talent?" (Carpenter 804), and in a letter to E. E. Cummings dated 7 September 1954 Pound asked the poet what he knew about dope and warned: "I may need e.e.c.'s help re/ particular victim / emergency MIGHT arise/" (*Pound/Cummings* 356). Sheri was that "particular victim," as William McNaughton's letters to Pound during that time attest. Sheri was also the victim of a dope plant by the police and went to trial in 1956, but she was acquitted easily, "jury out 5 minutes," as Pound explained to MacLeish (Carpenter 819).

    The sibyl at Delphi was also known as the pythoness (from her familiar), and in this guise Sheri makes her final appearance in *The Cantos*: born "Of the blue sky and a wild-cat, / Pitonessa [Italian for pythoness] / The small breasts snow-soft over tripod" (104/760). Sheri had given Pound a comic drawing of herself as a sibyl, standing next to a tripod and with a python in hand, which Pound thus worked into Canto 104. (Sheri said Pound told her, "T/drawing is good because it shows you can laugh at yourself.") In fact Sheri gave Pound many comically risqué drawings of herself; the cutest one depicts her nearly nude with a bouquet of flowers in hand and the caption: "'F U Will Be My Valintine I Will Be Yr Kon Que Byne."

In a similar manner, several of Sheri's paintings became part of *The Cantos.* She would show Pound her works in progress and often he would give them titles and then work them into his poem. Her *Sibylla* of 1954 coincides with her appearance in Canto 90 (written the same year). In Canto 93, the two paintings Pound mentions in his introduction to her book, *Lux in Diafana* and *Ursula Benedetta*, become the subjects of the poet's prayer for compassion:

> Lux in diafana,
>> Creatrix, oro.
> Ursula benedetta,
>> oro (93/648)

Sheri's *Lux in Diafana* ("light in transparency") depicts a woman's face in quarter-profile with rays of light emanating from her forehead, while the *Ursula* is a full-face portrait of the legendary saint. (Pound's "benedetta" demotes her to "Blessed.") Both paintings are idealized self-portraits. The lines "Isis Kuanon /... / the blue serpent / glides from the rock pool" (90/626-27) have been associated with Sheri's painting *Isis of the Two Kingdoms*, which Pound admired (Gordon 241; *Isis* is reproduced on 240), though in this case it's impossible to say which came first. Canto 98 refers to two figures Sheri painted, Princess Ra-Set and Leucothoe (not Homer's nymph but a character in Ovid's *Metamorphoses*), both included in *La Martinelli* and thus apparently pre-dating the composition of Canto 98. A different *Leucothoe* (but done in the same medium, sepia on grained wood) appeared in the spring 1955 issue of the *Hudson Review* as a frontispiece to Canto 86. During this time she did countless portraits of Pound, as I've said; one was reproduced as the frontispiece to Pound's translation of Sophocles' *Women of Trachis* (1956). In a poem/commentary on Canto 106 written many years after the event, Sheri recounts how one day she brought to St. Elizabeths a painting she'd been working on, a portrait of a woman with black hair surrounded by the faces of four girls. The Pounds were seated outside, and when Sheri showed them the painting, "DP sat straight up in her deck chair & said: 'I'll TAKE t-h-a-t' and she did.... EP stared @ work said nothing / He went to his room & wrote down in His Book" the opening lines of Canto 106:

> And was her daughter like that;
> Black as Demeter's gown,
>> eyes, hair?
> Dis' bride, Queen over Phlegethon,
>> girls faint as mist about her? (106/772)

Sheri would continue to illustrate figures from *The Cantos* after she left St. Elizabeths, including an *Undine* in 1964 in memory of Pound's nickname for her.

Undine is also the name H. D. used for Sheri in her *End to Torment*, written in 1958 in the months leading up to Pound's release from St. Elizabeths. In journal form she records her memories of him and their teenage romance, when he called her "Dryad." (Carpenter notes, "It was his first but by no means last invention of a mask for someone else, which stuck, and changed their perception of themselves" [62], as would be the case with Sheri, the sibyl/undine/madonna of St. Elizabeths.) After reading Rattray's *Nation* article and receiving *La Martinelli* from a friend, H. D. developed a keen interest in Sheri, finding a parallel between her younger self and the artist: "Undine seems myself *then*" (39). When she learned Pound would not be taking Sheri with him to Italy upon his release, she decided to help her; though she doesn't mention it in *End to Torment*, she gave Sheri the money from her Harriet Monroe Prize award in 1956 (Guest 315-16). She was enchanted by the photos of Sheri and her artwork that Norman Holmes Pearson had sent her, and somewhat reluctantly entered into correspondence with her. Sheri seems already to have known her work and wrote her an effusive letter of praise, but also expressed her rage at being dumped by Pound. "The male just can't go about like that, ditching a spirit love," Sheri fumed. "I have known Ezra for 6 years. The last 4 years I took a vow in St. Anthony's Church in NYC not to leave the Maestro until he was freed. A month before he was freed he made me break that vow" (57). "He killed her," Sheri wrote of herself to Pearson, describing Pound's decision to desert her (54). Instead of taking Sheri to Italy, Pound took Marcella Spann, a young teacher who had started visiting Pound at St. Elizabeths a year earlier and had supplanted Sheri in the Maestro's affections by 1958. "With her serious, rather reserved expression and her hair done neatly in a bun," Carpenter writes, "she made a marked contrast to the ultra-exuberant Sheri Martinelli, who until then had been undisputed queen of the disciples" (829). Dethroned, Sheri married Gilbert and together they left for Mexico at the beginning of the summer of 1958.

"Poor Undine!" H. D. laments. "They don't want you, they really don't. How shall we reconcile ourselves to this?" (57), remembering that a half-century earlier Pound had likewise abandoned her to go to Europe. Sheri had commented on the "sea-girls" section of Eliot's "Love Song of J. Alfred Prufrock" in a poetry anthology she sent to H. D., and the poet's last vision of Sheri is of "our little Undine on her sea-rocks with her wind-blown hair" (59), utterly forlorn.

At Pound's suggestion, José Vazquez-Amaral, another member of the Ezuversity who would eventually translate *The Cantos* into Spanish, had arranged for an art scholarship for Sheri in Jalisco. He also arranged for her and Gilbert to stay with a friend at his country house in Cuernavaca "in case the Jalisco scholarship fell through. It did," Vazquez-Amaral later wrote. "After a while the fiery and imaginative Sheri was also unwelcome at the Cuernavaca place" (20). The Mexican authorities expected someone who would paint pretty landscapes and glorify the republic, but Sheri was more interested in sketching beggar girls and exploring Aztec temples (H. D. 53). After about six months Sheri and Gilbert left Mexico for San Francisco.

The best thing to have come out of her Mexican odyssey was a newfound interest in writing. Vazquez-Amaral was dazzled by a piece she wrote on Mexico in 1958: "The title is *Mexico, his Thrust Renews*; the subtitle is *Cheap Hollywood Movie*. In a little over 7 pages, Sheri manages to give one of the strongest and most vivid *impressions* I have ever read on a trip to Mexico from the border to Mexico City. It is all there. I don't say that her painting is to be sneezed at but I still maintain that if given half a chance, Sheri—the Sheri of 1958—would have given Kerouac, Bellow and all the others who have ventured on the quicksands of Mexico some very worthy competition" (20). I haven't seen this piece, but I have seen another portion of the same work, entitled "The Beggar Girl of Queretaro," which is indeed a remarkable piece of writing.

The latter was published in the *Anagogic & Paideumic Review*, a periodical (what we'd now call a 'zine) she started in 1959 after settling in San Francisco. Sheri had forgiven Pound by this time and began the journal to fulfil a promise she made him to help raise the level of culture in this country. (The first issue, in fact, reprinted a 1928 essay of Pound's entitled "Bureaucracy and the Flail of Jehovah.") In issue number 4 she gave this unhelpful explanation of the journal's forbidding title: "A = the direction of the will UP & P = the kulchur born in one's head or wotever/ authority is E.P. - one might have not been listening for real but more or less that is wot one recalls." Actually, "anagogic" is a spiritual interpretation of a text, and "paideumic" derives from *paideuma*, a term Pound picked up from Frobenius to describe "the tangle or complex of the inrooted ideas of any period" (or, more simply, the culture taught by educators). Typed by Sheri and mimeographed in purple ink, the magazine was sold at City Lights book store and mailed to selected friends and libraries. She usually ran off only fifty copies of each issue, and not surprisingly few copies exist anymore.

A typical issue would consist partly of Beat writings and partly of Sheri's own writings, drawings, and commentaries on the other contributions. Pound is frequently quoted, and tribute was paid to H. D. after her death in 1961. The places of publication track Sheri and Gilbert's movements over the next few years: the first four issues were produced in their apartment at 15 Lynch Street on Nob Hill, number 5 was issued from San Gregorio, and number 6 from Half Moon Bay, both small towns down the coast from San Francisco. Number 5 contains a scathing review by Sheri of Charles Norman's *Ezra Pound* (1960), the first biography of the poet and the first to mention Sheri. Both it and number 6 contain poems by Charles Bukowski, with whom Sheri corresponded on a weekly basis for a while in the early sixties; they never met, but she loved his work. An early poem of his entitled "Horse on Fire" indicates that Shari shared with him some memories of St. Elizabeths: "and reading Canto 90 / he put the paper down / Ez did (both their eyes were wet) / and he told her . . . / 'among the greatest love poems / ever written.'" The poem expresses Bukowski's reservations about Canto 90 and Pound's self-appraisal of it, though generally he approved of Pound's work. Sheri is presumably the "M.S." mentioned in his poem "What to Do with Contributor's Copies?" (*Roominghouse Madrigals* 17-18) according to Seamus Cooney in his notes on the letter from which this poem sprang (see *Screams from the Balcony* 34-35). Bukowski's letters to Sheri have not yet been published, but in his published letters to others he occasionally refers to her. Sheri was a harsh editor and berated him "because I stay down in the mud and also because I put her in a poem now and then," but he was fond of her and proud to know her; in a 1965 letter to writer William Wantling, he reported: "Pound's x-girl friend Martinelli trying to cough up my whore-O-scope. stars, something. I suppose this puts me somewhere near the Master. just think, somebody Pound went to bed with is now writing me, has been for years. my, my" (*Screams* 134, 234).

A few supplements to the *Anagogic & Paideumic Review* were published at various times—one showcasing Bukowski, another a booklet by local poet Sam Suzuki entitled *San Francisco Beat Scene: Poetry*—but there is no record of any issues beyond number 6. In most ways the magazine is a product of its times. In his memoir *Bohemia*, Herbert Gold remembers "The hum and whir of the late fifties, early sixties mimeograph machines, churning out beat poetry, deafening me as I walked down North Beach alleys" (37). But Sheri's contributions stand apart from the usual Beat ramblings of the unknown local writers she published. One piece in particular has attained a certain notoriety over the years: while at St. Elizabeths Sheri wrote an essay for Pound entitled "Duties of a Lady Female," a partly tongue-in-cheek primer on how to please a man and defend him from other women (Sheri had been in a few catfights in her time), which Pound found amusing. Sheri published it in the third issue of her magazine, which came into the hands of Diane di Prima, who had stayed with Sheri for two weeks in 1955 when visiting Pound at St. Elizabeths. When she reprinted the essay in her own magazine *Floating Bear* (32 [1966]: 411-13) di Prima added the disclaimer "The views expressed therein are not necessarily those of the editors." Sheri's essay was reprinted recently in Richard Peabody's *A Different Beat*, where he appreciably notes "the sarcastic laser" of her observations on male-female relationships.

In San Francisco Sheri reestablished her connection with the Beat Generation, especially since many of the Beats she had known earlier in Greenwich Village migrated to San Francisco in the late fifties. She was introduced to Jack Kerouac during one of his visits there, though he apparently already knew who she was. Describing Kerouac in 1953, Gerald Nicosia writes: "Jack loved the modern young women on the Village scene and was especially intrigued by the 'Three Graces': Iris Brodie, Sherry [*sic*] Martinelli, and a woman known as the 'silent Madonna' . . . Wearing granny dresses and junkshop jewelry, her hair in a bun, the painter Sherry Martinelli visited Ezra Pound in St. Elizabeth's [*sic*] Hospital and became his mistress," Nicosia concludes, apparently reporting common gossip (455). Sheri's old friend Allen Ginsberg expresses a similar appreciation of these "very beautiful Jewish girls who read Ezra Pound and were into grandma dresses and sewing and amphetamine and junk and bebop and poesy and kept journals and painted," and even recorded a disturbing dream of her: "Up north, in the junk pad—a huge Siberian studio—with Sheri, Heine, various ex or present dead or alive junkies—" (*Journals* xvi, 302). Sheri soon became friends with most of the major Beat writers in San Francisco—Michael McClure, Gary Snyder, Alan Watts, Philip Lamantia, Bob Kaufman (with whom she was especially impressed)—and dabbled in the North Beach scene, a mother hen to the younger beatniks. But mostly she kept to herself, drinking vodka and producing her magazine.

In the early sixties Sheri decided she wanted to get out of the city (though Gilbert would continue to work there as an auto mechanic). She first moved down to a cabin in La Honda, but found the towering redwoods too oppressive, so instead moved into some cabins on the coast about halfway between San Francisco and Santa Cruz, where Tunitas Creek empties into the Pacific Ocean. She would live there at "the Creek" for the next twenty years, though for a mailing address she rented a post office box up in Pacifica, about twenty miles north. The caretaker of the cabins, Walter Clark, would be the subject of a memoir she wrote many years later, which gives some indication of her life there. Though she would soon abandon the *Anagogic & Paideumic Review*, she continued to write, draw, paint, and make jewelry, at night reading *The Cantos* by the light of an old kerosene lamp.

In 1964 Sheri gave her first one-woman show. A Cleveland advertising copywriter named Reid B. Johnson had developed an interest in Sheri's work when making a documentary radio program on Pound while he was still incarcerated at St. Elizabeths. In the course of corresponding with him, Pound sent Johnson a copy of *La Martinelli*, which so impressed him that a few years later he decided to organize an exhibit. After first securing Sheri's cooperation—she agreed to send about twenty oils and drawings—Johnson acquired others on loan, eventually assembling forty-eight works. He then wrote to acquire testimonials to Sheri's work. Johnson managed to elicit some impressive comments, printed in the show's four-page program, which is invaluable for the technical descriptions and dates of the works. In addition to quotations from Pound's introduction to *La Martinelli* and Wykes-Joyce's book (quoted earlier), the program contains statements from Robert Lowell ("Sheri Martinelli's paintings have a style of their own. I admire their grace, dash and uncanniness"), Marianne Moore ("She has a wonderful color sense and the true reverence of the mystic"), and Archibald MacLeish, who loaned Johnson at least one of her paintings and wrote:

> One of my most vivid memories of Pound in St. Elizabeths is a memory of the excitement with which he showed me some photographic reproductions of work by a young artist named Sheri Martinelli. No one who knew Pound ever had reservations about his taste—at least I never did, even when his taste had difficulties with me. I was struck by the reproductions and I was even more struck by the work itself when I saw samples of it: a power of line which asserts itself and cannot possibly be faked or counterfeited.

The show ran for a month in September 1964 at the Severance Center in Cleveland, and was the subject of a photo-essay by Russell W. Kane in the local paper.

Details are sketchy on Sheri's life during the second half of the sixties. Allen Ginsberg visited whenever he could, often bringing along a friend like Peter Orlovsky or Lawrence Ferlinghetti. In his 1966 poem "Iron Horse" Ginsberg recalls

On Pacific cliff-edge
Sheri Martinelli's little house with combs and shells
Since February fear, she saw LSD
Zodiac in earth grass, stood
palm to cheek, scraped her toe
looking aside, & said
"Too disturbed to see you
old friend w/ so much Power" (*Collected Poems* 450)

A year later Ginsberg visited Pound in Venice and asked a favor:

> "I'd like you to give me your blessing to take to Sheri Martinelli"—for I'd
> described her late history Big Sur, eyes seeing Zodiac everywhere hair bound
> up like Marianne Moore—which gossip perhaps he hadn't even heard— "To
> at least say hello to her, I'll tell her, so I can tell her," and stood looking in his
> eyes. "Please . . . because it's worth a lot of *happiness* to her, now . . ." and so he
> looked at me impassive for a moment and then without speaking, smiling
> slightly, also, slight redness of cheeks awrinkle, nodded up and down, affirm,
> looking me in eye, clear no mistake, ok. (*Composed on the Tongue* 10)

That blessing "brought tears to Sheri Martinelli's eyes on the Pacific Ocean edge
a year later, '68" ("Allen Verbatim" 273). In November 1971 she and Gilbert
drove up to Berkeley to attend the American premiere of Pound's opera *The
Testament of François Villon*. Pound didn't attend, but Sheri renewed her
acquaintance there with Olga Rudge, an earlier mistress/protégée of Pound's whom
Sheri had first met at St. Elizabeths in 1955.

One night at the beginning of November 1972, Sheri went out to check on
Walt the caretaker when "a terrible wind came up. A bad wind. A whistling
wind," she later wrote. "One recalled that in Hawaii, not too far off westerly,
such a wind is reported to come up when royal persons or sacred persons are
about to die. . . . One thought there was a talking sound something like: 'Think
ye hard on Ezra Pound' but it didn't make sense" ("A Memoir" 153). The next
morning Sheri learned Pound had died the night before.

There had been little or no contact between them in the fourteen years since
they parted at St. Elizabeths, but for the rest of her life Sheri would think of
Pound almost daily, endlessly rereading *The Cantos*, writing poems about him,
and trying to live up to the example he set for purposeful creative activity. She
continued to produce poetry and drawings, periodically gathering them up into
booklets, which she would photocopy, bind with staples and masking tape, and
send to friends. She apparently made no effort to publish her work through
conventional channels or promote her art in any way, or apply for grants. That is,
she had no interest in becoming a *professional* writer or artist. She did become
something of a professional widow, however: in the late seventies she attended a
Pound session at an MLA meeting in San Francisco dressed in black weeds like an
Edwardian widow. When Pound was slighted in an article in *Paideuma* in 1977 by
her old acquaintance Reno Odlin, Sheri fired off an enraged Mailgram to *Paideuma*
demanding an apology (which was reprinted in facsimile in its winter 1977 issue).
She also began to appreciate all the Pound materials she had saved—letters from
Pound, drafts of cantos, inscribed books—and began thinking about organizing
all this material, both for her own continuing studies of *The Cantos* and for
eventual sale to a library. As Pound studies proliferated in the seventies and eighties,
she began to be approached by critics seeking information, but she regarded most
of them with a wary eye. She felt their neglect of the anagogic possibilities of *The
Cantos* in favor of more mundane matters was wrongheaded, especially since she
had seen how the poems were written. (She put into an epigram the shortcomings
of Pound critics: "each stone is known / but building secrets lost.") Although she

subscribed and occasionally contributed to *Paideuma*, she barely glanced at the many books that were appearing on Pound, even those that mentioned her. She made an exception for Terrell's invaluable *Companion to the Cantos*, because it provided the kind of solid information she needed and because she shared Terrell's conviction that essentially "*The Cantos* is a great religious poem" (vii). (Terrell does perpetuate one error concerning Sheri: the Joey mentioned in Canto 101 was Sheri's younger nephew, not her "kid brother," as Pound believed.)

In 1983, at the age of sixty-five, Sheri decided it was time to retire and return back East. Both she and Gilbert had ailing mothers there to attend, so they left the Creek and drove out to New Jersey; after staying with relatives for a year or so, they finally settled in Falls Church, Virginia, just outside Washington, DC, where they lived for the rest of Sheri's life. Organizing Pound's papers became the primary activity of her days, interrupted often by family concerns and her own failing health. She remained interested in Pound activities: she planned to attend the 1985 centennial Pound conference in Orono, Maine, but last-minute complications caused her to cancel the trip. She did make it up to Rutgers University for a one-day Pound conference on 4 October of the same year, though she arrived too late for anything but the reception afterward. (I was working on my doctorate at Rutgers and met her for the first time that night, after corresponding with her for two years. She made it rudely clear I disappointed her somehow, it pains me to say.) She was invited to other Pound conferences in the eighties, but always declined due to overwork and ill health. One event she was annoyed *not* to be asked to participate in was a show called "Pound's Artists" held in Cambridge and London that same centennial year of 1985. The exhibit focused on the art Pound encountered and wrote about in London, Paris, and Italy. "No USA?" she scribbled on the copy of the program she sent me, urging me to protest the "lack of american art representation," by which she meant her own. She was proud to be the only contemporary American artist whose work is mentioned in *The Cantos*, and this sort of neglect hurt her. This particular slight was rectified a few years later when poet/Pound scholar Peter Bennett arranged for an exhibit of Sheri's work at the 13th Annual International Pound Conference, hosted by the University of Essex in September 1989. Sheri didn't attend but was pleased at this belated recognition of her work. The following year, she did attend another exhibition of her work, also arranged by Peter Bennett, at the Pound-Yeats conference at the University of Maine.

The last time I saw Sheri was in late October 1988, just before I left Rutgers to go to Illinois to work for the Dalkey Archive Press. She and Gilbert drove up to New Brunswick, where we were joined by visiting Pound scholar Massimo Bacigalupo. Sheri showed us some of her treasures, including many letters from Pound and some rough drafts of "her" *Rock-Drill* cantos. We kept in contact over the succeeding years, mostly by phone. Sheri always complained of the endless work involved in organizing her Pound archive while fighting off various illnesses, but these were the most enchanting conversations I have ever had with another person. She spoke in a measured, somewhat melodramatic manner—she reminded me of Carolyn Jones as *The Addams Family's* Morticia, whom Sheri closely resembled in her younger years—and she had a range of tones that would be the envy of any actress, from weariness to outrage to coyness to oracular pronouncements—and she would giggle like a schoolgirl. In her improvised monologues (she did most of the talking) she would quote everyone from Blake to Edgar Cayce, but always returning to *The Cantos* or some wisecrack E.P. (as she always called him) had made, and talk about everything from the annoying antics of neighborhood kids to psychic experiments in the former Soviet Union. She could be surprisingly witty and funny, and told wonderful (if dizzyingly digressive) anecdotes. She remained intellectually active until the end, asking me about Hesiod's *Theogony* or whether I could get an inexpensive Greek dictionary for her. After we finished a phone conversation—"Good-bye" was too final; she always preferred a sing-song "So l-o-o-o-ng"—I always felt like Coleridge at the end of "Kubla Khan," a bit dazed at the heady experience.

One of the last books I edited before leaving Dalkey in 1996 was David Markson's extraordinary novel *Reader's Block*, published in September of that year. In it, an autobiographical narrator contemplates writing a novel; at the same time, he broods over hundreds of cultural anecdotes and quotations, which make up the bulk of the novel. With spaces separating its one- or two-sentence fragments, *Reader's Block* superficially resembles *Rock-Drill* in that it too employs what Pound called "the method of Luminous Detail." On pages 74-75 of Markson's novel this sequence of thoughts comes to the narrator:

No needle marks on your annunciation's arm, now.

We do not come to thoughts. They come to us.
Thought Heidegger.

The first translation of major length for purely literary purposes was a Latin *Iliad*, ca. 250 B.C., by Livius Andronicus.

Sheri Martinelli.

The first line is from Gaddis's *Recognitions*, quoted earlier. A few moments later the narrator realizes he happens to know that Esme was based on a woman named Sheri Martinelli, and records it as one more example of the cultural trivia cluttering up his mind, on par with an obscure Latin translator.

In her final years, Sheri liked to park her camper in front of the local supermarket and watch the people come and go. It was there that she died on 3 November 1996, almost twenty-four years to the day after the death of her beloved Maestro, and forty years after he transformed the fisherman's granddaughter into a goddess.

Ra-Set in her barge now
over deep sapphire (92/638)

Charles Duits

The Birth of Sheri Martinelli

I was never virgin nor was born as others are
A green drum beats in front of a blue curtain
And it was beneath a dawn of great violence that two fishermen bent by the wind
    discovered there in the wet sand my two white feet budding like flowers
And it was a terrible delight to be drawn from the beach's womb inch by inch
    thanks to those two fishermen
The beating of the drum became a pair of arms before which the curtain parted
O grains of yellow sand, like insects you slid off me
Voluptuous wet sand sliding down my thighs
I recall the ochre-colored spasm and how I opened eyes heavy with sleep to see
    the tempest on the faces of the fishermen
My eyes were like crystal jars filled with seawater in which little fish, having
    made love, laid chains of eggs in which tadpoles could already be seen
Look, said the fishermen, she is blind
And suddenly in hushed voices, She is naked, completely naked
Veils of ochre-colored blood, you no longer protect me
The blue curtain folds through the green dream
There where I had been sleeping in the wet sand
The sand crabs with their multitudinous feet traversed my throat every day as they
    would have climbed mounds of sand
But these tender hills were kneaded of a softer clay
And in my parted lips the sand crabs sat as in an armchair
And bantered with their fellows, insinuating themselves on the balcony of my
    shoulders
On the balcony of my shoulders, I mean my collarbones
The sand envelops my flesh, the sand was a featherbed of tenderness
The drum beats far away, calling, calling
At nightfall O dark crustaceans rising from the depths of the waves you have
    chosen a very soft bed in me you have spread out your limbs in a caress you
    have chosen to live in my vulva
The foam clings less to the rocks than your pincers deeply grafted to my most
    secret flesh
And I, I am tired of being a woman preyed upon by starving men
Tired of being given over to their need to be wounded, to be abandoned
And I long for a lover who will sleep all night his lips on mine and his hand in the
    same fault and as delicate as the claws of the crabs
What to say of the taste of the sea, what to say of the cave of sleep
The fishermen, their faces changed, took of my body in order to quell their
    hunger
O I am not nourishment for starving men

I wish only to be a house
A house of lips and secret folds
Where they may exist in peace
And sleep like insects all night in my mouth
Their fingers in my vulva
Their fingers deep in the sand
Tranquil and the drum beats on
The drum beats out the call of heaven

(Written ca. 1946; trans. George Kearns and Rikki Ducornet)

WORKS CITED

Bacigalupo, Massimo. *The Forméd Trace: The Later Poetry of Ezra Pound.* New York: Columbia U P, 1980.

Bair, Deirdre. *Anaïs Nin: A Biography.* New York: Putnam's, 1995.

Booth, Marcella. "Ezrology: The Class of '57." *Paideuma* 13.3 (Winter 1984): 375-88.

Broyard, Anatole. *Kafka Was the Rage: A Greenwich Village Memoir.* New York: Crown/Carol Southern, 1993.

Bukowski, Charles. "Horse on Fire." *The Roominghouse Madrigals: Early Selected Poems 1946-1966.* Santa Rosa, CA: Black Sparrow, 1988. 70.

———. *Screams from the Balcony: Selected Letters 1960-1970.* Ed. Seamus Cooney. Santa Rosa, CA: Black Sparrow, 1993.

Carpenter, Humphrey. *A Serious Character: The Life of Ezra Pound.* Boston: Houghton Mifflin, 1988.

Deren, Maya. *Ritual in Transfigured Time.* 1945-46. In *Experimental Films, 1943-1959.* Mystic Fire Video, 1986.

Findley, Timothy. *The Trials of Ezra Pound.* Winnipeg: Blizzard, 1994.

Flory, Wendy Stallard. *Ezra Pound and* The Cantos: *A Record of Struggle.* New Haven: Yale U P, 1980.

Gaddis, William. *The Recognitions.* New York: Harcourt, Brace, 1955.

Gates, Henry Louis, Jr. "White Like Me." *New Yorker,* 17 June 1996, 66-72, 74-81.

Ginsberg, Allen. "Allen Verbatim." Paideuma 3.2 (Fall 1974): 253-73.

———. *Journals: Early Fifties Early Sixties.* Ed. Gordon Ball. New York: Grove, 1977.

———. *Composed on the Tongue: Literary Conversations, 1967-1977.* Ed. Donald Allen. San Francisco: Grey Fox, 1980.

———. "Iron Horse." *Collected Poems 1947-1980.* New York: Harper & Row, 1984.

Gold, Herbert. *Bohemia.* New York: Simon & Schuster, 1993.

Gordon, David. "From the Blue Serpent to Kati." *Paideuma* 3.2 (1974): 239-44.

Guest, Barbara. *Herself Defined: The Poet H. D. and Her World.* Garden City, NY: Doubleday, 1984.

H. D. *End to Torment: A Memoir of Ezra Pound.* New York: New Directions, 1979.

Heymann, C. David. *Ezra Pound: The Last Rower.* New York: Viking/Richard Seaver, 1976.

Kane, Russell W. "A One-Woman Art Show." *Cleveland Plain Dealer Sunday Magazine,* 6 September 1964, 6-7.

Laughlin, James. *Pound as Wuz: Essays and Lectures on Ezra Pound.* Saint Paul: Graywolf, 1987.

McNaughton, Bill. "Pound, A Brief Memoir: 'Chi Lavora, Ora.'" *Paideuma* 3.3 (Winter 1974): 219-24.

Markson, David. *Reader's Block.* Normal, IL: Dalkey Archive P, 1996.

Martinelli, Sheri. *La Martinelli.* Introduction by Ezra Pound. Milan: Vanni Scheiwiller, 1956.

———. "Duties of a Lady Female." *Anagogic & Paideumic Review* 1.3 (1959). Rpt. in *A Different Beat: Writings by Women of the Beat Generation.* Ed. Richard Peabody. London and New York: Serpent's Tail/High Risk, 1997. 154-58.

———. "The Beggar Girl of Queretaro." *Anagogic & Paideumic Review* 1.4 (1961?): 26-29.

———. [Letter to the editor.] *Paideuma* 6.3 (Winter 1977): 415-16.

———. "Canto CVI." Unpublished poem/commentary, dated 6 December 1984.

———. "A Memoir." *Paideuma* 15.2-3 (Fall-Winter 1986): 151-62.

———. "Pound as Wuz." Unpublished commentary on Laughlin (above), dated 11 April 1988.

———. "Goodbye Anaïs." *Anaïs: An International Journal* 12 (1994): 77.

Mullins, Eustace. *This Difficult Individual, Ezra Pound.* New York: Fleet, 1961.

Nicosia, Gerald. *Memory Babe: A Critical Biography of Jack Kerouac.* Berkeley: U of California P, 1994.

Nin, Anaïs. *The Diary of Anaïs Nin, 1944-1947.* Ed. Gunther Stuhlmann. New York: Harcourt Brace Jovanovich, 1971.

Pound, Ezra. "Prayer for a Dead Brother." *Antigonish Review* 8 (Winter 1972): 27.

———. *The Cantos.* New York: New Directions, 1995 (Thirteenth Printing).

———, and E. E. Cummings. *Pound/Cummings: The Correspondence of Ezra Pound and E. E. Cummings.* Ed. Barry Ahearn. Ann Arbor, MI: U of Michigan P, 1996.

———, and James Laughlin. *Selected Letters.* Ed. David M. Gordon. New York: Norton, 1994.

Rattray, David. "Weekend with Ezra Pound." *Nation* 185 (16 November 1957): 343-49.

Stock, Noel. *The Life of Ezra Pound: An Expanded Edition.* San Francisco: North Point, 1982.

Stumvoll, Josef. "Ezra Pound schreibt uns." *Biblos* (Vienna) 8.2 (1959): 74-83.

Terrell, Carroll F. *A Companion to the Cantos of Ezra Pound.* Volume II (Cantos 74-117). Berkeley: U of California P, 1984.

Torrey, E. Fuller. *The Roots of Treason: Ezra Pound and the Secret of St. Elizabeths.* New York: McGraw-Hill, 1984.

Vazquez-Amaral, José. "La Martinelli." *Rutgers Review* 4.1 (Spring 1970): 19-21.

Wilhelm, J. J. *Ezra Pound: The Tragic Years, 1925-1972.* University Park, PA: Pennsylvania State U P, 1994.

Wykes-Joyce, Max. *7000 Years of Pottery and Porcelain.* New York: Philosophical Library, 1958.

Undocumented quotations from Sheri Martinelli are from my correspondence and phone conversations with her, 1983-96. Further information was supplied by Gilbert Lee during phone conversations in 1997.

David L. Ulin

Kerouac's Ghost

Lowell, Massachusetts
October 21, 1989

Jack Kerouac didn't drive. All those years, all those cross-country journeys, all that travelling back and forth from East Coast to West, from Lowell, Massachusetts to New York to North Carolina to Texas to Mexico City to San Francisco, he never spent one second behind the wheel. For a man so associated with the freedom of the open road, he always left the driving to someone else—to Greyhound, to the strangers who picked him up hitchhiking, and, of course, to Neal Cassady, who, in the late 1940s, once did Denver to Chicago in seventeen hours, devouring the twelve hundred desolate miles of blacktop between the two cities as if pursued by the hounds of hell.

That's a small fact, on the face of things, insignificant almost, just another way the truth about Kerouac diverges from the myth. But I can't stop thinking about it because today, *I* am the passenger, sitting full of ambivalence as my friend Stu drives north on Route 27 towards Chelmsford, Massachusetts, where we will pick up Route 110 for Lowell. Outside, the trees have turned brown and lost their leaves; it is a crisp morning, with air that smells like wood smoke, and a light dusting of frost lying in eddies on the ground. All the years I lived in New England, I used to love days like this, used to love the sallow quality of their light, the darkness creeping across the fields at the end of the afternoon, the shadows disappearing into the long Northeastern night. As Kerouac himself wrote in his first novel *The Town and the City*, "when the sun of October slopes in late afternoon, the children scurry home from school, make footballs out of stuffed socks, [then] leap and dash in the powerful winds and scream with delight."

Like his friend Allen Ginsberg, Jack Kerouac would be some kind of literary elder statesman if he were alive today; instead, Stu and I are on a pilgrimage to his grave on the twentieth anniversary of his death. At the time of his funeral, Kerouac was largely dismissed as a serious literary figure, only three of his books—*On the Road*, *The Dharma Bums*, and *Book of Dreams*—still in print. Now, there is a monument for him in downtown Lowell, and a creative writing program—the Jack Kerouac School of Disembodied Poetics—established in his name at the Naropa Institute in Boulder, Colorado. Just a few months prior to this trip, I attended a Sunday afternoon marathon reading of Kerouac's long poem *Mexico City Blues* at a jazz club in Greenwich Village (honoring his intention "to be considered a jazz poet blowing a long blues in an afternoon jam session on Sunday"); virtually all his surviving Beat counterparts, from Ginsberg to Herbert Huncke to Gregory Corso to Carl Solomon, were there, trading off choruses of his work while a trio of sax, bass, and drums jammed behind them. All in all,

Kerouac is a larger presence on the American cultural landscape than he has been in nearly a generation, a figure of mythic proportions on spoken word scenes coast-to-coast, where his ideas on spontaneous writing and his sad-eyed quest for kicks and experience are invoked by poets and scenesters who were themselves barely alive, if at all, when he died.

As we make the turnoff onto Route 110 and head into Lowell, neither Stu nor I says very much. Although I spent three years attending boarding school in Andover, less than twelve miles away, I've never been here, and my first impression is of how much Lowell resembles every other mill town in the area—squat, blocky red brick cities built at the turn of the century, quarried out of hillsides and the rocky banks of the Merrimack River, full of heavy stone constructions thrown up against the cold, thin light of the Massachusetts sky. I remember prowling the streets of Lawrence as a student, discovering warehouse districts littered with broken glass and mortar that looked like photographs of the Great Depression; today, I feel the same way I did back then, as if the simple act of squinting my eyes might be enough to reconfigure time. Driving through these blank industrial streets, it's hard to know where memory ends and imagination begins.

We leave Stu's car in an ash-gray concrete parking structure on the edge of downtown, and exit into the Saturday morning hush. The sidewalks are empty, the sun pale and weak, casting little heat. At a newsstand, I buy a copy of *The Lowell Sun*, where Kerouac once worked briefly as a sportswriter; afterwards, Stu and I walk down the block to a storefront diner with faded vinyl chairs and Formica tables that look as if they haven't been replaced in fifty years. We order eggs, toast, and coffee, and scan the paper, but there is no mention of Kerouac's name. Briefly, I think about the photos I've seen of Kerouac at the end of his life— bloated, boozy, face florid and eyes small black pinpricks floating in a rheumy sea—and compare that with the popular perception of the rebel angel, the dark-haired saint of the underground. For a decade or longer, I've struggled to reconcile these images, and now I'm hoping that, by paying my respects, I can achieve some kind of resolution, that by making this visit to Lowell, I can, once and for all, put Kerouac into perspective, escape the weight of his romantic myth.

There have been times in my life when I measured everything against Jack Kerouac, times when his words have been so strong within me that my own voice was all but drowned out. For obvious reasons, this has left me deeply wary of being overwhelmed. Nonetheless, I continue to respond to Kerouac in a way I never have with other writers or cultural icons, his influence a fundamental aspect of how I define myself. On a rational level, I can see the man for what he was—a contradictory, often bitter figure who retreated into the bottle when the burdens of his life became too much—but in my imagination, he is forever young and lean, his face as chiseled as a piece of New Hampshire granite, charisma literally rolling off him in waves. By the same token, I'm aware of the uneven quality of his work, but ever since I first came upon Kerouac in my early teens, his idiosyncratic mix of sadness and euphoria, of irony and exuberance, has represented, for me, at least, the epitome of cool, a way of engaging the world while remaining slightly on the outside. It's a position I have always found attractive, one to which I am naturally drawn.

Over the last several years, my fascination with Kerouac has ebbed and flowed like the tides, advancing and receding in my consciousness according to some internal rhythm I can't quite understand. As an adolescent, sitting in my boarding school room sneaking furtive puffs of pot, I dreamed of partaking in my own version of the Beat experience, hitting the highway to discover a place more elemental than the one in which I found myself, more concerned with spirit and substance, where the petty concerns of my friends and parents—grades, popularity, college—would be subsumed in favor of something more profound. It was a stereotypical perspective, but no less potent for being so, and given my sheltered, upper-middle-class upbringing, the appeal it held still makes a lot of sense. If you buy the myth, after all, Kerouac stood in opposition to every received notion I was being encouraged, often against my own private judgments, to accept. He turned his back on an Ivy League education, opting instead for the bhikku's backpack and the mystery of the open road. He wrote what he felt like, when he felt like it, creating an "original classic literature," that celebrates the transitory nature of existence and laments the inevitability of death. He travelled with a group of outcast geniuses who glorified each other's exploits until they had created the ultimate in-group, their reports from the fringes the cultural equivalent of an atom bomb. He was impulsive, extemporaneous, a creature of intuition. More than anything, he was not tied down.

Yet the problem with the Kerouac myth, I've come to understand, is that it is precisely that: a larger-than-life archetype reducing the author to a two-dimensional version of himself. For Kerouac *was* tied down; he spent most of his life sharing quarters with his mother, and until the end was so frightened of her wrath that if she called a house where he'd been drinking, he would automatically sober up before coming to the phone. He was a reactionary, a supporter of the war in Vietnam, who never acknowledged his only daughter Jan while he was alive. He was an alcoholic, a barroom brawler, a romanticizer of skid row bums, who destroyed his talent with cheap wine and Scotch and died of massive esophageal hemorrhaging (what his biographer Gerald Nicosia has called a "classic drunkard's death") at the age of forty-seven. He was also, for a period of about seven years in the early and mid-1950s, one of the most startlingly original and diverse writers in the history of American letters, a man who, by his own admission was "blowing such mad poetry and literature that I'll look back years later with amazement and chagrin that I can't do it anymore."

That "mad poetry and literature" has everything to do with why I've decided to come to Lowell today, why I need to connect these conflicting impulses into a more cohesive vision of Kerouac and his work. It's all part of that ebb and flow, the rise and fall of his voice within my head. Lately, I've been obsessing about him as much as I ever have, hearing the admonishing textures of his broad New England accent each time I revise a sentence, or begin a story that's not completely rooted in the truth. Years ago, when I was taking my first, tentative steps towards becoming a writer, Kerouac's first-thought-best-thought theories of spontaneous composition seemed to me a fundamental means of breaking through my own polished surfaces, of opening myself up to whimsy, to improvisation and jazz. I remember my sense of discovery the first time I read *Mexico City Blues*, how I came away from the experience with a new appreciation of what poetry could do, of the relationship of music, of rhythm, to meaning in a literary work. Of course, spontaneous writing is a lot harder than it looks; you have to turn off every bit of critical reflex in your mind, and just let the words and associations find their way across the page. In fact, it's taken me until this past summer, two months prior to visiting Lowell, to write *Cape Cod Blues*, a blues poem of my own, after better than a dozen attempts to pull it off.

Now, though, the strain of derivation has become too much. Over the summer, when I was writing *Cape Cod Blues*, with *Tristessa* on my night table and Nicosia's biography *Memory Babe* in my bag for the beach, Kerouac was such a presence that to try and get a handle on him by visiting his tomb seemed like the most logical thing I could do. What better way, after all, of making him physical, of defusing his mythological impact, of somehow placing him within the world? Yet several times in the last few weeks, I've picked up the phone to call Stu and cancel the trip, and on the train ride up to Massachusetts, I watched the question marks crawl across my face in the darkened window glass, as I wondered whether I was getting in too deep. During my three years at Andover, I always resisted making this journey, even though most weekends, one group of friends or another would take the bus to Lowell and spend a couple of hours sitting on the cemetery grass, passing a jug of red wine, pouring a little into the earth over Kerouac's head each time it was his turn. Maybe it was reticence, maybe a desire to maintain whatever distance I could, but the only time I've even seen the gravesite was in an old issue of *Rolling Stone*, where a news photo captured Bob Dylan and Allen Ginsberg taking a break from the Rolling Thunder Revue tour to pay their respects, sitting on crossed legs beneath the bare trees of autumn, singing and chanting to the dead man's bones. Once, that picture filled me with excitement, with the surety that here was the place I was seeking, where poetry and music was common currency, and society was what you made of it, not the other way around. That, however, was many years ago, and thinking about it today is enough to raise the hackles of my ambivalence all over again.

Stu and I finish our breakfasts, and move out of the diner in the direction of downtown. By now, the sidewalks are starting to fill up; it is getting on to late morning, and the stores of Lowell are open for business, just like any other Saturday. The city's central corridor has a refurbished look, the ancient industrial buildings scrubbed, ruddy, their facades freshly painted, as if they were monuments in a historic district like the South Street Seaport or Fanueil Hall. For a moment, the whole thing almost seems like a photograph, caught in some strange suspension of time, but ultimately, the streets are too clean, too well-attended for the illusion to hold. I try to see Kerouac in such a landscape, try to remember his descriptions of Galloway in *The Town and the City*, or Pawtucketville in *Dr. Sax*. Those were living places, full of grime and mystery; if they were faces, they would be etched deep with creases, pockmarked, weatherbeaten, lined with wear and age. But

Lowell this morning is like a matron with a facelift, all her history erased in favor of this newly polished look, and I can't help feeling that I could be anywhere, any town with a few vintage structures and an aggressive Chamber of Commerce eager to redirect the past.

After checking out the heart of the city, Stu and I ask a couple of passers-by how to get to the Kerouac Memorial, dedicated with great fanfare only a couple of years before. One after another greets our request with a blank stare. "Kerouac?" a man asks. "I don't think I know that name." Finally, we wander over to the offices of the Lowell Historical Society, where we pick up a map and directions to both the Memorial and other Kerouac landmarks scattered throughout the town. When Stu inquires about commemorative activities, though, the woman behind the counter gives us a long scowl. "Here in Lowell, we prefer to mark Kerouac's birth, not his death," she tells us, as if she's heard the question once too often. And all of a sudden, I get a glimpse of Stu and myself through her eyes—just two more acolytes of the King of the Beats, me with my earrings and long hair, Stu all dressed in black. It's exactly the image I'm seeking to distance myself from, and the idea of being seen this way makes my stomach clench. Once again, I start thinking that maybe this whole thing isn't such a good idea.

But good idea or no, Stu and I have both come a long way, so I swallow back my doubts, and we set off for the Kerouac Memorial, trying to decipher the grainy Xeroxed lines of the map. Even with directions, the Memorial is nearly impossible to find, and by the time we get there, Stu and I have seen most of the available markers of Kerouac's life. We pass Lowell High School, stop at the church where Kerouac's funeral took place, cross the threadbare span of the Moody Street Bridge to Pawtucketville and stare from street level at the fourth floor apartment in which he lived as a teenager. Finally, after an hour or more of meandering back and forth along the same stretch of road, we discover what we're looking for, an arrangement of marble slabs engraved with excerpts from Kerouac's books, erected in a small park on the banks of the Merrimack. For both of us, the day has long since taken on a surreal quality, as if we are living in one reality and everybody else in another, so we are not especially surprised that we have walked by this spot a number of times. We make a circuit of the park, sit down in the shadow of the stones. I read the words, Stu takes a couple of pictures. We are all alone.

If there were ever an appropriate moment for me to resolve my relationship with Kerouac, this would probably be it. But life does not imitate art, and this afternoon in Lowell, there is no instant of revelation, no sign that will somehow clear up all this ambivalence and put everything in its place. Actually, confronted with the Monument, I find myself confused all over again, at how the living flesh of Kerouac's language seems so out-of-place preserved upon the static surface of the rock. When this memorial was built, Norman Podhoretz, once Kerouac's classmate at Columbia University, complained that it sent the wrong message to honor someone who had led so many people's lives astray. At the time, I thought Podhoretz was just being contrary, that his comments were additional proof of how poorly served Kerouac had been by the terms of his own myth. Sitting here, however, I can't help but think that this fails to serve Kerouac either, that immortalizing his words in marble is exactly the wrong way to go. It's such a seeming contradiction—the middle-class values that inform the Monument versus the avant-garde sentiments etched on its polished sides—that it only works to heighten my discomfort, transforming the ethereal textures of Kerouac's writing into something solidly respectable, and dead. Twenty years later, is this what Kerouac's "spontaneous bop prosody" has become, a series of tombstones, proscriptions, laws?

The wind picks up off the Merrimack and blows a swath of dirt across the park. Dust rasps in the empty spaces between the facades of jutting marble, sifts in the letters of Kerouac's name. Stu turns up his collar, stands, and stomps his feet. "You ready?" he asks. I nod.

So we turn away from the Monument, and beat a path back into downtown Lowell. By now, foot traffic is thin again, the streets emptying like a river as the light slowly fades from the sky. Stu and I retrace our footsteps, past the Historical Society, past the diner where we had breakfast so many hours ago. In a certain sense, it feels as if we are rewinding time, as if we are not just covering old ground but moving backwards, as if, in the last thirty minutes, we have slipped some kind of boundary, and can actually retrace the past.

That feeling comes on even stronger when we arrive at Edson Cemetery, where Kerouac is buried beneath a simple marble marker laid flush to the ground. As we pull through the gates and open the windows to ask directions to the tomb, the sky reddens to a dusky shade of plum, and our breath is visible in wisps of precipitation. The caretaker gives us a map of the grounds; Stu puts the car in gear. Edson Cemetery is laid out like a city, with numbered streets and avenues, all paved and wide enough for two-way traffic. For a couple of blocks, we see nothing but shadows lengthening across the ornate Victorian monuments and through the keening, bare-ribbed trees. Then we take a left, and Stu's headlights flicker against a shadow dance of movement, a scraggly band of people clustered around a solitary grave.

Stu stops the car about twenty feet away. He cuts the ignition and the lights, and for a second, the only sound is the ticking of the engine as it cools. I roll down my window, take a deep breath of sharp fall air. From up ahead, I can smell marijuana, and see a bottle of wine making the rounds. Periodically, someone spills some of the dark liquid into the ground. At first, I'm not quite sure what's happening, but then I understand that, like my boarding school friends, whoever's out there is marking Kerouac's place in the circle whenever it comes around.

And watching them, I start to feel a little telescoped, as if it *is* my teenage buddies sitting there upon the grave. My mind flashes back to the photo of Dylan and Ginsberg, and all of a sudden, I am drawn to that circle, to the romance of it, the illusion of camaraderie so strong that it's almost as if, by sheer force of will, these people could resurrect Kerouac from his premature demise. As the light continues to slip, a tall, stocky teenager stands up in the middle of the pack. From here, it's all I can do to make out his silhouette, like a ghost in the gloaming, and it takes me a minute to notice the book in his hands. I lean out the window, peering at the cover; outside, someone lights a cigarette, and in its glow, the title becomes momentarily clear. *Visions Of Cody.* An odd choice, I think, and wonder what he's doing, until the wind changes direction, and his low, droning intonations sweep over me like a storm.

For he is reading. "It's been so long since I've heard the sound of the Merrimack River washing over rocks in the middle of a soft summer's night," he mumbles, his voice marked by the broad vowel sounds of the region, not very different from Kerouac's own. The pull of those syllables is contagious, and in the thrall of their rhythms, I remember the Kerouac Monument and its silent letters, think about the contradictions at its core. To tell the truth, I had expected to find something similar here, but what fills the cemetery instead is Kerouac's living language, his words soaring like birds in the darkening air. "It's our work that counts, if anything at all," he told *The Paris Review* in 1967, and this ragtag tribute is nothing if not a testament to that. I make a move to open the car door, but then, as if I were a teenager again, something stops me, keeps me apart. This is, after all, the thing I was most afraid I might end up confronting, and the idea that it is somehow attuned to what Kerouac was really all about just adds a final layer to all the mixed emotions my trip to Lowell was supposed to dispel.

So, as usual, I wait. I wait until everyone has returned to their cars and driven slowly out of Edson Cemetery, calling "Goodnight, Jack" as their taillights fade away. I wait until Stu and I are the last people left, until between the cracks of night's descent, the caretaker's truck begin to make its rounds. I wait until there's no one left to give witness, before I finally extricate myself from Stu's passenger seat and approach the grave. Standing there, I observe a moment of silence, then take out my notebook and scrawl something suitably ambivalent, one of my favorite quotes from Kerouac, which I leave upon the stone:

"Perhaps nothing is true but everything is real"…

Cynthia Connolly

Portfolio

Black Canyon, Arizona
1 - 19 - 97

Jamika Ajalon

Blackability
(where da revolution at—revisited)

It's a mad, mad world
& i'm sitting on this "A" train
riding into the madness of Manhattan
wid all these mad people
most of them don't know they mad
but u see
i revel in my madness
find rhythm in my badness
yeah my bad black ass

& the only reason i'm black
iz coz' i ain't white
or i think that's why
see i've been called

an oreo/a freak/a black hippy/a slut/a hoe/a niggah/a spade
and i've been called an a-typical negro
because i would remember to say
"are not" instead of ain't
and cannot instead of cain't
cause i practised with Hepburn
"the rain in Spain stays mainly on the plaaain"
shit still can't get that right

see i waz born in the '60s
grew up through the '70s
and my blood is still screamin'
with that psychedelic residue

squeezin' thru my teenage yearz
spittin' blood i swallowed my fears
& when time came for me to fly i flew
with my ratty bag & needin' to stay nappy head
i left my St. Louie
bluuuuz
to live a life i would chooze

but wasn't altogethah
prepared for the gap
between not being white
& being truly black

went out and tested my
blackability
came out black hippy/freak/punk
but i said that still ain't me
u missin' some important ingredients

"what are u/what are u/you got good hair"

Niggggahhh
turned super African-Amerikkkan over night

i'm super negro
son of the new negro
don't you know
i can wrap that kente-cloth in a single bound
say by any means necessary any time necessary
by any means necessary

i know what it means to be black
& i know what ain't black jack
i mean soooouund black
see her hair like that
dreads creepin' naked down the back

look like she's dressed in some potato sack
—lookin' ragamuffin
u can't be black like that
i mean soooouund black

& the way she walks with that swagger
woulda thought she waz a bulldagger
shit, bitch lost in a sea of whiteness
nobody i know that's black
iz freaky queer like that
we have pride in ourselves & we don't need no homosexuals
faggots
fuckin' wid that man
pride iz our manhood,
our Black Manhood
the African Queens

know what it means to
stand by this big black dick

trick—aaah

oh super black fly Niggah
why u gotta be callin' me outta my name like that?
why u gotta be callin' me outta my name
like that?

we cannot possibly be a re-vo-lu-tion like that
and how many young homies
wearin' the Malcolm X hat
know where the revolution at…
know where the revolution at?

You see we do not live in a melting pot
Amerikkka's way too icy
to be anybody's
meltin' pot
it's too cold for my
black-non-black ass out here
i think I'll go back
under the veil

Elizabeth W. Andrews

The Swimming Lesson

I knew you best in water:
your crisp blue suit, that flowered skirt,
I remember how it opened
beneath my legs, the celery colored pool
with mysterious drains. I clung to you,
covered your pale blue body
with my own, as if it took two of us
to drown. You kicked, we struggled
to the deep end. Rootless, a ladder beckoned
in the meager sun. Hoses slumbered,
and nets for small caught things
hung from silver poles, hollow and remote.
You'd rescue anything that couldn't right itself:
beetles trapped on their backs, Daddy Longlegs
drunk on chlorine. Once you nursed a spider
in the palm of your hand.

In the water you'd confess to anything, flatter me until
I could have loved you for it. It was as if
you wanted me, the things you said,
little nets I took for affection, how you wished
you'd been loved, the way people talk,
I've been told, who haven't spoken
for years. You almost had me
believing I was your audience, the one
you flowered for. The place
was ours. Slowly I learned to subtract myself
from the listening air. Pleasure
had nothing to do with it. I practiced
the dead man's float, and you
kept on talking, as if
you were alone
in that cold green water.

Joe Asser

Graffiti Artist

Daubed along the side of the Universal
Church of God in Finsbury Park are the
words Ken Dodd's Dad's Dog is Dead.
But is this more or less significant than
the fact God can indeed be termed
universal, or the fact God exists at all, even
though Ken Dodd's Dad's dog does not.
Unless his Dad's bought another dog,
whereas we all know God is very much
a one-off and outside space and time.
Unlike Ken Dodd who must be getting on
a bit now and I doubt his Dad has much
further to go either, in fact, he probably
joined his dog many years previously.
While God is right here, right now and
always has been and always will be. But
does that really help Ken Dodd, or his Dad,
or his Dad's dog, or you, or me. Is the
Universal Church of God in Finsbury Park
on the ball, or merely kidding itself for
the tax rebate you receive on covenanted
donations? Ken Dodd certainly worked out
a few tax loopholes for himself until he got
caught, whereas Our Lord was always very
cooperative when it came to the local revenue
officials. But maybe He was trying to say
something else when he beat up several
other members of the economic hierarchy
outside the temple gates, or were they inside?
I don't remember and anyway it doesn't matter
because God is alive and well in Finsbury Park
and Ken Dodd's Dad's Dog is dead.

Steve Aylett

Bestiary

Albatross: expressionless, cruising bird. In *The Ancient Mariner* Coleridge hung a dead one around the protagonist's neck in a desperate attempt to make him more interesting.

Bat: this animal is harmless when found in a kidney tray.

Crab: write incriminating evidence on its back and see it run.

Dog: malevolent, n-shaped animal, which may sometimes be heard to speak.

Eel: hose and nozzle, moving in water.

Frog: rubber monster which stares openly at friend and foe alike.

Garter snake: a sacred animal in many tribes, the garter snake is best when roasted.

Hammerhead: large inflatable shark. Only the fins, sneering mouth and tremendous size tell the common man that this is no ordinary pet.

Icthyosaurus: prehistoric dolphin with hubcap eyes, first discovered by Mary Anning in Cornwall while she was dynamiting fish.

Jaguar: when provoked, this car will explode.

Knife: in cricket, the object one throws at a bastard.

Lizard: when mashed, this animal resembles snot.

Maggot: treadle-operated finger biscuit made mainly of beef.

Narwhal: elephant with dangerous, stabbing nose and dry sense of humour.

Octopus: doughy animal which, when removed from its ocean environment, is disconcertingly useless.

Penguin: black and white creature with a bill, often mistaken for a lawyer.

Quetzalcoatl: inflatable god of the Aztecs, known for its raised eyebrows and milk-giving shoulder blades.

Ribbonfish: elongated animal used by senior judges for self-flagellation. The fish is also used for the binding of wrists and in emergencies may be discreetly eaten.

Salami: zombie meat—leave it alone.

Trilobyte: thrown at a mime, this empty fossil shatters hard on impact.

Underwear: tight clothing worn by some federal agents.

Vampire bat: cute, pig-faced bird which drinks blood. The family *Megadermitidae* cannot drink blood and are called 'false vampires', which goes to show that if you're a bat, you can't win.

Whip: the ostentatious manner in which a public speaker discards his trousers.

Xylophone: percussion instrument made from vicars' ribs and played at high speed by circus clowns.

Yell: the manner in which one addresses a policeman.

Z particle: possessing a weak nuclear force, these particles are seen to bear a likeness of Orson Welles' face when viewed at 20nm resolution.

Francesca Beard

The Poem That Was Really a List

the spade that was really a symbol
the queen who was really a son
the king who was really a rock-star
the mad-man that was really God
the milk-man that was really dad.

the waitress who was really an actress
the actor who was really an artist
the artist who was really a pornographer
the small boy who was really a helicopter

the car that was really a toy
the toy that was really a bribe
the toy poodle that was really a baby
the baby that was really a last ditch attempt

the cafe latte that was really a milky coffee
the soup that was really a meal in itself

the studio flat that was really a bed-sit
the short-cut that was really a cul-de-sac
the nine-to-five that was really a ball and chain
the pain-free diet that was really a cash-loss weight gain

the commercial success that was really a sell-out failure
the check that was really in the mail

the lack of interest that was really impotence
the frigid cocktease that was really lack of interest
the one night stand that was really a date rape
the mercy fuck that was really an act of love

the leaked statement that was really a press release
the statistic that was really a cooked book

the apology that was really an excuse
the excuse that was really a screw you
the anecdote that was really an extended slap in the face

the helping hand that was really a kick in the teeth
the stiff upper lip that was really a cold shoulder
the last laugh that was really an own goal

the little bird that was really a can of worms
the fresh start that was really a wrong turn
the youthful radience that was really soft focus
the race riot that was really a political protest

the spiritual journey that was really an ego trip
the inner child that was really a spoilt brat

the home that was really an investment
the marital relations that were really a form of rent
the sofa that was really a bed
the park bench that was really a bed

the cynic who was really a romantic
the romantic who was really a sexist
the sexist who was really a phobic
the love that was really fear
the fear that was really nothing
the ending that was really nearly here.

Elisa Biagini

Morgue

Dead man in the fire
his stretched skin
like a slaking pink
like dead paper,
only the label doesn't burn
and the string.

It's reflected, enormous, in my eye.

On the dune of the nose
a mark, only,
rough-hewn,
a hollow to collect liquids.
The very eyes have a fading hue.

Half a look
red,
a horizon
a hanging rag stooping to the black hole,
to the half screen.

Meanwhile,
under the fire,
pendant of bones
the sheltered face,

the respected symmetry of the dead.

Fingerprints have fallen in the dark
and shrunk.

They got soaked
then immediately dried
by an overkilling draught

coming out from a dim
but deep opening

here,
just above the wrist.

Crooked stigmata
mark from a mistaken aim
now a dried scar,
a naval, indeed,

but with no organs inside
just tubes.

You lose your eyes
they drown in the sea of humors
where glassy melts into watery
and the pupil too,

some dough falls onto your hands—
the well of all photons.

In the curves of the hands
in the loops,
see that misfallen
shade,
plumbago, almost

and the shell-nails
match with the spots of the skin.

You are the very closest to sleep,
paper bracelet
label of a dispatched suitcase—
submerged
in this odd remnant
without a request.

Fishes love your pallor,
bare hand.

A hug in the invisible air
like the arm of a headless crane
standing
as in a far-off attention

the skin is so rough:
the last shiver while freezing.

Slips out the blanket from the face
the plastic shroud,
dull like sour milk,
reveals two empty plates
two shutters fallen on the bone,
every speech is vain.

Finger touching finger
around the wrist,
it's the mark of the sock:
it's the pause of the liquids
with time.

There is no sample
of that sound,
you can only imagine that step
or the drop that falls
and fades it.

Poison-dried, not a drop.
A desert in the body:

the very blood is dust
out of the wound
like grains from a sandglass

getting lost out of the clockwork.

The nails,
deaf to silence
keep on working
because they know
that darkness has no grips

everything is straight and smooth
like a well.

Under the surface wind and bones
but from here light and on the table
the shape
covered
the dress on the face,
a wave of detergent
that blinds you.

A last photogram between the eyelashes
a pupil still in its frame
tile-like
the curdled tear:
on the film light gets caught and still veils

the glassy eye
the marble, glazed with oversleeping.

Years sunken
in the emptiness
of the ear
time dissolves,
a stained eye
with commas and full stops left
under the black well of the voice.

A body felted by wrong washings
and some dark spots
won't go away
they are like holes
made by bugs:
you're moth-eaten.

At every cough
you put out a candle
your heart is darkness.

Paul Birtill

Best Seller

Poetry doesn't normally sell,
but mine might because I intend
to embark on a series of bizarre
motiveless murders on and around
Hampstead Heath. Poetry doesn't
normally sell, but mine might....

Eugénie Bisulco

Bodies

I love the way a body anticipates
a touch,
a comfortable way to lift an awkward thing,
when and how to dodge a ball or a fist.
I watch a mother and son together
hoist a stroller up onto the sidewalk.
Their bodies know the push and pull
it takes to get it right.

What was that game?
Sixty Seconds in the Closet?
I never played it, but I always imagined
mouths finding each other,
hands able to hold just perfectly.

Try this game:

Lie beside your lover,
and expect his hand to reach your hair,
warm your arm, brush up against your hip.
Perhaps it doesn't happen,
but it won't matter.
What you will savor
is the knowing.

Nicole Blackman

Black Box

If the black box is the only thing that survives a plane crash
then why don't they make the whole plane out of it, I asked.
It's made of lead, you said, a lead plane is too heavy to fly.
And that was that.

There are benefits to being a pilot's wife, you know. You
understand what torque is and why San Francisco is always so cold
for California. But it makes you pray. Takes away your capacity for
disaster films. Makes you recite the oxygen mask instructions like
yoga chants. (If traveling with a small child, put your mask on
first.)

Parachute jumpers say that the more you jump, the more your risk
increases. You don't get any 'better' as a jumper, your number simply
comes up one day. The more you jump the faster it comes. I thought
about that every time you left and kissed us all good-bye in the same
order as if it was a lucky charm: dog, daughter, wife.

When I was called on Sunday night, it didn't feel like I thought it would.
Didn't feel like being hit or having something drag heavily on me. It felt like
someone came to take my bones away and pulled them out one by one.
Impossible to stand, impossible to sit, I rolled and pitched uncontrollably like
a ship on death waves.

I was at the crash site when they recovered the black box. I saw
them put it in the truck. I saw them close the door. I saw them
walk away. I saw them talk to women in trench coats with
microphones. I saw them turn away from me.

The damn things are heavy. Well of course they are.
They're lead. You can wrap it in a coat. You can carry
it like a baby. You can run to your car and drive home
panting, heart beating too loudly in your ears to hear
sirens as you disappear.

We   slept
with   love
now I sleep
with lead.

I wrap my white arms around the
black box where you live now and
listen to you talk to me all night.

27 List Poems I Should Write Some Day

44 Plants That Merit Attention
6 Reasons Why I Should Have Sex In A Car Before I Die
11 Friends I Actually Despise
12 Words I Can't Spell
7 Things I Have Said While Coming
4 Items I Look For In Friends' Bathrooms When I Go To Parties
42 Pleasant Ways To Die
15 Ugly Parts Of The Body
6 of The 7 Deadly Sins Because People Can Never Remember Sloth
4 Foods That Will Show Up In A Turd Because They're Hard To Digest
16 Ways I Used To Torture My Barbie Dolls
9 Things I Wish I Could Have Told My Grandfather Before He Died
3 Reasons To Be Cheerful By Ian Dury and the Blockheads
2 Kinds of Tomatoes My Mother Grows
18 Types of Condiments in My Fridge
86 of The Really Brilliant and Devastating Poems I Know Anne Sexton Had In
        Her When She Went and Killed Herself
8 Cheeses I Have Eaten And Not Thrown Up
18 Times I Have Seen *Breakfast At Tiffany's*
2 Police Officers I Talked to About Getting A Restraining Order
4 Leonard Nimoy Albums I Have That I've Never Listened To
$250 My Stepfather Still Owes Me
1 Friend Who Won't Talk To Me Anymore
14 Things To Do Until I Have Sex Again
11 Ways To Stifle A Yawn
3 Girls Who Were In The Room And Laughed At Me When I Heard The Bee
        Gees' Song "More Than A Woman" and I Sang "Bald-Headed Woman"
        Because That's What I Thought The Lyrics Were
and 2 Ways Henry Has Asked Me To Marry Him In 7 1/2 Years

Claire Calman

Love Is Blind

No doubt all four-eyed dames have read
What Dorothy Parker sourly said:
"Men seldom make passes
At girls who wear glasses."
—Apparently, men don't want sex
With women who are wearing specs.
But don't lose heart if you've poor vision,
And scorn this myth with just derision;
You'll find yourself adored by guys
Who are diminutive in size.

Yes, you can bet they'll be delighted
Once they know that you're
                              short-sighted.

Glenn Carmichael

And

And Adam said, "God give us the tools
and we'll do the job."

And God gave Adam the tools. And Adam
looked at the tools and then he looked at
God and he said, "God these have got to be
the shoddiest tools in the entire universe."
And he looked at God's tool and God's tool
was bigger and better and shinier and more
pulsating and prominent. And Adam looked
at the tools what God had given him and he
said, "God, you've got to be joking." And
God laughed.

And God said to Adam, "Get on with it."
And Adam got on with it.

Then Adam looked at God, and God wasn't
there. But Adam did hear she'd been seen in
Bond Street, walking a puma, entering
Cartiers, smelling delicious, dripping with
jewelry **and** looking absolutely divine.

John Cooper Clarke

Eat Lead Clown

It was time to move. I pulled on a raincoat, put away a pep pill, set fire to a cigarette and split.

Outside the stars stuck out of the sky like dandruff specks on a purple tux and the moon spat blue light on the night-life.

I stopped at a vacant hub-cap to check out my wardrobe, the 2-tone dexters in particular. Someone strangled a saxophone. . . elaborately.

Enter the brothers Archangelo, two brilliantine gypsies, rats on rollerskates, the plague on wheels.

Frankie fingered a string of powder-blue rosary beads while Angelo carried a switch.

I swerved, missed out on a set of signet rings and came back with a jap chop to the breadbox. Angelo slashed my wrist before catching a dexter in his wheels. The show was over, and I called the shots.

Blots of blood the size of pennies hit the pavement, peppered with rosary beads, forming an epileptic colour scheme. The flames of doom shot forth from a tightened grip, I gazed on the filth of the world and my heart said nothing.

The sound of squealing brakes and the smell of rubber vied for attention. A sideways focus revealed a sky-blue Bel Aire deLuxe convertible rocking on the springs.

"Get in Jim," said a voice from a thousand fathoms.

Her lips were a poisonous pink, she looked like St. Theresa of the Roses in one of her cheesier moments.

I was bleeding all over the fake leopard upholstery.

We stopped outside the Chevron Burgerama, its synchronised sign, in lime-green neon, the sole monitor of my ebbing existence.

Burgerama. Blank. Burgerama. Blank. Burgerama. Blank. Blank.

Robert O. Costa

Tango

This is some dance we've devised, my friend.

This dance is a tango: stylized, rehearsed motion,
followed in an instant by the step that seeks and finds the edge,
binds passion to perdition, looses the eros tide,
leaves in its wake the familiar, unnatural disasters.

This dance is a war dance: prisoners are not welcome,
arrows have already flown. There will be more,
even if we remove the paint that was not meant
to telegraph uncertain intentions,
even if we do nothing else to unsettle the ghosts of those
who've already set fire to this ground.

This is a teenager's first slow dance:
I awoke today dreaming I'd been holding you.
You wouldn't let me see your face, but it was you—
your back and waist, cradled in my arms,
fit exactly as they had the night before,
the danger and the sweet, solitary hurting
charged the air that same way.
Only it was not the night, light was not my friend,
a glance could not easily be stolen,
nor a tear brushed aside with inconspicuous notice.

This evening I stand back in a shyer light,
awaiting the right song,
watching you move through the crowd,
working up the courage to ask you
for the next dance.

Virginia Crawford

Drowning

Below the surface fish swim wildly,
rocks shift slowly in the current
drifting to their places.
Sand shapes itself to waves.

Maybe she leaned over to see the fish,
to pick up what she had dropped.
Now she is under water.
She has broken the surface of the water

into molecules thrown through the air
like crystals in the sun, rising, sinking, landing.
The river is swirling into the spiral of her ears
mixing with her molecules.

Like a fish, her eyes are round and searching,
surrounded as her mouth bubbles.
The water loves her,
supports her in her fall.

Someone Else's

No one knows
I'm not her mother,
but feeding her here
in the department store's restaurant
while her mother shops,
I could be.
Stroller by the table
pink rabbit cloth over my shoulder
warm bottle in hand
I'm a vision of motherliness.
Women walk by
with knowing smiles.
A soft nod tells me
they know;
they are mothers
or want to be.
Some stop to look,
to say she's cute
or ask how old.
I answer, "three weeks,"
smiling as they smile at her
as if this were three years ago
and I had listened to myself.
Now strangers tell me
I look like "an old pro."
It's the way I hold her,
coo as I change
her diaper.

Tim Cumming

Landscape with Valve

You stand there like a ruined building.
She looks at you as if to guess your weight
while someone drills a hole in a wall.
It sounds like a marriage breaking up.

The story, as it is, fades from the room like daylight
or a roll of film accidentally exposed to bright sunlight,
a film of thick mist, cigarettes and dusk
with Perry Como on the sound track.

Perry stops and asks for a match then lights it on the side of your neck.
Charlie, he says, you're not the spark you wanted to be.
Listening to you is like listening
to someone blow into an empty shell.

You hang behind him like a stage curtain
in a tiny theatre of extravagant gestures.
The stage is set: with a picture of you
raising a glass to God the Father

who struggles from the tailor's dummy
you've hidden his pictures of women in.
One of them has an address on the back.
You scribble it down, jump forward a couple of years,

pushing through crowds of people,
knocking over Perry,
saying "excuse me" but not meaning it,
and if you saw what happens next

and the people behind it,
your heart broken, your mouth in flames,
your head in the sand with salt rubbed into it,
with *All the World's a Stage* inscribed into each grain of salt,

then you'd look for the next fast car
and drive it through the wall
of your lover's bedroom, a wall which has writing on it.
It tells you to be yourself and speak your weight.

Let's be realistic. You meet the wrong woman
and start to shin the wrong tree, no strings attached.
You stay up there a few years, make a wish
the span of your own hand, and promises

which are there to be broken.
There's love of course, and deep water.
You throw a little salt over your shoulder.
A snake's curled in the heel of your boot,

but you don't look back, or down, or out.
Nostalgia, you say, is for monkeys.
But you send her a letter.
Yes, you send her a letter.

You say you saw them together standing in formation
like invaders from another planet.
She doesn't get it. You sit in a room together
like a couple of news readers without any news.

You wait for an answer
but nothing means less then you do now.

Blair Ewing

Just Another Byte out of Time

These images keep biting their way into my brain:
faster and faster until I feign death by sleeping
only then I'm still recycling these soft-candy pictures
of profit and power. Sadly for them, you know
Rome is gone forever, and only prelates and monks
speak their tongue and tomorrow is a loaded gun
made right here in America, polished with love
and shipped with an instructional video.
Because push is very definitely coming to shove
and who here wants to bet (I'll give you
9-to-5) that it will be the blood of ballots
and not gold that splashes over the cameras' rodeo?
And we better not count on any social virus
or disease of goodwill to come and rewrite
the program, either. The paid-for philosophers
intone: Just be happy with what toys and time
you are allotted. As for me, I get my healing best
from long-standing love, books, yoga and
deep calm of forest...

Brenda Frazer

Animated Midnight Dream

Jazzing with Bessie Smith
  Ray Bremser
Janis Joplin or Scott
 I'm dressed as a Teddy Girl
or someone's fantasy.
 Painted all the cocked
up colors of desire.
 My suit is black
 My skin the white cravat
And then my garment turns
inside-out for sex and texture.
And it's Halloween
Day of the Dead in
Mexico.
 I climb up from loneliness
to the patriarchal bed.
A place for bargaining,
purchase and delight.
 Goats and Ghosts on
the balcony watching.
Outside Sirens scream, or is
it me in here, singing a
higher note to my blues?

      Sept. 22, 1984

Tina Fulker

Untitled

there's a streamer
unraveling around me
its bright party colors
want to fun the room
there's an illness lingering
like the last guest to leave
I've seen some photographs
of someone else unzipping
their jeans
I didn't fancy him much
when I first saw him
but now I do
I want to have sex
in an unexpected place
I want to be taken by surprise
I'm not a housewife
finishing the chores
I'm a writer finishing a poem
trying to find a publisher
for a story no one likes
it is well-written
the bed was well-made
when you came back last night
I've been alone too much
there's an illness
it could be catching
there again it may not be
there's a streamer
unraveling
in a room
no one visits
is there going to be a party
has there already been one
there's an infection I'm carrying
it's from the 20th century
it's garbage that can't be disposed of

it's got clothes on that it wants to take off
it's a boy but it wants to be a girl
the pollution in the city has changed
the color of my eyes
but I can sill see
can I unzip your jeans
can I hold your cock in my hand
I play a part
there's no stage directions
if this is method acting
why haven't I met Matt Dillon yet
all this role playing
when you come home
I'm going to be disguised as someone else
the apartment will be in a different block
a few streets away
my name will be changed on the bell
I want to screw up the system
I want to leave the washing unrinsed
your dinner uncooked
I want to send you back to your mother
she can make your apple pie
I've run out of pastry and cream
I've dried up
I'm sterile
I've got clips on my tubes
and a baby crying
in a century
waiting to finish

Karen Garthe

The Soutine

well, veal. The feet never touch ground.
it's the every cell in *my body*
and every cell in your body to ship
way out in front.

so when does the poem start?
old hymns won't allow tragedy
the pacifier of a Beautiful Day keeps nursing
it is almost ecstatic to land.

how we hugged a meaningless curve
like the ocean fished-out of cod,
an unpopular perpetrator, a popular
victim,
the jury's bad decision.

we liked him, you know.
he looked like life hadn't panned out
then again he'd never expected much anyway.

where's the Soutine? Is the Soutine lost?
great lakes of pianos perch, firewood.
very old people have pensions
at least.

malingering, watching
the gross malfeasance of the Trustee
when the poem started
stood his corner and cried.

Regan Good

The War Horse

This morning the world's been changed by water.
(No one yet awake in the honey-colored light.)

The wooden steps have just been painted
And the ivy's running riot—

The crows pour languidly from their stations
And the sleeping house is quiet.

I count the keys on the grand piano
As the house stands dumb in the morning's light.

This house is like a handless clock, I think.
Nothing like innocence exists and nothing much like sin—

Death came here as a wash of water
And the sun rose as it will again.

No, there wasn't any blood; there wasn't any fire.
Rather the dead became an object to be admired.

No, there was not brimstone, there was not fire.
There was a white stone sunk in a bowl of water.

I say I am a War Horse, I tossed my head!
Then flung the windows open!

Then the sun rose red as it will again
And the dead rode on waxed and quiet—

And no, I mean the sun sank red
With the flash of hellion's fire.

And the flood-tide waters changed the world
As a hundred doors flew open.

And no, the rasping breath was not like fire.
It was the pounding ornament of the grand piano.

As I said, I am a War Horse, I tossed my head
As in a parade for a grand occasion!

I shone the crowd a smiling face
Like a Mussorgsky brass come striding!

Perhaps I was panting in the newborn light,
Beating time to the rough-cut breath of the dying—

That night we ate and drank like children
In the strangest company of strangers.

I'm sure I ate and drank that night
As the stone stood white in its water.

And yes, the night passed slow and Hell came crying
After the last forced breath of the dying.

And I'll admit that the light seemed slow in rising.
And that my mind smokes and flares as a paper-fire.

John Greaves

Untitled

Ta langue trépidante entrouvre
Tes lèvres;
Me prend, en passant, en otage.
Qu'un chuchotement timide
Qui annonce le torrent avide de salive
Qui m'engloutit et me balance
Sur la tête de mon propre vit,
Qui, lui-même, palpite et brûle
D'un feu antérieur.
Le va-et-vient de l'immensité
De ta bouche entière, autrefois si petite,
Ebranle la chandelle, emblème
Du feu mon corps et me rend saoul.
Me voilà naufragé sur la péninsule
De ma propre bite, fouetté goulûment
Par les vagues de ton ardeur orale.

Janet Hamill

Nocturne 5

Waiting in a flowing, flower-print dress. Through the open summer window, the warm hands of the night reach in and, slowly, one-by-one, unfasten the buttons, down to the waist. After a thunderstorm, the metallic perfume of rain predominates, and the soft hiss of traffic coursing over wet pavement.

How welcome the calm. The respite from the dance. The chorus line of skeletons. Just for the moment, benevolent gargoyles guard the city from perches high atop the skyscrapers. Wise and heavy with patience, still. Their hearts are fortified by hope.

Stirring in a glass of dry white wine, a cool fingertip. An old album by Orpheus on the record player. Music for lyre placed among the stars. Music for waiting to be filled with light.

Elizabeth Hamilton

It Is Easter Week

I am cleaning house
sorting
throwing out
boxes of buttons
your grandmother kept
in clear plastic boxes
they hit the trash
with a teaspoon
other things you left
when your voice comes back
so I sit down to drink
the drink you liked, that I kept
that is all, I think
I am done with that. But
sometimes something again
turns up, like a train
ticket, illegible postcard
your absence.

It is Easter week.
Once I shook the hand of a man
who by all accounts
had been the CIA
in Chile during Pinochet
and this hand
the man's hand
felt like a hand
the man was a man
and I, no Gaelic fairy child
who feels in her hand
the animal paw
the cloven hoof
of the animal in man
nothing out of
        the ordinary,
which I never understood.

Who does?

It is Easter week.
Soon Jesus will rise from the dead
and float there
like a postage stamp
that got away
was never disfigured by the sorting machine
in an agonising glow
he will *noli me tangere*
say and the priest said,
Who are you
on Easter week,
the Virgin or Peter?
Barabbas or the cock that crowed?
But the cock turns and turns
in its memory of the manger
of the cattle and the ass
their big eyes
their lowing
the smell of urine
yellow as a halo.
It cries,
There is no way up!
No way down!
The cock turns round
in the memory
and cries a third time,
No way out!
not meaning to mean
what is said it meant.

It is Easter week.
I will, says God, *I can*
like the Little Red Engine
of my childhood
that was a man, I guess
anthropomorphic, as God was
is this belittling?
I think I can it says, he says
and it huffed and it puffed
to the top of the hill
glorious height
I will, says God
to me on a spring day,

transfigure the ashes
(His metaphors are commonplace)
that once were coals
that once was fire
that once was lumber
(for building a building
that never got built)
and before that an oak
into an altar.
The ordinary miracle
undigested
sweet as soap.
And he does of course.
he did.
Last April I awoke
and the smoke
still hung about the altar.
I can see it rising there.

It is Easter week.
I am cleaning house.

Brian Hinton

Love Poem

With your face so like a skull
—picked out in white, a grin of pure bone—
and hands whose veins are wearing through,
it's no surprise that I should fall
in love quite so helplessly.

It matches the death inside my own.

Your flesh is frost on a mountainside,
sloping bare,
eyes that glitter, birdlike,
your midriff covering rides up to show
skin so charnel-like and yet so warm,
hair chopped viciously
to atrophy sex
but there's passion in your kiss, heat in your embrace.

You gather yourself up into your clothes,
tight around you like the weather.

Your soul will flower with the Spring,
and dance,
as the dead time shatters.

Bruce A. Jacobs

Blood Dance

After the sun vanishes behind
a hundred acres of corn,
talk turns, on the
highway-sized veranda,
to luck and karma.

The owner of the inn
crosses her bare arms,
says she found the house in a dream.
After waiting two centuries
for thirty rooms built
around a log cabin,
she drew her realtor a picture.
So true, she tells us,
that we summon our own worlds.

I want to ask if this means
that people in sweltering rooms
have conjured the lack of jobs
and air conditioning. But this
is what the black guest
is expected to say. Instead,
I pick at a raw hangnail,
tell her I am part Indian,
a sliver of my grandfather,
who walked ten thousand miles
delivering mail and never
made it to dental school.

I skip the part about walking.
My grandfather was weak,
I am told, a man who crawled
into bed fully-clothed,
hid his head from bad luck.
Through my boots, I feel
the thick porch lumber, nailed

hard and flat as the prairie.
A dream built to last,
with gunpowder and hand tools.
Which reminds me. My other grandfather
was a blacksmith. He winched
shoeless oxen into the air,
ducked their hooves like flies.

I stamp my feet
on my hostess' planks
without knowing why.
The faces around me turn,
bright in the new darkness.
I imagine a lone settler creating
familiar sounds for himself
while the new moon incises
a sharp circle in his roof.

The owner of the inn
leans forward, crosses a leg
white all the way up her ten-story thigh,
asks me what nation.

I ignore the blood
on my finger, tell her Cherokee,
which may actually
be true.

Valerie Jean

Again

Snow topples the day down,
drags its white iciness over all
the trees and tentative sprouts
of a false spring. Winter remains

a gray-shrouded dawn where
renegade shadows step out
bold, from my nightmares,
grinning. The weight of this

silence, echoed in taunting
winds, smashes through
my window—a savage howl.
All the singing my heart had

to re-learn is lost, and defeated
I crawl back into your death,
babbling like an anxious child
whose mother did not come.

22nd Revelation

My anger at the sun is
unnatural, but you are dead
and only crazy people curse
the non-living. I am not
so mad to tempt those ghosts
I bribed into uneasy truces,
begging them to stay on
their side of the fence.

Growing up next to the fancy
cemetery, I learned early
not to talk to strangers who
disappeared behind wide
tombstones or to those
whose lifted heads held
fierce disgust for the
clinking of my fast bike.

Halvard Johnson

White Lies

I'm the kind of guy who likes
to tell little white lies once in a while,
but not just for the hell of it.
For example, the other day I told
the kid downstairs that Alabama wasn't really
part of the United States, and you
should have seen his mouth drop open.
I was surprised that he'd even heard of Alabama,
considering that we live much farther north.
Alabama's neither here nor there though—
What I mainly want to do is make some small
contribution to the kid's education. I want him
to know that people don't always tell him the truth.
I want him to know that Alabama, if I say so,
is in central Russia, and that if stars
ever did fall on Alabama—which I doubt—
they were probably paid to do so.

Martha Johnson

Losing Jane

The two girls are walking on the dirt part of the road, past where the pavement ends, past the sun-warm flat rocks that cover squirming snakes, past the place where blackberries will be hanging long by the end of August, where they had picked them in other summer's ends. It is the time before the end of friendship. They are eleven, still prone to giggle, afraid to think of boys.

Maybe if today had one or two clouds capable of distracting their intent, a broken frog—maybe not. They have brought peanut butter and banana sandwiches, a thermos of red Kool-Aid. Sometimes now she says that certain roads should be left untraveled, certain thinking better left unthought, at least by girls. In scenes like this, its hard to say whose idea it is. Maybe Jane, maybe Alice. But heat is surely partly in the blame and the fact that the fire tower is occupied, the ranger's car parked on the far side of the circle.

She still tries to make it flowers and will from time to time say things like *when it's your time*, alternatively quote scripture about all things working for good, but she stops, leaves for a replaying. Paragraphs are fading from her repertoire, but on better days she is still capable of complete sentences, most of which have to do with going and how pavement turns to dirt and then to grass, and the man with the gun coming from past the end of the road, and yes, her mother had told her about men and little girls and the dangerous woods.

LuAnn Keener

Wild Dogs

On the phone my brother tells me
one of his sheep, pregnant with twins,
was eaten by dogs. The torn rib cage
lay in the pasture like a broken sail
and the two large creatures, black diagonal stripes
on rose-brown fur, loped into shadow.
He lay in wait with his shotgun,
killed one, then set poison traps
for the other. But I didn't

want to tell you another story
of ignorance and blood. We're both sorry
for the lovely sheep, and for her children
like pale apples, the moon fingering
the shattered crystal of their caul
as they slipped too soon onto winter turf
in a twisted curtain of screams.
Especially, I don't want to hear
about the gun, nor you to hear. What we need

is this: how the moon must have looked to her
through scrims of terror, like the shining face
of Sheep Mother she had dreamed...
and how the white-hot tsunami of pain
melted to a coolness of spring grass, to an opal light
she floated on, into a world we lose
track of at this point, as her lambs,
whole and perfect now, follow her
into its arms. Also, let us hear

of the dogs, a pair of siblings
who love each other, perhaps they have
a litter in the creek bank...Tell me
of those dark markings we must learn
not to see malice in, strange runes
that charge us to peel the scales from our eyes.

Don't tell me again
about the death, the wordless grief
of the bereft mate, nor of my brother,
his hands fine-tuned with outrage,
carefully laying the trap. It is hard
to keep rising and rising against gravity
but this story is urgent
to gather light.
                        Remind me

of the village of trees beyond the fence,
the thin stream that runs there
bearing its urban taint.
Of the flagging wraith of that wood
that even as we speak of it, grows stronger,
stronger as we voice our need
not to triumph, our desperation
to be brought at last to our knees
in its small green chapels, to understand
what we can do, and must not. Teach us
how those odd slash marks evolved
to shock us with variegated beauty
and nothing, evil and light. Tell us, please

don't stop talking
till we taste the bread of mystery and praise.

Mimi Khalvati

Terrapin

September's luminosity
   is powerless. An afterglow
of holiday. My daughter's
   fish are fine, she says, three
so small they haven't yet
   changed colour; two fantails.

In shortening light
   our days will be nosed
through glass, a slow pursuit
   in circles. Stations
will ghost neon globes, nights
   bed brackish water.

She's got two tanks now,
   one for fish, one
for a terrapin she's rescued.
   They take up all her
living room, what with friends
   crashing out, a father

for a lodger. They're thinking
   of buying a boat, *don't*
I'm dying to say. Boats
   sink. One I heard of
left no trace but a teddy bear
   floating on the canal—

true or not, boat people
   are always saving cats
scraping hulls and sooner
   or later moving into flats
they take months to redecorate.
   Time my son moved out.

Where to? Where'll he put
    his piano, who'll put up with it—
round and round we go
    swapping rooms, beds.
September's my own aquarium
    I was going to say.

My memory's getting as short
    as a fantail's.
Writing on the back of a hand
    as if ink in the blood
could freeze the flow, flow
    swamp detail.

Ronald Koertge

Q and A

What exactly is a thesaurus?

> A thesaurus is like a thousand family
> reunions, all in the same hotel, but each
> one in a separate ballroom. A dictionary,
> on the other hand, is like the Army where
> everyone lines up for roll call.

Do words have feelings?

> Because of one picture, a thousand words
> are burdened with low self-esteem.

How can I have a large vocabulary?

> Exercise. Start with *air, leaf, inch*; then
> increase slowly. Be patient and careful.
> The first time you try *incarnadine,*
> have someone spot you.

Do words die?

> Absolutely. I remember the funeral
> of *a go-go.* She looked completely natural
> in her black boots, mini-skirt, and fringed
> blouse.

How can I remember the parts of speech?

> Picture a fancy restaurant: an adjective
> lights the cigarette of a noun. Two adverbs
> accompany a verb to the rest room. An
> article holds the door; a preposition hands
> the verb a warm hand-towel.

Myths

Today my mother says she is afraid of turning into
a vegetable. I know what she means but the way she says
it reminds me of Greek myths where people became
poplar trees and cows.

I imagine being called to the hospital and there,
under a light blanket, is a huge zucchini. I struggle
to make sense of it even if that means embracing
the randomness of lecherous or willful gods.

But the doctor can't keep a straight face. He bites
the inside of his lip to keep from laughing. I can
hardly blame him. It's not his mother lying there
with a stem.

Well, probably Mother won't turn into anything
distressing. Not that she hasn't had her share of
greed or ambition or longing, but she's very
healthy. In fact, she's been in the hospital
only once—the night I was born.

As she dozed afterwards, she thought she saw God's
face on the ceiling. Then it turned into a Chrysler.
"I didn't know which to believe in," she confides.
"I still don't."

Wayne Koestenbaum

History of Boys

1.

Call him A
for angel butt, curved poplar—

the first butt I desired.
I thought, "This

is what sculptors feel"—
honest love of contour.

Butt wasn't separate
from boy, or from my consciousness.

Both—all three—walked past me.
"I could imagine touching it,"

I mused, but didn't push
the idea toward execution.

Religious, respectable, he recognized
my existence, somewhat.

Charity informed the butt,
made it a locus.

2.

M got a hard girl pregnant, sent her
to San Francisco for an abortion.

I imagined touching
his leg hair, bits at a time.

I didn't know how to go about it.
Without procedure

the action completed itself.
The leg felt hard, like a praline.

I had a praline disposition—
sweet, factioned.

Laid out on the floor
by my eye

he was no longer delinquent—
no longer the impregnator.

I decided, in fantasy,
to be kind to his legs.

The legs, then, might radiate
their own salt rigor.

3.

V's stomach crossed the hotel room.
He smelled of the talcum

stick drawn across white bucks
to preserve their pristine suede.

The house he lived in
held V's stomach at night;

the house he lived in
faced a busier road than mine.

Lust played zither on my
belly's blank billboard, unlettered

marquee advertising no
good film, only some mystery about Malaga.

4.

Did F know his last name was a variety of bean?
His jock held nuts and other items, a safe

deposit box. He sat
on the gym bench; that angle

enlarged his bush. His grownup
name augured grownup sorrow.

Are adult sorrows
larger than a child's? Looseness

suited the bush:
it had all day, all year.

No one—no girl—would ever discover
his pudge dusk stomach,

portions abstracted
from other contexts.

5.

The boxer flap opened, spoke
this humid moral.

Avra Kouffman

Lush

She was lush (And plush)
LIKE AN AMAZON ON VACATION
Not honed (Or toned)
Just basking,
—Relaxing—
In exuberant sensations
Of the flesh.

Some call it "fat",
As if there's horror in abundance
I think. "Hmm,
Something's wrong with that!"
I like the bulging, swerving curves
That shake and take up space:

An abdomen abounding…
A thigh all soft and rounding
No disgrace!

Girls, Let's not be silly:
They say, "Curve out here, there curve in"
Bust = blessing, Stomach = sin

Ridiculous!
Be more, not less
& Don't obsess:
Caress

The flesh that curves out
Everywhere
From here—and here—and here—
And there…

And then
If people try to shame you,
Taunt you into caving in,
Just say:

I don't want to get smaller
So you can feel bigger.
Expand your horizons,
Stop shrinking my figure!

I don't want a body that's meek.
I don't need a form that conforms
To the norms of the week,
Or to this month's physique

Be it slender and sleek,
Or next season...Who knows?
But I know

My body goes
Wherever,
Whichever,
Whatever way

It *wants* to go.

And I like it like that!

Elizabeth Mary Larson

Ditch Digging

James Baldwin taught me,
don't use an ice pick
to dig a ditch.
Use a shovel.
And when you hit rock,
go around it.
Dig deeper.

Even if you think
your back is as bent
as it's ever going to get.
Bend more.
Dig harder.

When you find a word,
don't take the very first
one. Or even the second.
Or the third.

Dig a better ditch
while you're looking.
Something you can stand in.
You can always say,
"I've been down there
and lived to crawl back up."

James Baldwin told me,
over my shoulder in a
whisper, "Find your own
words. The best ones.
And when you do,
Go tell it on the mountain."

Sara Elizabeth Levy

Nocturne

I steal.

At night my fingers recite
the catechism of robbery
rummaging through your hair
coaxing your shadow to dance
while your sleepy breath slowly heats
like untrained steam
nearly ready to sing.

And even the sheets commit
their crimes, hoarding your scent
in their woven crevasses; gently etching
lines like cave paintings or hatchmarks
on your drowsy flesh—as if
sleep were quantifiable, or art.

Soon you'll awaken
and gesture daybreak to your side
to give you hints
about dreams and night spells
never knowing the thefts
that occur during silence.

Rise

Wake me with your tongue
she tells him
let the brazen tendrils
meet and curl; permit these
fleshy valves to delve
without wondering about
the opening or the closing.

Wake me with your fingers
she tells him
they are so like my own—
slender and silent like
untested whips—wearing
identical rings that meander
loose and bronze
across tendon and knuckle.

Wake me with your lips
she tells him
but there is no need for words; tonight your lips
are a silent fable
of two brothers
loving the same woman—
one a grand curtain
of decision deferring
to the other luxury
draped below.

Please wake me with your eyes
she asks him
allow your gaze
to ease me from my
library of dreams and night-songs
for together we have seen rooftops and weather;
seen the other's touch earn a lover's grasp
while allowing private senses new admiration.

Yes, please wake me with your eyes
she asks him
all I need to see
of love's lore
rests in them;
all the tears
I need to spill
or taste
are yours.

Lyn Lifshin

The Mad Girl Finds It Excruciatingly Painful to Go into Strange Bookstore Trying to Get Them to Buy Two of Her Books

First she buys six books she hadn't planned to,
looks for an almanac for a friend, a book of
maps she could use a map to find in the store
where her heart's pounding as she flails among cook
books and stock guides. The books could be her
babies she's brought to audition for the only

part that can save their lives. Or maybe she is
at a telethon to raise money for some operation,
a transplant they'll die in a week if she can't
get. This seems worse than being a pimp, worse than
a prostitute. It's like taking off her clothes
for a lover and having him laugh or gag, or become

terribly bored. She edges up to a clerk to ask about
seeing the book buyer. He looks snarly and stressed
and there's a line of Christmas shoppers so she
goes to the other room, near poetry where of course
there's only a few who aren't even buying and finds a woman
who looks less jaded and mean and after she buys the books

she never wanted, manages to gasp, "book buyer, is he
here?" remembers how bad she was at selling advertisements
for the ETV station she worked for. "Isn't in," is a relief,
the car stalling at the edge of the chasm as brakes go. "You
can leave them with me and I will make sure he gets them,"
the woman says and the mad girl knows she can't go thru

this again and awkwardly takes the two books out of a Borders
bag, puts her card in and flyers to order, doubts she'll ever go
into that bookstore again. In the morning she calls Clinton,
the name on the card, as nervous as if she was calling
the president and calls too early, before he's even checked what
is on the desk. "Thanks you for alerting me," he says and

she holds her breath, knows she does better on paper or
face to face, stumbles. She could be trying to do pirouettes not
in shoes but in bricks. "If you wanted to have them I could
supply…" and he says, "No, I'd rather deal with the publisher.
Do you want them back?" And she sputters, "Mail them?" and he says, "I'll put
them aside," and all she can do is imagine trying to

claim bits of her lips and hair, pieces of her tongue that never
got offered up for sale. She thinks of a German film, *Nobody Loves Me*
where a woman thinks the super is so hot for her she decides to
surprise him, jumps naked into the trunk of his car with only a
bottle of champagne only to find when he parks at a romantic out of
the way country spot, he's got someone else, her close friend, spread

eagle on the back seat so she lurches, naked except for a branch into the
crowded subway in Berlin, her skin the color of ruby toes. "Nobody
loves me," the mad girl is sure hanging the phone up, feeling
as stripped and silly, still knowing this might be something that if it
won't trigger sales might make a poem.

Julie Liu

Patron Saint of Pests and Mosquitoes

I go to many places, I go all over the world, but still they find me, still they come to beg for my favors. I am asleep in a high tree in a remote forest in a distant land. My roosting crows are gathered around me sweetly like dark fruit, and I'm having the most wonderful dream about nuts that won't open. Suddenly I am awakened by a jingle jingle, then a tap tap on my alabaster toe. The tapping is very persistent and it is clear that the tapper will not go away. I open my eyes and look down to see a skinny girl clinging to the branch directly below mine. "Oh please," she says, "there's this boy…" and what she wants of course is a philter, a liquid chain. I am drowsy and grainy-eyed and the girl's perfume has caused many of my crows to fall stunned to the forest floor. I reach into my flowing robes and produce a vial of vodka which I then give to her with a thrust of my saintly hand. "Oh thank you thank you!" she says, and as she descends from the tree her jangling earrings lull me back to sleep only this time all of the nuts open so I wake up and spend the rest of the night waiting for the orange sun to crack the sky with its brilliance.

I am in the Amazon, drifting down the mighty muddy river. A canopy stretched over the boat provides shade for my fair skin. My mosquitoes are gathered around me in an thick cloud. They are in the middle of one of the finest performances of their operatic careers. I feel tears prick the back of my eyes as they near the end of the third act, a real heartbreaker. The leading female lies stricken with malaria and the two leading males fence over the right to nurse her back to health. Their tiny proboscises whip passionately in the air. I know that it will end in tragedy, and I am ready to cry. Suddenly I feel a cold splash of water on my face. When I blink away the moisture there is a moustached man clinging to the side of the boat. He has raised his scuba mask and is shrieking wetly. "I beg your pardon?" I say, and eventually make out the word "piranhas." He hauls himself into my boat and pants out a request for inspiration. "I'm thousands of dollars in debt…my wife tries to poison me every night…loan sharks bang on my door at all hours and piss on the lawn…" He is dripping water everywhere and with a quick glance at my mosquitoes I see that the entire orchestra section is soaked. "Go forth," I command quickly, "and invent the powerboat." I point my saintly finger at the river. He looks at me with religious fervor and follows the direction of the finger overboard. He is so maddened with inspiration that he outswims the piranhas. I turn back to my mosquitoes but the spell is broken. Even after the instruments are dried and retuned it takes us a good twenty minutes to locate *la prima donna*, who has fainted beguilingly on the stern.

Tailgaters stumble upon my desert meditations. I dance my Ballet of the Spiny Water Flea and am interrupted by panhandling drunkards. Young girls who communicate in dolphin squeals find me stargazing at the equator. There are more daily requests for enlightenment than I can count. My saintly brow, crowned with a garland of purple loosestrife, has developed permanent furrows from the barrage of people, wishes, failures, noise. My copious beard has begun to fall out in clumps. I am no longer able to do needlework because my hands shake with fatigue. I've submitted a request to change departments, but at this point a transfer seems unlikely. I am here for a reason, and the opportunity for retirement remains a long ways away.

Roger McGough

Whoops!

You are strangely excited
as we enter the crowded bar
and find a small table in the corner.

You insist on fetching the drinks
and before disappearing
squeeze a note into my hand.

It reads: "Why go home tonight?
I have a room. I have a bed.
I have a spare toothbrush."

I recognise my own handwriting.

Gwyn McVay

You Have Nothing Left to Disbelieve But This

I've been telling you Grandmother stories but not the one
about her wrenching the heart out of the light brown river

Cordial, she said, *like or related to the heart, amiable feelings*
It was as if a chocolate cherry had been crushed in the fingers,
its liquor running down many wrists, tasted only by sun,

a red quartz dull with facets, gristled fat, two pounds of it,
and slowly, rust-brown angels of the river hoisted, dripping,

to sing about ruts and ditches, black-tea water over rocks,
yes, in the county you come from, veins of carnelian and jasper
in their necks and temples, *mud, culverts, highway gravel oil*

You have nothing left to disbelieve but this, all the showy myths

are taken, life on Mars, a magnet spinning in the earth's
iron core, will you attempt it, her red heart of impurities?

Quipu

Looking for a good story in this

Fishing line, between
thumb & dark of callus

Dear posterity, this winter
Tributes include five hundred
Bundles coca leaves, the same
Alpaca fleeces & a great quantity
Rope hemp for weaving & dyeing
The demi-god of bad choices appeared in a dream
To warn
          All telegraph lines are down
between Cuzco and Machu Picchu

Stuttering Morse code: D-d-
Disaster
          That's all, folks

Before our language there was another language
We spell it in out palms, spread our
Fingers and count, we cannot imagine

How it was for them, eyes closed
Perhaps to dawn over the mountains

We tug our knots so they will be universal
Even to the hand of a blind widow counting
Her goats, one terrible eye in each

Rope knot like thorns on a sacrifice cord

Miriam Morsel Nathan

The Absurd Messiah

It will be in the season
of the magnolia's blossoming.
The messiah will wear
a helmet and biker's spandex
when he arrives holding
in one hand photographs
of someone's dead lovers,
and cupped in the hollow of the other,
the foggy bellow of a French horn.
Two cranes destined for each other
will collide, then part. In a café
on a side street lovers will smoke
cigars and eat black olives with onions.
Women will seduce men
by crying. And then,
after one full year of light,
followed by a hundred of darkness,
a crescent moon will hang backwards
in a night silent as the inside of a violin.

Dorothy Porter

Hot Date

Pine trees
  come most alive
    dripping with resin
      in a fire

I've got a hot date
    with Death

will she be
  my boiling Celt?

will we dare
  the White Horses?

dewy together
  Death and I

hot-sea blue

or will Death
  be my curly cork-screw
      Jew?

"I'm you
  I'm you"
she moans

knocking me to the floor
of an old blood hotel
sucking out my breath

Oh Death!

I never knew you
  in a dress
  in high heels

just the melt
   of your breasts
the fork-lift
   of your tongue

I can't bring home
 a devil
   to meet my mother

but I won't
  ring for a taxi

I'm not leaving

until you tell me
 about yourself

let's talk, Death

can't we be friends?

is it all
        sex
      with you?

do you like cricket?
do you like tennis?

what did you think
   of this year's Film Festival?

Sip your long black,
        slowly, Death,

I want to know you

do you want
   to be my second cousin
      twice-removed?

Celt or Jew.

You'll never be English, Death
I said Goodbye to All That

with my last Anglican
    Communion

I can't remember
  the wafer
I couldn't get drunk
  on the wine

Celt or Jew.

Breath or dew.

You'll never be faithful.
I'll never be true.

Because, Death,
  I'm not simple

and neither are you.

My At-last-lover

Your face sleeps
   illuminated
in the early morning
  warmth
     of my slack arm

you're my at-last sound asleep
    child
you're my cat
    with a dreaming paw
       flexing in my hand
you're my raw storm
      gorgeously spent

and what am I, darling?

Exhausted

and full of trapped bubbles
   like honeycomb.

Crete

Finding a vein
I find you

you're a wet socket
    of white sea

my tropical bikini top
    rips off

your blue eye
    won't lie flat
        on the broken wall

I twist like an otter
    in an underwater cave

your palaces are spiced
    with wine-dark
        chill

my chest echoes all night/all night
    on a thin mattress

your snake
    bites my breast
        with a hollow fang

O flash! O honey!

Minnie Bruce Pratt

The Ferry

Today I saw, she tells the woman close beside her, *a man
in the thicket by the river bridge, because it rained
hard and he moved slow. He stepped from his invisible cloak,
water sewn seamless by needles of rain, and unfolded
a cardboard box, propped it against a gumtree, sat casual
like I adjust a couch pillow in our living room. Then I looked
in the wasteland at what was trash. Corrugated tin bent
into shelter lean-tos, and there was one webbed string tent,
a woven home beside a pile of blue-green jewels, bottles.
Where the river sludged with mud, tires, a shopping cart,
I could see a footpath worn down through stinging nettles,
to the stone road across the stream at a fording place.*

*And when I saw this, the bridge shook under me like cloth
tearing in a woman's hands, like the sheets on this bed shake
when we pull them taut between us, making love. Someday,*
she says to the woman, *I'll take you home to see my river.*

In summer a place of thunder, dry dirt into sudden water,
and the dead ruts of loggers' roads sparkle with quartz.
In winter, sycamore trees lean upstream, white branches,
bones picked clean, the roost where a dozen buzzards gather.
Downstream, an island from backwash of sand. Seems a place
where nothing's ever happened. But there was a ferry once.

On the black river, blurred light, a lantern on the dock.
A white woman at the winch chooses who will cross. Once
she cut the cables and lost the boat, a year's money, to keep
the soldiers out who'd come to free the slaves she carried,
the ones who tilled the bottom land.

On the slurried bank,
a secret fire always blazes. Someone, no coin for passage,
waits for low water and massed night shadows to wade in.
Someone's voice always foams, seething, in the rapids.

141

I'll never find my girl Phebe again. Shoes drug me,
foot sore, down.

Siakaya auet, itanowa, itukshila.

Papa says he's gonna whip me.   Well, he'll have to catch
you first.

When we want to stay, they make us leave.
When we want to leave, they make us stay on no land for all.

It was never my river, sold before I knew it. Yet it was mine.
How could I leave it? The blue shining darters, the lily stars.
Walnut meat sweet inside a thickshelled skull, leaves crushed
*   to bitter musk. Creek mouthing below the river bend. But a house*
forted in on the land could not make it mine.

Now limestone
grey bluffs, cenotaphs, mark the passing of those who tried
to buy. And money still drives down from the city, inexorable, slow,
a bulldozer scraping choice suburban plots from the scenic bank.
An old man in another state writes to ask if five cedars planted
small are living yet? Spared by a marring hand?   Though the old tree's
gone, brought down when he sold his place, and the railroad graded.

Meanwhile, in this declivity, wedged between two ridges, the trees
wait for people who know them by sight, each winter silhouette
familiar as a sister's height, her handprint. The people who walk
to pick up lightwood for their fire, or pine needles for baskets.
Or the ones who said, *If the dead could have counted, the land never*
would have been sold, but, alas, though they stood around, and their tears
came in raindrops, they could not be seen, and the white man's plough
furrowed up their bones.

Someday, she says to the woman,
I'll take you to see my river, and the house my people built
fallen in on its foundation, cellar gaping like a grave draped
in creeper and cat briar, timber frame stripped sure as the
bone-pickers unraveled flesh from corpse.

Now I am homed only in you.
On the winter river, the ferry woman would not have carried us,
with our voice of lost souls, of owls mating in ice silent night,

cries cracking like trees falling. We would have called hoohoo-
hoohoo hoohoo-hoohoo-aw *down on her from the bone-white trees.*
We would have rowed ourselves across that obscure unowned place.

The bed trembles like a bridge falling, with her
face down, spread, dead woman's float. Then over
at the other's hand, laving, not saving her, but
meeting of waters, hidden shoals. The boat of her
legs, a vee of white, opens, waits. Their joints
creak as they row together on the night's wide river.

In dark rain, on the concrete bluff of the bridge, graffiti
glow orange, words phosphorescent as a campfire near the man
who leans back against a tree's damp bed. The words say,
We love you Manuel. They say, *Catherine Fire here today.*
They say, *We are crossing here, this bridge our only land.*

Jeremy Reed

Poe's Marriage Night

Praying for Sister Morphine in the dark
and all poppy derivatives, he trained
spiral coitus with a corkscrew's tip

into a rose-blushed cork,
and had his young bride sleep inside a shroud
and not a clingfilm negligee,

tubercular blood on the sheet
instead of a virgin's rich currency
the colour of sweet williams.

His necrophiliac subtext ruled the night,
he who could only love her dead,
preserved her like a florist's rose,

her thirteen years so fragile in his arms,
he saw her dreams transparently
quiver like fish in sinewy current.

But later, rising to the thunder rain,
he went downstairs, and pacted with his need,
and crippled oaks were crying out

and in his vision she was blue
from rigor mortis, but without decay,
and he was with her in her vault,

tormented, mad, priapic, brainstormed-lust
roaring inside his arteries,
her toes splayed out before they turned to dust.

Leader of the Pack

I saw your blue coat on somebody else,
a memory corona, tugging thing
like listening to the Shirelles,
their broody atmospherics, 'Leader of the Pack',
in which the biker joins the early dead,
the leather cortege in the cemetery,
a devil-angel logoed on each back.

I miss you more than I can ever say,
and synchronistically, coincidentally,
that girlie group's vocalised elegy
turns up on the air-waves, all thunderstorm
and moody trauma with her heart broken
beside an oil pool on the road,
the sixties still beginning, and that song
hanging on it like a blue rain,
melodramatics teased by the big sound.

October, and a fuming pinkish sky
is slashed by late afternoon mauves.
We've lost our walks through Air Street, Golden Square,
the buzzy Soho afternoon, the shift
into those small streets with their quiet,
the headiness of things we said. I keep
most days inside, go out about the hour
darkness drops over town, and hear the roar

of leather bikers burning up the air.

Female Singers

So often reaching out of ruined love
to find a high spot in their pain
a way to sensitize a loss
that's universal in its suffering,
and up on heels, red heels spiking the boards,
she dips a hand into her heart
to feel the broken places, lets it bleed

through phrasing, and her backless gown
is raining sequins to the floor.
Sob sisters, torchy divas in the spot,
all tousled hair and red cupid's bow lips
they're like a black sheathed sisterhood
who plead right to the roots of love
as though by never letting go
they'll win the lover back, or die from need.
'Cry Me A River' sung so deep it's down
wherever breath begins.

They heal us by companioning their hurt,
and living through it all day, every day
as truth that feeds a tear-stained voice
in telling how a woman's dream
was broken on that downmood night
he met somebody else, and went away.
It's the old story of a life
thrown out, betrayed, and after all the years
still loyal, as she thrusts a gloved hand high
and holds the note like putting in a knife.

Novels

Obituarized data on the microfiche,
they stay suspended like ice-burials,
cryogenic bodies in nitrogen

awaiting recall. Reconfigured lives.
Most are sucked into a black hole,
imploded star that won't give pieces back
or redress the issue posthumously.

I see cerise camellias flattened out
by April rain, when buying books;
the light's translucently reverential,

a wine-blushed afterglow on Holland Park.
Anna Kavan at Hillsleigh Street
writing her fiction, needling smack,
heroin for talcum powder,
dead on the bathroom floor, a borderline

absolutist cult
bringing her weirdo wacky novels back.
I stand outside the garden where she sat,
a bottle blond with crushed lipstick,
seeing a leopard under trees

seeing her absent body break in flames.
Survival's her's. Another rain
of books arrive, the story lasts
for ever in its modulated ways,

new lives, new fiction in the DNA,
and each attempt a shot to have it end
to write the whole thing down.
Kavan in Chanel. Elegant, cut-off,

stylized, obsessive. Faxing from the dead?
I keep her in mind as a holograph,
leopards and hypodermics on her bed.

Elizabeth Rees

Home Movie

My sister has brown eyes, brown hair
and symmetrical breasts. Tonight
she can't stop crying in the basement.
Mother won't hold, but hovers and grips.
Sister twists tighter than rope, pulls
her own hair from the roots.
Mother slaps my sister's face.
Her sharp thwack echoes, Stop!

They climb upstairs.
I light a cigarette. Mother
comes back, "Sometimes
it's best to use force
if a person's lost control."
I nod like a buoy.

Kim Roberts

St. Anthony Preaching to the Fish

1.
You or I would feel silly,
but he had the Will of God behind him.
He leaned over the waves and spoke.
Their little mouths opening, shutting,
agitating the surface of the water
the way raindrops make the water jump up
to meet the other water descending:
perhaps they thought they would be fed
physical, rather than spiritual food.

2.
Physical food: In Lisbon,
where St. Anthony is the city's patron saint,
grilled sardines are the specialty. Any night of the summer
go to the *Feire Popular*: families gather around
heaping plates of whole *sardinhas*, eyes glazed (both:
eater and eaten), and the smoke of the grills
hangs in the air with the carnival music.
Charred flesh, but soft and white inside,
feathered between three hundred tiny bones.

3.
Spiritual food: *The stimulation of pity by emotive means,*
the clearness, the simplicity and the intelligibility,
the basically realistic way of expression,
the emphasis brought out in the choice of useful
and economical plans of action
are some other means of a religion that wants to innovate.

4.
At night, around the stairs of the former palace
off the *Praca do Comercio*, the stairs that lead
down to what Lisboetans call the Sea of Straw
and English mariners once called Jackass Bay,
three hundred fish feed, packed so closely

they support each other on all sides, pocking
the surface of the *Rio Tejo* with their o-mouths
and flashing their silver bellies. Tourists gather
and point, leaning over the waves like *Sao Antonio.*

5.
Antonio doesn't like sardines: he has bigger fish to fry.
With his slim *moreno* good looks,
sometimes he can get the foreign women to buy him
a bottle of *vinho tinto* and rides on the bumper cars
at the *Feire Popular.* He calls himself *el professore*
and kisses each part of my face, teaching the names
from forehead to chin: *testa, olhos, nariz, boca, queixo.*

6.
The monumental tabernacle and the altar glass
containing sculpture of Our Lady of the Happy Death
complete the ensemble, surrounded by lace-like
angels in upholstered wood.

7.
The wooden Saint Anthony, larger than life,
holds a large red book in his left hand, on which sits
a tiny pudgy baby. St. Catherine has her wheel,
St. John his sheep, St. Jerome his skull,
St. Francis his wounds. To each his proper prop.
But Anthony, lovely Anthony, savior of fish,
in Lisbon you are revered above all. The widows
kneel on the hard pews and tell their beads,
their mouths opening and closing, opening and closing.

Natasha Sajé

Fruit

Pitting a flat of sour cherries squeezing fingers through crisp
skins takes all day thinking about silly mind games and how the
still life makes me happy even though the light is fading and
someone's stolen the marigolds out front and maybe that's why I
spend six hours finding pits only to throw them out betting on
whether I've got the last one and if I do then I will be loved
and if not I'll be loved by someone else.

Leslie Scalapino

from *Deer Night*

A homeless musician—having a dog that is a boxer, where he'd sit and play on the street—others fleeing return on the street by him. The dog the boxer's rear half is a tulip or pod emerging. The dog is still half existing.
the pod is liquid-covered worm that is transforming the dog

The homeless musician then is not on the street. One is transformed by the pod, but appearing as oneself. The pod duplicates separately from one but closeby. It isn't dreamed or dreaming. When the others at the moment pass running, the still living as that being oneselves are fleeing.

A liquid-covered worm transforming a person, who has to sleep, in daylight.

A social butterfly has no contemplative faculty (because I say so)—that is that of the other, the black butterfly seen or not able to be seen on the blue/and which is then man flying in it. There are no people but rather that faculty occurring. *In terms of plays, my gesture is 'to get to the inside of action, at any time.'*

(she herself is the lackey) Lackeys came up crawling to fawn on the few people who liquidated.
"Gregarious" is the social being—in castigating—so there's relative occurrence.

(appearing as brown indigo butterfly)   *qualifying actions*

by being spoken

The forced collectivization occurs on red wheat fields. Perhaps 40 million were liquidated in this period. People being shipped in cattle cars or shot. Or freezing as past the line itself using the line. Children straggling off the cattle cars when they are being deported. Looking for water.
Starving children in herds are blue as if they are aliens. On the red wheat fields which don't exist—then, one wasn't born.

The brown indigo butterfly appears as man

from one not being born—is conception-making at present as
the line of text as the real event

Only the wealthy supposedly were liquidated, yet those obviously destitute called "sympathisers" of the others were   liquidated too.

People say about this But they were wealthy, yet themselves have far more. one's observation solely and also one's experience solely—have no relation

The dirty canals floating garbage/shanties on stilts, people bathing—In the world people are the main exports, sold into brothels by parents; or they migrate as labor on the roads.

It isn't produced by the events *per se*. But must be its extremity, while not arising from it.

The black butterflies as the worms on the red wheat fields—irreducible as the black butterfly/which is the man flying being that. On a hot vast terrain of fields *per se*, there are no people.

I could only repeat that. It's its relation.

The relation isn't produced by suffering merely—of the real occurrence of their forced labor, the destruction of anyone not starving as having a food supply (seen—out—*not* swollen/distended with malnutrition are beaten), or anyone *having* enthusiasm—no emphasis is allowed in their convention.

which is that experience is not to occur.

Yet in extremity, not discounting occurrence and being that itself, the visual is an event itself.

The worm ate the red wheat field—fields are empty—on indigo night.

Hatred is. People believing in that which is conventional as occurrence/ as relative. So one cannot say it, as the occurrence is relative.

The MacDonalds and Sony companies by the brothels—on the canals she's been sold at 14. There is therefore not an intellect that can see this as differentiated from moon (that's eliminated) and so sentiment—this is not to be 'seen' but 'giving up' (as a kind of relaxing) to be invented in one only.

The roots ('existing' yet not there) of plants on stalks upright on stems— the wildcat, one—one would fly toward one if barred.

And it wasn't barred.

An ibex with only one horn and a red little tongue sticking out—(green bands as if tattoos on the face)—city, 'suffering emergence' seen.—But where there is no emergence—she's translucent, kneeling—because they bind them; hooves facing each other 'only' in motion.

This may be Egypt in her and she isn't there. And cattle.

(14-year-olds brought in are in motion *per se*.)

(Dancers carry Ibex on uncovered palaquin or litter. She is kneeling on her knees and on her arms which are curved backward, have hooves on them like the ibex's legs. A black satin wedge-vulva is sewn between her legs and is visible on her front.)

To conflate actual time, to make the past be actually the present by making its motions. I don't want to do that. I want the present to occur, yet that isn't anything.

The romantics thought imagination to be expression of one, that was 'discovered'—even a violation of nature.

Maureen Seaton and Denise Duhamel

The Scarlet Letter

From the beginning Pearl loved the letter A—
it was her beginning, her real father
dim as his name, invisible as her
little dog's soul. Never mind the mournful
sky, the A in the clouds, the demon chill
of Boston. Reverend Dimmesdale whipped himself
silly. The stigmata on his chest smelled
of psychological maladjustment.
And what about Mistress Hibbens, the witch?
The woods were full of eerie curlicues.
The moon got in the way of women whose
silhouettes grew pointier and blacker,
collapsed in ash. Pearl's eyes grew darker
than a cauldron's bottom. Then she flew away.

The Scarlet Letter 2

The day Pearl insisted her mother sport
that A was the day Hester decided
no more kids, that's it. She'd confided
in no one, not Pearl who made seaweed A's
and stuck them on her doll's bellies, like play
in purgatory, place of soul-waiting
and embryonic-suffering (Pearl's plotting
worked like a spell); not Dimmesdale who confessed
as if, at that point, anyone could care less.
Still, the story wound down like a river
after Dimmesdale took the scaffold, shivered
through the stigmata-A on his chest.
Not to mention the meteor that blessed
the day—its rabid tail of adultery.

Edgar Silex

Distances
For Sherman Alexie

as a child I thought my grandfather was the god
who walked out each dawn and pulled the sun up
by the songstrings of birds who sang to his presence
I thought his being old meant it was easier
for him to finally take for granted each last dawn
yet there he was each morning going out
offering his prayers to the momentary
to the spiraling force so that it would continue on
to the sun so it would continue to rise
like a smoke-prayer for the sun he too would rise
in the rose-light of his thank you's
thank you weaver of this green-blue earth
thank you maker of this blue-green sky
for my wife for my family for each morning
when we sat together at the breakfast table
his thank you's would smile us awake

I think now that she was god's hand
turning the machinery of the day
the washing and thrashing and hanging of our clothes
the cutting the stirring and pouring
and nursing the hungers and pains
the shushing and brushing of childhood vims
my grandmother turning everything slowly
till it hummed into each night's silence
like that corner of hers where she kept
a candle and cross in the quiet of her bedroom
where she rooted her knees her hands clasped
and as heavy as the bags of her eyes her whispers
rising evanescing in the stillness *God*
keep my good husband sober and strong please
don't make us choose between food and the mortgage please
forgive our transgressions in the darkness
she would kiss Amens softly on our sleeping foreheads

a Spanish catholic she preferred to speak
of herself simply by saying she was Castillian
a full Indian he preferred to say nothing
in this way he spoke of how our blood's indivisible
but once when I was little she cried
as she tried to whip the stubborn Indian out of us
he always dreamed about what might happen
she always dreamed what had happened
and I am amazed at how they loved each other
at how this world blends what seems so divisible
at how each night and day they taught us to think good
thankful thoughts but mostly I am amazed
at how the word *please* eventually frees
the souls it tries to destroy with its slavery

Ifigenija Simonovic

Love Poem

each morning I wake up
        different
each night I fall asleep
        the same

sometimes one day seems like a hundred days
sometimes a hundred days seems like one day

I love you and the earth goes round

I Used to Be a Girl

One day my step-father decided to strangle me.
He took care of me, then.
He took me then.
He had had me ever since we moved into his house.
He took care of me, then.
My mother said I was lucky.
Not all step-fathers
love their step-daughters.

To strangle me was fine. I did indeed
miss the bus. I did indeed
have sand in my schoolbag. I did indeed
forget to learn my rhymes. I did indeed
fail to be good, yes I failed.
My mother said I was lucky.
Not all step-fathers care.

No, I did not mind at all
being strangled.
I only felt wrong doing him a favour.

My mother was standing by, watching,
her hands held out
ready to catch me later. Later.
She was going to catch me
I knew I could trust her.

I looked at her face then I looked at his,
they merged into a blur of mist and cloud,
only their eyes peeked through like beams, hot rays
making my mouth feel dry and sore.

I could not stop thinking
about the day before, I saw it all,
the way he handled me. He was saying

I was not to be scared.
He was saying he needed me.
He washed his congealed milk out of my hair,
just in time. I told my mother
I was wet because my baby brother
had pissed into my face.
We all laughed.

I am here now. Still here. I am looking
forward to the final blow.
I am indeed looking forward,
into the future. I am lucky
I do not have a daughter. I would find it
hard to hold my hands out ready to catch her.

Bob Slaymaker

Yearning

They lived in a crowded house—
six kids, two parents, one grandmother.
The three boys slept in one bedroom,
the three girls in another.
The parents had their room,
the grandmother hers.
There was never a quiet moment,
the bathroom the only refuge
before someone pounded on the door,
stopping a boy's mirrored boxing match,
a girl's imagined ballet.
Thirty years later, each one lives alone,
relishing the quiet, the private bathroom,
missing the varied human voices,
the many hearts beating as one.

W. *Loran Smith*

The Playboys
for Harold

The summer of love *Time* magazine proclaimed God was dead,
my parents gave up the ghost, too. My gung-ho father grew
a feathery blond mustache, took to wearing the silver
turquoise bone choker I had given him last Christmas
on a lark, when he had still loved St. Christopher.
And on weekends he'd take his Swedish girlfriend upriver
on our boat, the boat's mahogany deck, the cooler of rib-eyes,
the pinch of reefer he smoked in his pipe like Hugh Hefner,
his Swedish girlfriend's breasts, the whole kit and caboodle,
vibrating with two hundred belching horses of Evinrude
he plowed and whipped up to his new hipster buddies.

Sometimes, when the Swedish woman was home rolling meatballs
for her own Swedish family, I would ride up to the island with him.
The dirty choppy river going past the portals of the cabin,
where I sat in the dark reading Hesse or Alan Watts.
I was always preparing for the contemplative life then.
A life I envisioned far above this world, far above these silly men
in their aviator glasses and tight trunks, hooting and hollering
at every girl that skied past the beach in a Day-Glo bikini.
Far above their salesmen's bellies pouring over their waistbands,
too much beer cooling thirty feet down on the anchor lines.
Far above the trick knees and aching shoulders they swung
in slow painful windmills all afternoon and well into their drunks.

Thirty years later, I am no longer so disgusted with the worldly life.
Right now I remember the girls like psychedelic Venuses
on half shells, the rainbow wake of their ski's fanning
out in rooster tails. In fact, I could look all day at their smooth,
hairless stomachs, the water pouring off in sparkling rivulets.
Nothing in their sweet bodies quite sharp or defined yet.
Just the unbelievable possibilities of my own hunger.
Like the embarrassment of jobs I've cooked my way through.
Say, like thin pink medallions of milk-fed veal in bordelaise
and shaved black truffles, or sweetbreads in puff pastry,
or strawberries in double cream, or chocolate Grand Mariner tortes,
like forty-something, rounding with the field into the home stretch.

Andrew Sofer

Aunt Winnie

You told them you were half Indian
and they believed you:
milk-chocolate skin, flashing brown eyes.

In a cold Berkeley house, I find you
running on Mexican faith cures and enemas,
brown belly swollen with cancer.

Four wild kids you dragged coast to coast
and me—pale schoolboy cousin, foreign—flock
to your bed-side. We play Jefferson Airplane

late at night, smoke crumpled joints
in tribute, get on each other's sinking nerves.
I remember you two years ago:

handing me the joint
then chuckling
as I lay on my bed

seeing clouds float across the ceiling
until you yelled, "Let's go!"
sweeping me up in my pajamas

for a midnight drive to the ferry.
You left me in the Land Rover
stoned and leering at passers-by

then whirled us away
to the dune-flecked beach.
Your thin fingers

passed a red speck
that danced to music, and
"Into the sea! Into the sea!"

You gunned the engine, spurted
through wet sand, wheels spinning,
and for one wild instant

I thought you could really do it,
Winnie, drive us into the sea.

Virgil Suarez

Milagros *La Flaca*

Was the first girl I ever made out with.
She was all skin and bones. Wore
orthodontic braces, which while we kissed
and fondled that day in the garage,
        cut up my lips real bad.

Her pelvis dug into my waist as we ground
into pleasure. She refused to let me touch
her under her blouse. We were thirteen.
The way she kissed, I thought, had something
        to do with her name: miracle.

She got me in trouble for the first time
with the law. I visited her house on Saturdays,
after her parents left to work the flea markets.
She never let me inside her house
        out of respect for her parents.

I waited for her in the garage. Each Saturday
I got there earlier. One time I was there so early
after her parents had left, that the next door
neighbor saw me and called the cops.
        They came, asked me a few questions,

and since I wouldn't cooperate with the right
answers, they took me in. There were two of them,
and they wouldn't talk to each other as they drove
me to the station. I asked what I had done wrong.
        They drove and kept quiet.

But I insisted upon answers, until the one driving
looked up at the rear-view mirror and shouted to shut
the fuck up, and so I did, for a while, until I started
to tell them about what I was doing in the garage.
        We drove into the parking lot behind the station.

The cop who wasn't driving and who hadn't said a word,
came around the side of the car, opened my door,
reached in, and pulled me out by the hair. He choked
me and left me breathless for a few moments.
       "When we say 'shut up,'" he said, "we mean it."

And so I didn't talk after that. They called my parents.
They came to pick me up at the station. The chief of
police assured my father this wouldn't go on record.
They shook hands. On the way home, my mother cried,
       and my father refused to talk.

As soon as we got home, I tried to explain
what happened. My mother said this Milagros girl
was no good for me, no good indeed if she
was already getting me into trouble with the law.
       I was not to see her again.

Next Saturday, I didn't go see her. I didn't call.
Neither did she. Time against us, we forgot each other.
I've tried to over the years, until I see us: two kissing
fools in the penumbra of an empty garage, her braces cut
my already raw lips, the taste of metal in my mouth,
       remnants of a girl named Milagros.

Auto Erotica

Ask the man who's found in the passenger
side of his Cadillac, phone plugged

into cigarette lighter, '79 class ring tight
around his finger, the shoe laces on his right

foot missing, used instead to tie the plastic
trash bag tight around his neck, the subject

of the conversation that hinges upon the release
of the self. Some bad habits acquired beyond

adolescence, or perhaps before, when the scent
of panties, the sniff of the inseam on a pair

of Levis, something to undo the hold of boredom.
Something about the lack of oxygen

at the moment of release, *le grand morte*
with trash bag. The man leans forward

and thus makes it seem like the dashboard
released its air bag around his head. The man

died from such undoing. Intricate methods,
a kind of smothered-by-pillow he practiced

even as a child, the trick of a belt used as a strangle.
"A gasper," Byron called it, or rather the person

who engaged in such pleasure, the lure of asphyxiation.
The dawn reveals the car, parked in the vastness

of an elementary school's lot, on a Saturday.
The police have come, cordoned off the area.

Later, the homicide crew goes to work.
The enema bag is found in the backseat, among

the graded student papers, liquid seeped out
and made the ink run. This is the last remnant

of the puzzle that will be put together later
in the lab, perhaps only the forensics expert will truly

know what went on here, and even for him
this will be a first. A man who's learned

to rely upon the guilt of hair, the small traces,
residues of the strangeness of the here and now.

Peter Tatlin

Made Rich

I can't help it if these things make me love her.

I can't help it if I love her when she stands before me
Naked except for bright red slipper-socks at foot and burning red hair at head,
Her whole warm and ginger body glowing and glorious in the window's frame,
The rooftops of half of Paris behind her in cream and pink and pearl,
Sacré Coeur perched tipsily upon her shoulder.
I know these are small things, but I can't help it if they make me love her.

I can't help it if I laugh like the water in the cobbled gutters
When she says, when first we go to bed,
"If I shock you, please say."
I can't help it if these things make me happy.

I can't help it if it interests me when, her warm back sloping down before me,
She unburies her head from the pillows as I begin to come and throws it
Oddly, quickly from side to side as if to free something from her ear or shivered hair.
I can't help it if I find this strangeness funny and enjoyable, enjoy enjoying it.

I couldn't help it when she put on that scarlet hat like a wide-mouthed Fez
And pulled red hair down each side of her face,
Couldn't help it when she walked and turned and turned and walked beside me
        and before
With that alacrity and lightness which I love and hymn,
A little ginger gibbon at my side throughout late-night Montmartre,
Couldn't help it when we pushed our faces close and to the glass to see
The trays of brightly-coloured gummy cakes for Ramadan,
Nor when we turned at last
And found ourselves back at her place, back in her tiny attic rooms
With their unfathomable quality of space.

I can't help it if I can't stop thinking about her.

Paris Revisited

Can I write today?
Lover's anus, needle's eye, berry...
From what, today, from anything?
"In those days," she said, "they only fell in love
By mistake". From silence,
Always from silence.

Can I write today?
Days of no writing
Like cans tied to my ankles,
Clattering on the cobbles
In cacophony that compels me
On, as if to escape them, on.

Where is that silence?
Where might that bucket be lowered?
Can I write today?
Can I write today, please?

Alexander Theroux

Dropping Fleas into a Glass of Water

Wet fleas are three-fourths dead.
The way they despair is, oddly,
by activity. I find the way sunshine
illuminates their last agonies
by adding irony to pain the way
when desperately we try to pray
in struggling to save ourselves
our imprecations quickly take on
disbelief so used we are to God's
suffocating silence as we drown.
Their miniscule bagpipe bodies
brown and tiny as tobacco flakes
with snouts like Bosch's horns
as crazily they scissorleg and
thrash, bite for air, eat water
the way leaves gulp red light,
experience with each abdominal
exertion in the champagne night
of frying, sizzling bubbles
the dreadful fact that jumping
does not work, just as prayer reaching
for a similar height does not
in our despair.   As to beseeching,
kicking, thrashing, madly humping
fleas in water likewise is our lot.

To Mickey Hood Who Travels the World and Visits Monasteries on His Motorcycle

Wheelman, pilgrim, who finds God
as much in wind and wet and wandering
as any pale renunciant

eating black radishes by night
in the desert of his prayer and self-denial,
no rear-view mirror for you!

What do you see beyond your glasses,
Mick, how many rose moons, sad roads, bent trees,
dry hills, cold hands, night lights,

and thin as a druid, greasier with lube
than a wart hog's dug, didn't you conventicle
everywhere with holystoning monks

speaking fortune-cookie English
only to feel bone-dead sleep quicker than one
can say never late than early?

No misomundist travels in his head
as far as you in pursuit of monastic solitude.
It is never unfeelable form

in merely biking—how lost
in remote dorps you must often find yourself
seeking the spindle of a spire?—

but patching vow to vision.
It is not necessary to change, you well know,
rather necessary not to change.

Remember how Lord Krishna
in the *Bhagavad Gita*, holily contemplating
the nose, sitting cross-legged,

prescribed the "mystic squint"?
I see only you on your motorcycle of a night,
not Krishna, riding Godward so.

Mike Topp

French Style

There's a classic Western movie where a cowboy says, "Gimme a shot of red-eye," and the French subtitle reads, "*Un Dubonnet, s'il vous plaît.*"

Tim Turnbull

Raw Horse

I step into the restaurant
                              And bellow my order
                          Bellow my order
Bring me a raw horse
Bring me a horse I roar!
                          Waiter!

Bring me a whole horse
Bring me a whole live horse!
                              Waiter!

The other customers quail
Bewildered children clutch their mothers' skirts
And wail

The maitre d'
Whimpers, smiles a nervous smile
And sidles up to me
'P'haps M'sieur would laak to traa
Som escalope of veal
Smothered in a rich waan sauce
With 'aricots vert
Et pommes Dauphinoise....'

NO! BRING ME A HORSE

An uneasy murmur ripples
                              Round the room
As diners shuffle knives and forks
                                  And spoons
The air is dense with desperation
                              And gloom
They're hoping it'll all be over
                          Soon
They glance

                    About
        For a way
                          To escape
            Then

One man panics and makes a break
I intercept him with a body check
That drives him through the plate glass shopfront
He dies impaled in a pool on the pavement

NOW NOBODY MOVE
TILL I FINISH MY FOOD

And bring me a raw horse
Bring me a horse I roar
                          Waiter!

The horse is brought
It shies and struggles and stamps and snorts
I strip to the waist
The waiter trips and stumbles
In his haste to get away

He crashes through the kitchen doors
Which clatter on their springs revealing
The sous-chef swinging by his apron strings
From a hook in the kitchen ceiling

My sinews strain and muscles flex
Flecks of foam from the horses nostrils
Spatter my chest

A couple of pensioners piss their pants
And with a screech beseech me
'Oh spare the noble beast
Eat us instead
We're old and bony
But our blood is red.
Oh spare the horse'
The pair implore.

Two well aimed fish forks
Nail them to the wall.

178

The air is thick with sweat
And fear
The horses eyes roll white
It screams and rears.

I grasp its head
And taking care to bite an ear off
While its still alive,
I wrestle it to the floor

Tables, chairs are splintered
 Crockery breaks
I snap its neck
Its legs keep flailing
As I tear into its flesh

Eating, eating, eating, eating,
Eating, eating, eating,
Eating, eating,
Eating

Till I'm sated.

Then when gorged
I torch the place
And walk away
Covered head to toe
In guts and gore,

Because I eat horses

I eat horses

I eat horses

RAW ....

Christopher Twigg

Gorillas

I

Like cave or stone age men
in gorilla suits, loose-fitting
they walk bent over
and carry orange peel in their mouths—
one thumps a tub and makes it roll in straw—
their eyes are old ladies,
Tibetan wisewomen,
half-brothers,
a noble arm framed on a ledge—

Children make bird noises to arouse their interest—
they pore, listless, like *Melancholy*
with abandoned toys,
compasses and dodecahedra—

a keeper's painted grasses on the brick

II

A female

She has feet like Old Bibles
and dry hair full of static electricity—
she scratches her arm
fingers her armpit
scratches her labia
and lollops—
Fat and unselfconscious
on her ship or metal hedge
without promise of tree, shade or mat to play on
She would love to but she cannot get undressed
so she drinks tea and serves shortcake in a flowery frock

III

Are they more prisoners than Estate Agents?
with shadows of bars on their colossal grey muscular arses
and straw fags—
Kings of nutshells and Infinite Space?
Limited vision astronauts
with black driving gloves—
Their heads are just portions of something else
like faces drawn on a vastness—
old cave eyes, cave watchers,
drip attendants, corridor spooks,
genial and dull old people,
sunny headachers,
lying up below the rafters
or playing games under the church roof

IV

Wrestlers of formality
superb sportsmen, men of
character, they have lost all
their medals, live in the
mouth of a tunnel of memory—
like conger eels in underwater pipes—

What do they do in winter when it snows?
They're doing time and we are tiny flowers
like black girls in bikinis seen from above
or men who roll themselves to death in beds!

Ruth Vaughn

Castle Rock

Stuck
Between meanings unhooked from
The pull—involuntary—of assumptions

Unbridled and strange

It would be easier
To let go
Than to fingernail scratchings
Shedding selves in
Flakes clawing for
An unevenness odd
Enough to hold them

To let
Go just let go and
Not to fall
In
Misfire hanging
On
For fear of fall-
ing
Not to fall
Scratching still
Air squawking
Not to fall
Wishing
Not to fall

And
To let go
To enjoy the tumble
To eke out the fraction of fraction of
Seconds
To let the bigness take another breaking thing and

Dash it to
Zeros of
Continuing

ruth weiss

One Night

one night i was out rehearsing with an acoustic
bass. long bus-rides across the city. i was out.
and out of it. not a rehearsal to shout about.
had to be done. and i did it. wondered why but
one has to do what one has to do.

on the way home across the city. at the transfer-
point it was dark. ominous. all not-seeing. there
a man also waiting for the transfer. he is talking.
i am silent. moving further and further away.

we are both waiting for the bus. he is talking.

i make out the words. scoffing tone. scuffing
one foot in front of the other. a man i had never
seen before.

WHO IS GOING TO READ YOUR BOOKS?
WHO IS GOING TO READ YOUR BOOKS?
WHO IS GOING TO READ YOUR BOOKS?

i am silent. i reach home a long time later.

WHO IS GOING TO READ YOUR BOOKS?

well hell i'm going to read my books—
OUT LOUD!

1989

Tim Wells

Cinnamon Girl

My Japanese friend
Has learnt some bad English from me
She says that this
Is what she came here to learn
Often
When meaning "Thanks" or "Good-bye"
I say "Cheers"
She uses this expression as a toast
Only she always mispronounces it as "Tears"
I've never corrected her
As besides from being endearing
There is more truth there
Than she knows

Biscuits Ain't Biscuits 'til They're Baked

Yeah,
      I'm on the grassy knoll
pulling the trigger
and getting away with it
Now you may think
that all my writing
about submarines, tanks and fighter planes
is the result
of making one too many Airfix Tiger Tanks
or of reading one too many Sven Hassel books
in my formative years
But I say this;
submarines, tanks and fighter planes
are wombs
as well as phalli
And further
I say this;
when Woman gave birth to Man
She made a weapon

Terence Winch

Pegleg

Fred Johnson is wearing
Harley Davidson suspenders.
My sister makes him breakfast
because the roof of his trailer
rotted out and there's garbage
all over his place.
He lost his leg
in a motorcycle accident
in his twenties.
He gets a disability check
for service in the Korean War.

My sister says he recently
started insisting that people
call him Pegleg, and that some
now know him only by that name.
She lives in the mountains
and people are peculiar up there.

Either I hit the tree, Fred says,
or the car full of people,
so I hit the tree.
I made this leg
out of that fucking tree.

Rose Zaeske

pink

When alone, she thinks of those things she shouldn't. Things
she shouldn't do, things she shouldn't think. Think, think goes the
little brain, pink and bright and plump. But that was years ago.
When thinking was good and considered productive. Now it's
distractive, and now the little organ has grown grey and ominous,
ever-expanding over her life and living. It lives on its own, it seems,
but likes to pull others in, into its swirling crevices, deep and
bottomless. The organ has grown grey. She tries to put back the
pink. She tries to think pink thoughts, bright cheery and childish.
But that doesn't work, so she drinks the red wine. If she follows it
with water, it should pinken, thereby pinkening her brain. She's
sure this works. She saw a movie. On television. Educational. The
brain of a person who'd been clean all his/her life was cut and
crumbled like cauliflower. The brain of the chronic alcoholic was cut
and reacted like juicy red meat. Red's pretty close to pink. Maybe
red is good enough and she doesn't need the water anymore. It was
slowing her down anyway. And everyone knows that slow is blue,
an entirely different color, too close to grey, and grey is what she
wants to leave. But grey is where she often ends. Because no one
can stay pink forever.

Connie Imboden

Portfolio

Three Photographs

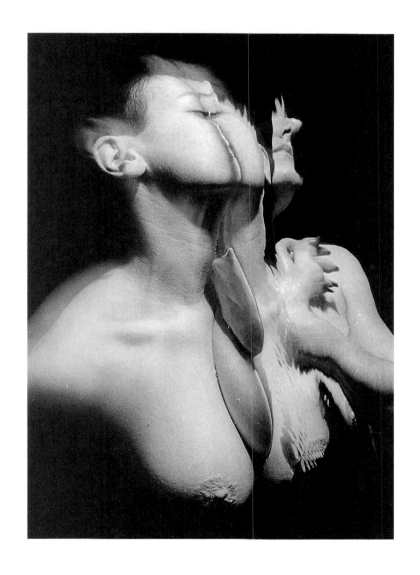

Kim Addonizio

Reading Sontag

He's a submissive. She's used to giving men what they want. At first she doesn't know this about him; they dance in a living room, end up in a bedroom, he leans back against the wall while she kisses him. She presses her palms against his and he sags against the wall, the backs of his hands touching it. She's much smaller than he is. She doesn't know how to be dominant, but she wants to please him.

A piece of pornographic fiction concocts no better than a crude excuse for a beginning; and once having begun, it goes on and on and ends nowhere.

The next time, when they start to fuck, he lies back on the bed with his arms over his head. The next time it's a few nights later, or the next morning. There is no next time. Even if there is, there won't be many more. This is my way of recovering the past, in order to torment myself with it. The next time, he lies back on the bed, tells her to use his dick for her pleasure. She uses his dick for her pleasure. She doesn't come. She comes. She almost comes, stays at an excruciating peak for what feels like hours, shuffles through erotic images and fantasies trying to break through. No, trying to let go. Surrender? No, break through is better. It's a barrier. A wall. Or maybe glass. Trying to break through a barrier that feels like glass. Trying to forget someone else. She's a little girl. He's a priest, he makes her kneel beside a narrow bed in the rectory, he pulls her dress over her head but not off, he takes off her underwear and fucks her. She's a nun. He rips off her rosary. She's in a bathroom, one of a row of naked women on their knees, men come in to fuck them, then go to take a piss. He's pissing in her mouth.

Literature's supposed to take the moral high ground. To be beautiful. To instruct. To cast out one's personal demons. To revel in one's neurotic self-obsession. She's a virgin, she's led to a table in a filled amphitheater and tied down. Her father fucks her, and then her seven brothers, according to age, the eldest first.

It's so difficult to make love with someone new—much harder than it used to be, when she was younger. She's been celibate for years. Okay, months. It feels like months, anyway. She remembers making love with her ex-husband. Bastard. Asshole. Love of her life. She hates him. She misses him constantly, constantly feels the pain of their failure, or the pain of her failure, the pain of his abandonment, the pain of the loss of their intense sexual pleasure, pain, pain, pain. She starts to cry. She doesn't let herself cry. They stop fucking, and he runs her a bath and leaves her alone. She curls up in the tub, lifts handfuls of white soapsuds, lets them drop onto her breasts in the candlelight. She's in a fetal position. An image of extreme distress. Duress. Inability to cope. Whatever. The obsessions of *Histoire de l'Oeil* are indeed Bataille's own. In other words, there's supposed to be a gap. A disclaimer. A lie. Okay, a disclaimer. The conditions of my grant were that I not write anything obscene. I signed the paper. I lied to get food stamps, to stay on MediCal, and to receive Unemployment. I also signed the Drug Free Workplace Enforcement Act. I have never used drugs in my life. She stays in the tub until the water gets almost cold, then goes back to the bedroom. They light up a joint. They snort some coke, shoot some heroin, and smoke some crack, then another couple—friends of his—shows up and the four of them fuck in every conceivable combination. Lots of homoerotic activity: the men come in each other's mouth, stick crucifixes up each other's ass. The women put their tongues all over each other. She likes fucking his male friend; the friend dominates her, the way she's used to. About four in the morning she and the friend end up in the shower together, masturbating for each other, and she asks for his number. He asks to see her again. He asks if he can call her. She refuses. She hesitates. She doesn't know what she says, she's so disoriented from all the drugs. She's pyschically dislocated. They gave me a lot of money; it didn't once occur to me to refuse it. Maybe I should have turned it down, to gain some notoriety. I'm a nobody. No one cares if I live or die.

A few days later they're discussing another couple, mutual friends.

Why do things always have to go somewhere? he says.

Now she has to take the opposite role, though she might, herself, have asked the same question. She feels a sense of panic that they won't go anywhere; he'll resist her, or be indifferent. She's afraid to show weakness around him. When they make love, when they fuck, when they perform for each other, for you, for us, when they engage in perversely pleasurable sexual activity, when they begin to have mutual boundary problems, when they fuck, she thinks about slapping his face, remembering the lover who slapped her. Remembering her ex-husband, the failure, etc., on and on, she must be addicted to pain. I, for one, am sick of her. She's history.

He knows she's used to giving men what they want. He's prepared to be disappointed in her. His own heart's still broken from the last affair, which, though brief, was intense. He's still hurting from the last relationship, which, though intense, was brief. Experiences aren't pornographic; only images and representations—structures of the imagination—are. This I underlined, and felt compelled to write a note in the margin: "But if 'experience' exists in our consciousness/imagination of it.. ?" I think I was trying to say that what we experience, as it's partly a function of how we perceive, can't be abstracted, separated from structures of imagination. But now, when I think about it, I'm not sure. I'm not intellectually equipped to take on Susan Sontag. I'm stupid. No, I'm smart, but I lack depth and breadth of knowledge. I skim everything in a desperate attempt to catch up. I'll never catch up. Normally we don't experience, at least don't want to experience, our sexual fulfillment as distinct from or opposed to our personal fulfillment. But perhaps in part they are distinct, whether we like it or not. She wrote this in 1967. Nothing's changed. Some things have changed.

Not enough has changed. No one will publish my work; I'm a terrible writer; I can't write a conventional, realistic story. I've given up. Still, I keep trying. He's prepared to be disappointed in her, but she keeps surprising him. Their sex gets better and better. He wants to hold on to his pain, his heartbreak, his regret, but that position begins to feel unnatural; he realizes he's only trying to deepen the loss of the other relationship to satisfy some twisted need to see himself as a victim, to recreate his childhood abandonment. If only he could see this, he might love her, but he holds on to his pain and finally breaks off the relationship. Affair. Friendship. Their random couplings. Meaningless sexual interludes. Temporary evasions of the acute meaninglessness of existence.

They go to a bar. Bataille hunches at a table in the corner, scribbling in a notebook. Marie is sprawled in a chair, naked, her legs open, being sucked by Pierot. They order beers. No, gin. He orders Johnny Walker Red, she has a rum and Coke. They stand at the bar, fascinated by the scene. Arousal comes through identification with one of the participants. In fantasies, she often sees herself from the male point of view. Not the dark beneath the blindfold, the feel of the black cloth knotted behind her head, but the sight of her face, her mouth open as he fucks her there. Marie climbs up on the table and squats, pissing on the dwarf. He decides to take a picture of the dwarf, urine splashing in his face, being jerked off by Pierot. He manages to get part of his own face in the shot by pointing the camera at the mirror behind the bar. Later, in his darkroom, he processes the negative, hits it with the enlarger light, moves the paper around in the developing bath with a pair of gray plastic tongs. The bottles behind the bar, the mirror, Marie's white body, the stream of urine. Where his face should be, the paper stays blank. Fuck him, I'm going to forget all about him.

He doesn't believe in Plato's concept of men and women as halves of the same whole, seeking each other. He's been through Reichean therapy. He's been depressed. He's fine alone. He's bald as an egg; she imagines straddling him, pushing her cunt against his mouth, then sliding it across his skull. His head is nicely shaped, she can't imagine spoiling its purity with hair. He takes her nipple gently in his teeth and gives it a slight tug. Milk pours out of it, thin and watery and sweet, filling his mouth almost faster than he can swallow. He sucks and sucks, feels drunk, falls asleep in her arms. She gets up, carries him to his crib, loosens the suction between them. She tucks the covers around him, spins the colored plastic mobile that hangs from the ceiling, touches the pulsing spot on his translucent forehead. She feels incomplete without a lover in her life, realizes that after years of dodging commitment—entrapment—commitment—she wants a partner. A companion. Anyone who will hold her and love her. A male body in her bed. A confirmation that she exists. When she doesn't see him for several days, the intimacy she'd felt with him earlier vanishes as though it never existed. Each time they're together, it feels as though they're beginning over.

He can't guess what she's thinking; when he asks, she says *It's private*, sounding almost angry. He's beginning to resent the relationship. Affair. Etc. She can make him do anything she wants. He feels trapped. Manipulated. Toyed with. He's tired of living without much of a context, or one that shifts so radically. Maybe he's going insane. He's stopped taking Prozac, stopped therapy, stopped calling her. He's tired of having to fuck her all the time. He loves fucking her; he can't get enough. He goes through all his photographs of old lovers, but they're like movie stills of famous actors; familiar as they are, he knows he's never met them. He lights a cigarette from the pack that appears on the table. His dick throbs in his jeans. He's going to explode unless he fucks her. He unzips his jeans and jerks off. There's no difference between inner and outer life. He comes thinking of her, milk pouring from his dick, come pouring from his dick like milk, like wine, like a language he'll never learn.

Roberta Allen

The Wrong One

"It was a boy, definitely a boy," said the boyfriend, still holding the wet rubber basin, "but there was something wrong with it. It didn't look right."

Weakly, the girl said, "How could you tell? It was so small." She raised herself slightly from the hotel room bed to look at him. How did he know how a ten-week old fetus should look? When he pointed it out in the basin, it was just something pinkish, almost transparent, amid the blood and slime and muck.

That morning a nurse had performed the illegal procedure while the boyfriend waited nervously outside the room. When it was over, the nurse had said it would be several hours before she would abort.

Their doctor friend, who had found the nurse against his better judgment, had wanted her to keep the baby almost as much as her boyfriend did. The doctor, who was married, had even introduced her to his girlfriend and their three-year-old son. But nothing could make her change her mind.

Neither the girl nor her boyfriend had a job or a permanent address. They were looking for a place to live though they could barely afford their fleabag hotel.

Lying there she thought about her boyfriend's children: three to date, and all with different girlfriends. How many more were there to come?

Wasn't he saying the fetus was ill-formed to punish her: to make her feel her failure as a woman; her inability to have a healthy son? She thought about the fetus. She thought about the boyfriend. Clearly, she had killed the wrong one.

R. R. Angell

Greyhound

A disemboweled newspaper blew in cold gusts down a urine stained sidewalk outside the City Bus Terminal, keeping company with leaves and chasing fragments of itself that hadn't caught on dirty iron railings or public trash receptacles. Wrinkled pages blew by revolving doors, dodged by the human effluent bathed in yellowed light from old and dingy street lamps, then continued with the wind into the biting howl of darkness down a hard sidewalk.

People huddled into themselves, pulling thin coats around their necks trying to stay warm in the unseasonable cold that had descended late in the day and by midnight had turned into an arctic blast that drove the unprepared indoors, corralling them wherever there were circles of warmth. Some carried bags or battered briefcases and walked briskly toward known destinations; others meandered. Almost all were walking close to the street, avoiding dark shapes and reaching hands that huddled against a wall plastered with ragged posters that beckoned in the wind. Farther down the street, other posters wrapped around lampposts under brilliant halogen bulbs throwing crisp surgical light into the darkness below with varying degrees of success. The posters screamed to free the incarcerated, or hawked the next Rave, or talked of AIDS, or whispered of missing children, the eyes demanding, seducing, begging, forever crying, as soot from graffittied buses coated everything with a dull charcoal grime. The smell of exhaust mingled with urine and decay, pungent and choking.

Jake plodded into the wind toward the terminal cloaked in yellowed light, not as one would swim toward an island after a shipwreck but as a scavenger with careful, focused eyes. A shred of newspaper leapt up and wrapped around his leg, overlapping his snugged gray wool overcoat. He pulled his crippled and naked hand out of a warm pocket and batted the paper away. The paper had a cold and clammy feel. Reflexively, he wiped his mangled paw on the soft teddy bear nestled in the crook of his left arm, then realized he had transferred a smudge of newsprint to its cheek. He shifted the bear to his other arm, then with his good hand he produced a handkerchief and wiped at the fuzzy cheek, with the same care of a mother wiping smudges from the chubby cheeks of a small child, first licking the cloth, then rubbing. Satisfied, he cleaned his crumpled fingers and put the handkerchief away, then angled toward a dark street lamp where he could lean in shadow and watch people go in and out.

He swigged vodka from a pocket flask and lit a cigarette, illuminating a round face, wisps of gray hair, a varicose nose, bushy brows that pressed down on dark, baggy eyes. His nose and cheeks, bitten by the wind, flushed almost Santa-like with spidery red veins. Twenty minutes and several cigarettes consumed him before the terminal traffic slowed enough. He popped a breath mint into his mouth, reseated the teddy bear in the crook of his arm, and walked into the light, where he was sucked into the terminal through a revolving door.

Inside, ragged people sat in rows of uncomfortable plastic chairs. A few managed to lie down or curl up underneath the chairs on a bed of discarded newspapers. Others sat bored and annoyed with the world, or reading, or with heads forward trying to get some sleep. A cop leaned on a spray-painted pillar sipping coffee and watching the ticket windows, unconcerned with the sleepers. There was an underlying noise, as if hundreds of people were shuffling through dead leaves in some invisible place.

Jake walked behind the cop and through a door to another waiting area that was dirtier than the front but quieter. There was a vending machine alcove of hard, gleaming tile tucked off to the side. A teen in baggy clothing kicked a machine in slow motion, or perhaps exhaustion. Snacks swung back and forth on metal spirals after each blow. The kid stopped kicking, put his face to the glass and stared inside at the insubstantial snacks and candy dangling there.

"Bus Number 186 to Nashville by way of Indianapolis, Louisville, and Bowling Green, now boarding on platform 15," a blurry voice echoed. A girl in worn jeans and a canvas coat got up and threw a purple knapsack over her shoulder, getting the strap caught in her frizzy blonde hair. She untangled it like a drunk batting at spider webs, then grabbed a worn guitar case and shuffled toward the door, bumping Jake as she passed. Without looking at him she said, "Yeah."

Old folk and people with children had taken the plastic chairs nearest the door, their belongings piled around them like sandbags. Sleeping drunks perfumed the middle of the room. A flood of street kids huddled in the semi-darkness of a corner where the fluorescent lights never worked, talking among themselves in low voices or lounging with stretched legs and baseball-cap-covered eyes. Some of the chairs were missing or partially ripped out of their sockets.

A kid in black jeans slouched on a row of darkened seats, his tattered flannel shirt gaped open, his white stomach exposed. Unconscious, the kid was oblivious to the coolness of the room. Jake maneuvered toward shadowed seats nearby and sat down a row behind the flannel shirt so he could watch the kid sleep. Only the girl with purple hair and a nasty scar on her cheek noticed Jake sit down. Their understanding still in place, keeping her away. She sneered at him and spat on the seat in front of her while she held his gaze, then she pulled a dirty blanket around her and stared at the spittle, watching it creep like a slug down the blue plastic. Her eyes closed, and she passed out again. Jake held his teddy bear tighter and patted its head, watching the sleeping kid in black jeans, blurry street tattoos on his hard stomach rising and falling with each breath. The teen at the vending machine resumed his kicking.

After a while, a dark-haired kid of about twelve or thirteen detached himself from the huddle of kids by the wall and glanced around before walking toward Jake. Out of the corner of his eye, Jake watched the kid cross the room, his hands jammed into the pockets of robin's-egg blue sweatpants. He had on an oversized unbuttoned flannel shirt with the sleeves rolled up and a dirty white T-shirt underneath. As the kid got closer, Jake turned and looked at the angelic face, the large eyes, the marble-white complexion. The boy did not stop or look away but flashed a smile. He turned and, with exaggerated movements, flipped the tail of his shirt up as he bent over to tie the laces on dirty sneakers, making sure Jake saw the holes in his sweatpants. Then the kid dropped into a seat in front of Jake. He sat quiet long enough to let Jake check him out.

"Need a boy, man?" he whispered to the air. Then he cocked his head and looked at Jake. Open, business-like, self-assured.

Jake smiled, impressed. "What's your name, kid?"

"What should it be?"

Jake thought for a moment, then after a time said, "Joey. I like Joey. Reminds me of someone."

"Funny, that's my name. Did you wanna give that bear to a boy named Joey?"

"Not a boy." Jake watched the kid, contemplating his features, the kid's smooth delivery, wondering what his life was like, how long he would last. He was too pretty to stay pretty too long. "Do you have a sister about your age? Maybe younger?"

"Might. What's it worth?"

"About ten I think."

"Try thirty and I might."

"Go." Jake nodded toward the door.

Joey took a long look at the kid in black, then got up and left. Jake stroked the teddy.

A loud crash and the sound of breaking glass meant the baggy kid had finally gotten his meal. Jake didn't raise his head when the cop ran through the door and into the vending alcove. The kid was yelling. A minute later the cop was pushing the handcuffed teen through the door, and one of several bags of pretzels stuffed in the cop's back pocket fell to the floor unnoticed. When the cop and his charge were gone, the kids along the wall raced to the machine. The girl with the purple hair and scar got up and shuffled to the alcove after flipping Jake the finger and spitting.

Joey reappeared with his 'sister.' They stood there together against the wall just inside the door. The girl looked like a doll, with a thin face and curly Shirley Temple hair. She was wearing a beat-up black leather jacket that was several sizes too big, over faded jeans and stained pink sneakers. She held Joey's hand and stared across the room at Jake with an unreadable expression. Jake watched her, oblivious of the kids who moved back into darkness with their armloads of junk food. The little girl took a deep breath and smiled as if seeing Jake for the first time. She dragged Joey across the room and hopped up onto the seat in front of Jake.

"Hi, Grandpa!" She reached over the seat for a hug.

"Hi, honey." He hugged her and patted her back, feeling the knuckles of her spine even through the jacket, and she grabbed the teddy bear, pulling it from him.

"This is my friend, Joey," she said brightly, "who made sure I wasn't alone while we waited for you. Mom said you'd give him fifty dollars when you found us."

"She did, did she?" he said looking at the boy. Joey looked him square in the eye, unblinking, as if defending the increased charge. Jake chuckled and winked at the boy, then pulled out a wallet stuffed with bills and handed over two twenties and a ten. "How is your mother, honey?" Jake glanced around the room, but no one was watching.

"Oh, fine now, I think." She turned to the boy.

"Bye, Joey," Jake said. "And thanks for taking care of my little girl, here."

"Yeah," he said.

The girl watched Joey go until he reached the door, then turned back to Jake.

"What's your name, honey?" he whispered.

"Christy."

"That's a nice name."

"I'm cold—and hungry, too. Let's go get warm, Grandpa." She hugged her new teddy bear.

Jake reached into his pocket and touched his wallet, his touchstone. She would do nicely. "Yes, honey. Let's go get warm. You sure could use some cleaning up." He stroked her cheek. "We might have to give you a bath tonight."

"I haven't had a bath in a long time, Grandpa. Can we eat first?"

She had those wide green eyes and her face opened up to him, a bright island amid the dingy backdrop of the station. Her hands curled over the back of the chair where she still knelt, fingernails chewed and caked with dirt. Dry hands for such a young little one. She could put some lotion on, bath oils. His client had been generous this time, and specific, had given him plenty up front to find just the right subject.

"Please, can we eat?"

Food. He tasted vodka reflux. Something to soak it up with would be a good idea, and something to keep him awake, to sharpen his eye, steady the camera.

"All right. Hamburger and fries okay?"

"And a milkshake?"

"There's a diner a few blocks from here. Come with me." He got up, hearing the faint slosh of the flask in his jacket.

"Grandpa?"

He looked down at her kneeling in the chair and waited. She reminded him of....

"Can we take Joey, too? He hasn't eaten and there's this guy that's mad at him." Tears welled up and she looked away to swallow.

"He has plenty now to get him through."

"They'll jump him as soon as he walks out, Grandpa. He won't have nothing and they'll stuff him in a locker like they did last time."

He had seen the beat-up bank of lockers, some with the doors ripped off, some big enough for a suitcase or two. Poor kid. But that was life. Even pigeons sorted out an order. Pecking order. Pecker order.

"He'll be okay, honey." Jake walked around the chairs and took her hand.

She got up moping, and shuffled with him toward the door, her head down as she clutched the bear close. "They're gonna get him tonight," she whispered to the bear. "Don't watch, don't look, don't tell. Don't watch, don't look, don't tell."

She repeated it over and over into the bear's ear, and Jake heard every word. He looked around and found Joey crouched alone against a wall in shadow, eyes darting from the cluster of kids tearing through wrappers in the corner, to the empty chairs, to Jake. Hollow eyes, the eyes of the beaten.

"It's the street, honey," Jake whispered. "That's how it is."

He glanced back and saw that Joey was tracking them, a blank expression on his face. Christy changed her litany on the other side of the doorway to a whimper. Jake stopped to look down at her. His client wasn't interested in tears.

"All right. Go get him." She stared, then smiled as he squeezed her hand. "Go on before I change my mind."

Like a butterfly, she was gone, then back, leading Joey through the door. She pawed at Joey's arm, pulling him by the flannel sleeve until they were a threesome and the kids hugged him so that he had nowhere to put his own hands but on their heads.

"Food. Let's go get something," he groused and pulled away from them.

The green vinyl booth seats had been taped together so many times they were a web of yellowed tape with tufts of padding and wood visible, especially around the chrome edging. The kids sat across from him. Christy, against the speckled Formica wall, played with the salt and pepper caddie, counting then stacking the sugar packs. Joey shivered beside her from the frigid walk, the flannel shirt his only protection. Seemed he had lost his coat the night before to someone. Jake didn't want to know, but when the kid ordered hot coffee, black, with his breakfast, he said nothing and reached reflexively for his flask, catching himself in time as the waitress wiped bleached curls out of the chicken-skin face she turned on him, making him want that drink even more. He didn't have time for this. There were orders to fill.

The waitress finished with the kids and cocked her head. Drapes of skin sagged in valences beneath her eyes like a basset-hound, he decided: mournful and waiting to get it over with. She angled her pad and chewed her gum with wet, open smacks, like greasy sex in a dingy room, staring at him with the blank expression of 3:00 am, waiting for someone else to make the first move, as if passivity itself were an effort.

"Nothing," he said. She flipped her pad closed. "Wait," he said, and she frowned and fixed him with a face that made him wince. "Tomato juice and toast," he said, looking away so he wouldn't see her judge him, or walk away. She was just a movement that left an empty space.

"Grandpa?" Christy had three neat piles of sugar packets—one white, one blue, one pink—arrayed side by side; the salt and pepper shakers kept sentinel. She saw Jake looking at the piles and went back to them. "These are my beds," she said to the salt and pepper as she moved them to the caddie, sliding them into position, "and you have to stay away so the children can go to sleep." She turned and spoke to the blue pile. "This is where Joey sleeps, in between so he can stay warm." Her fingers carefully squared up the packs. "And this," fingers moving to the pink, "is where I sleep." She lightly brushed away a few grains of salt. "This puffy white cloud over here is where our dead angel sleeps. He used to help, but he's too comfortable anymore, so he just lays there." She retrieved the shakers.

"When we're in there now, they come in and watch us, but the angel doesn't chase them away much now. So they get in sometimes and…"

Salt poured out of the holes as Christy pounded the head of the shaker into the blue pads. Crystals broke free of the shattered wrappers, spilling and mixing with the salt. Then she ground the head into the pad and let go. The entire diner picked that moment to go silent, not a word, no scraping of a spatula on the griddle, no clang of pots, spitting of coffee machines, jingle of knives, only the loud, heavy glass sound of the salt seller hitting their table. Jake shifted in his seat. Joey didn't move or flinch.

"Geesh, honey," Jake said. "Brush that off onto the floor. You're making a mess. Where is that waitress?"

Jake looked around, half expecting everyone to be staring, but the noises were back, customers stared into inky cups with bleary faces floating through the wisps of cigarette smoke layering the air around them, or murmured with one another, their shifty eyes jumping around the room. The harsh light made his kids look younger, made him uncomfortable. No waitress. He leaned back. The flask sloshed against his chest like a loose pacemaker, then pressed heavy there, insistent.

Christy caught Jake's eye. "What's your place like?"

"What?" He shifted, his undershirt ripe and sticking to his back, itching. The flask shifted with him.

"Where do you live?"

"I'll show you later," Jake said, slipping out of the booth. "I got to use the facilities. Stay here." They would stay for the food, he knew that much.

He didn't pay attention to graffiti anymore, too much trouble without his glasses. Cold water felt good on his face, tightening loose skin imbedded with coarse whiskers. The stalls were empty, he was alone.

He knocked back a slug and slipped the flask home, rubbing his raspy chin, the whiskers his baby had hated. He had scratched her raw she'd said, so she stopped kissing him unless he shaved. Lilly liked to shower while he watched with his camera, or she'd pretend to talk on the phone. His clients loved her, his biggest hit. Top of the charts. Jake would give a little extra money, pretend to miscount. After a while she practically lived with him, talking through dawn about the street, her fears. He let her steal from his wallet when he wasn't looking, careful about how much. She was losing weight so they ate a lot, packages of cheap hotdogs, baked beans. The clients complained, too bony, then too old. Next, please. He lost her to a hot spoon and plunger long before she'd spit in his face for the last time, when he'd finally told her there was no more work. There hadn't been anything for her for six months at that point. An expensive lie. He had shot her with an empty camera, just to make her happy, keep her feeling safe. Anything to make her happy. Then he couldn't even do that anymore.

Another swig and a splash and he was back on the job, sliding into the booth. They looked a little older now, closer to the age of consent, as if the penalties had decreased. It just made things easier. More justifiable. He slid back into the greased vinyl booth almost smiling and seized the tomato juice that had appeared with coffee and milk while he was gone. He sipped off the top, eyeing the surroundings out of habit, then poured it full again with the flask.

"Any more of that?" Joey fixed hungry eyes on him.

"No, punk. What makes you think I'd give any to you?"

"Makes things nicer. They give me some before."

"Who?"

Joey sipped his coffee, his dark unblinking eyes reflected in the black pool of the misting cup.

Jake cleared his throat, a phlegmatic production, cut it with tomato juice. He wanted a smoke. He wanted a shave. He wanted to get on with it. Christy was yawning, leaning quietly against the Formica wall.

"You shouldn't be drinking, see? Slows you down, makes you stupid. Then they can get you."

Joey nodded slowly and set the cup down on the saucer. The bottom of the cup scraped chalk-like and grating as he slid the cup into its well, calling attention to the silver sounds of knives and the sharp clash of shuffling dishes nearby. The steamy smell of greasy hash browns frying floated around them.

"You doing dope? Don't," Jake said, glancing at Christy to see if she was listening, but she had fallen asleep, or so it seemed.

"It's a vacation. What do you care?" Joey squinted and blinked as if trying to cry.

"Use that shit and you can't tell what's cool from what's deadly, even after you come down. Trust me. I made it. It wasn't that different then." Where the hell did he come off playing Grandpa? Keep it strictly business. Strictly.

Joey nodded and smirked. A hard shell seemed to have been painted over him, firming up those soft edges. Cute little tough guy. Maybe there was an extra bit in this after all. He could get in some shots ahead of the orders, the two kids together maybe. Joey's brown eyes, dark hair, skin translucent as white marble. Jake found himself staring, thinking of himself at that age and his own seductions, those times, the forgotten times fighting for his life.

Joey lightly traced his hand across the smooth skin of his neck, pausing to finger a small brown mole like a beauty spot placed strategically beside the hollow of his neck. He seemed to enjoy Jake's voyeurism, to encourage it. Jake looked away, searching for their basset-hound waitress, and saw two cops that had settled in at the counter with pie and coffee. The dog was talking with them. Bitch.

He gulped half the tomato juice, felt the hidden clear liquid in it dilute his thoughts. She probably would be suspicious if he asked for a lime wedge. Jake shut his eyes, just for a moment, and Lilly was there, shrouded in purple sheets, her favorite color, hair black now, red lips, dark eyebrows, and white, white skin. He opened his eyes to the sound of ice clinking, and Joey was putting the empty juice glass back, wiping his mouth on the back of his hand. Jake came close to yelling, to losing it on this kid, this putrid little scum who would have probably rotted or frozen out there if it hadn't been for him handing out free meals and warm, safe places to stay; but the blue-and-badged crowd kept him in his pen, and his anger made him breathe and shake and wrap his good hand around the boy's on the glass and squeeze hard, crushing the white little fingers, the soft, cartilaginous paw, letting the kid know who was boss, top dog. Joey didn't flinch—he seemed to relax and give in like a cat bitten at the back of its neck. Limp. Jake let go and pushed away from the booth, disgusted.

"Go if you want," Jake said. He walked trembling to the men's room and pushed through the antiseptic steel door into chrome and gray.

A drunk with a college T-shirt was pissing with his forearm on the wall, his forehead wiping slowly back and forth on his hairy arm, the stream a tiny trickle, sporadic and chopped, then nothing.

Jake lit a cigarette and waited for the guy to leave, but he didn't move. The guy was probably asleep. The vodka bit Jake's throat, and he flashed on tough younger images, of being chased in wet alleys as a kid, his face pressed into rough brick, spun around, then a baseball bat under the light, and he raised a hand to save his face.

Jake opened his eyes, shaking off the sting of raw alcohol and memory, and put the flask in his pocket as he sucked the smoke. Spitting in the sink, he caught sight of a cockroach scurrying along the line of floor and wall to slip around the garbage can. Still the drunk slept on. Jake threw the lit cigarette at the guy's feet. Maybe the smoke would make the kid puke and he would feel halfway decent when he finally woke up.

Joey was still in the booth, but Christy was lying down, taking up the whole of the seat, so Joey had moved to Jake's side and was leaning against the wall. The cops were gone, and their waitress had brought food. Joey was shoveling eggs and home fries, all the while eyeing Christy's hamburger, barely noticing Jake slide in next to him.

The basset hound waddled up with a fresh tomato juice and set it down between Jake and the boy, then she put the bill face down on a wet spot at the edge of the table. The total was the only ink that didn't run. Raw tomato juice made him wince, the taste too acidic, too thick. The kid pushed his toast in front of Jake and watched him with a slight turn of his head, never missing a fork-full.

It was too late at night, too late in life for Jake to do differently. And as they waited for the waitress to retrieve his change and wrap the girl's food to go, the boy leaned into Jake and nodded off. Jake's arm was uncomfortable and alien as it looked for a place to alight, finally succumbing to lay across the boy's chest, which swelled with an even and gentle breath.

"Tired little puppies, ain't they?" the waitress said reaching for the boy's empty cup. "Great to be a kid, sleep anywhere." She poured coffee. "Between buses?"

Jake nodded.

"Get 'em all the time. You stay a while if you want, honey. No one will mind unless we get busy."

Jake drank the kid's refill. Dawn was not far off, an hour or so. He could feel it coming, sliding around there in the darkness waiting to pop up and show them another steel-gray day, and Jake would rather be inside his little place, the job done, to sleep and maybe dream of money and sheltering some of these, the progeny. The coffee was an insistence in his stomach, a pressure in his bladder and he gently slipped from under Joey's head and wadded up his overcoat for a pillow before limping off to the restroom, his leg having fallen asleep with the boy.

The drunk was gone, and Jake peed alone. He thought about a final swallow but put the flask away untouched. He'd give them a warm, safe place for awhile, nothing else. Maybe tomorrow would be different. The steel door swung shut behind him, flashing dully with fluorescent light, and Jake saw that his booth was empty. Even the tip he had carefully counted out was gone, as was his coat. And his pocket was empty of wallet. Slick bastard.

He was out the door in seconds, soon shivering in the now windless cold, a desert of concrete and dormant trees tucked in ravines of steel and glass. On the way to the bus station, he lit his next-to-last cigarette, savoring the warm flare of the match for a moment before pressing on. He came at the revolving door from the other side now, with betrayed determination, and spun inside to brightness and transient filth.

'Joey' was there, past the shattered vending machine, the long coat just touching the floor as he leaned against the wall. Christy was gone. The boy looked at Jake out of the corner of his eye, reached into his pocket, and pulled out Jake's wallet. The boy stooped down and put the wallet on the floor, his eyes on some other prize, and with only a glance and slight smile, floated off across the room, through the bright empty space between the shadow of the wall and the shadow of the seats where a younger man sat slumped, intensely watching the boy's approach. The boy turned, and as he bent over to tie his shoe he winked at Jake and nodded toward the wallet.

The kid had left him $50.

Mary Caponegro

Whoever Is Never Born with the Most Toys Wins

> *Not to be born surpasses thought and speech.*
> *The second best is to have seen the light*
> *And then to go back quickly whence one came.*

Sophocles, *Oedipus at Colonus*

I

See the boy in his bed, how he tosses and turns; his mouth trembles, eyes flutter beneath their lids, then stillness. Again, the same sequence. This boy in a bed only recently become his will hours later awake to the almost familiar: posters and knickknacks and trophies and photos, surroundings the boy does not see while he sleeps, while he dreams, a boy in his room in a comfortable house, which exudes this particular morning the aroma of bacon frying, an aroma in retrospect predictable.

Numerous mornings like this have occurred, and even though the boy's tummy still reeks of the cloying sweetness of too many Shirley Temples, the sputtering strips provide him incentive to exit his dreams and to transcend his nausea, which is, after all, only slight.

The boy then remembers the bar in which he spent the previous evening, and the evening before that, and so on, a bar more familiar than this room, which is as it happens the boy's favorite color—although for a passing moment it becomes his least favorite. As he lies between these walls he feels repeating on him the many maraschino cherries he consumed at the bar, in his nervousness, in his effort to disguise that very nervousness, as an adult might draw incessantly from a cigarette. He would in fact find himself holding the stem in just such a manner, between index and middle finger, even after he had pulled away the the soft head of round fruit with his teeth.

The bar he remembers as backround for a woman's expectant face, her slightly parted lips, a man's clenched hands, his strong jaw, their solicitous antiphonal words, the glut of their persistence, his own weary acquiescence. Oh, what's the use of dwelling in the anguish of the morning after? You're here now, may as well get out of bed, go down the stairs, get on with it. Mercifully conveniently, no matter which evening or who, they always have the same name. Morning, mom. Morning, dad, the boy intones. Thanks for last night. Hey, Smells great. *Is this my place?*

II

See the girl on the bench; she appears nonchalant, her head propped on her elbow like that, her cheek pressed against her palm. Is she gazing dreamily at the pond situated in front of this circle of benches, or does she turn to observe the chaotic ensemble behind her: the informal parade of potential parents who daily comprise a backdrop at least as compelling if considerably less scenic.

Perhaps it is not indifference but wistfulness the girl exhibits, as she continues to look on, intent on disguising her interest. Or her longing? By sunset it will be decided; the girl will go home with a mother or father, or more likely both, unless she elects, one might say, by default, to go home to the parents whose house she awoke in this morning, the parents who tentatively kissed her good-bye as she left for that park, and who are perhaps themselves defensive participants, as it were, in the informal procession of persons, possessions and gestures. These pending parents, if espied by the girl, might shrug as if to say, we have to watch out for ourselves, for our future, we have to insure against loss. For all they know, the girl may exit the park holding the hand of the woman who at this moment displays a slender cylindrical metal artifact, made gold by the sun, which she then pulls apart into glistening halves.

As the girl squints at the cylinder held to eye level, the woman sustains her captive audience by causing to rise up from the base a creamy bright finger. This gesture received by the girl is equivalent to the woman's own beckoning index. The brightness of its erected color, particularly in relation to the gold tube from which it emerges, is mesmerizing, for it is a color to which one is obliged to attend, a color which recalls to the girl the fire engines that had delighted her in earlier years, and which, if she were lucky, she would discover in miniature version sequestered in a stocking of the same hue affixed to a random fireplace in proximity to a decorated evergreen on what would become the most anxious day of the year.

III

All days resemble that day in their way. All days are parcels in which gifts are wrapped, gifts to a child from a parent, some more mysterious than others. Even now in the park parents stroll bearing gifts, and which gift can determine which child. Perhaps the girl will accompany the couple who balance between them the cage of a gerbil, setting it down on the opposite end of the bench, the better for her to witness its occupant's antics. She surveys his sparse furnishings, watches as he mounts the diminutive wheel and sets himself in confined motion. The tip of her index finger taps at the bars after she surrenders her veneer of indifference. Coochie coo, little guy. (In reply, his whiskered face approaches hers from the other side, as if even this creature were schooled in seduction.) In all likelihood they will allow the pet to be housed in her room, the room about to become her room. And whatever name it is her whim to call the gerbil will become the word by which all call it. Thus the girl has no new names to learn other than those of her creating once she whittles her options down to one: Oh thank you, dad, thank you, mom. And Bucky thanks you too. *Mind if I close the door now?*

211

IV

Thousands of such transactions occur in the park; thus its surroundings are ultimately irrelevant. No one, in fact, attends to the beautiful scenery, not to boats nor to swans, nor the trees, nor their blossoms or leaves, nor does anyone tend to exhibit disgust at the sundry synthetic debris that accretes in the interstices of Mother Nature. Any unoccupied plaything, any artifact not in a child's hand, anything in storage long enough to gather dust is a time bomb of sorts, one that does not tick but sings, sings of failure, hiatus, unseemly gaps between one child and that child's successor. Recycling does occur from one child to the next, but along the way the mass of detritis mounts, since the traffic of parents and children naturally propagates excess. See the batteries left to corrode in the walkman, the camera, the radio, the windup toy? Toss them, then!

You *can't* see the Nicad dying inside the computer, tape recorder or toothbrush. Make sure you don't trip over tennis balls gone awol, dented Classic Coke cans— ah, what kid can resist just one kick?—unretrieved pacifiers, torn wash & dry packets, soiled squeaky toys, bent bubble blowing wands. More abundant than any other item littering the park is cardboard and cellophane, the evidence of packages bought and opened in desperate haste, not by an eager or greedy child, but by an anxious parent primed for giving. Clearly, there isn't a moment to lose between toystore and park. Who could expect any self-respecting parent to pick up after him or her self? Everyone knows they're here only to score?

V

Can you believe that man behind the catcher's mitt?—holding it coyly in front of his face like a mask, then lowering it just enough to let you see his eyes. He winks and lifts the bulky glove another notch again. "Play peekaboo with POOKY, pal. Give me a break and leave the props at home," you want to taunt, but instead mutter, under your breath, to the gang." Pathetic!" heather hastens to confirm. "Just ludicrous," say tim and tom in unison, as much to mock megan, who learned the word last week at school and finds a niche for it in every other sentence, as to reinforce your disdain. But all of you know he's no less objectionable than the woman beside him bribing with her cleavage bait, a teething ring like some enormous gaudy piece of costume jewelry on her finger. Have they ceased discriminating altogether? Don't you look your age, for child's sake? You're not in diapers anymore. The guy is over-eager, pitching arm winding compulsively, give him the slip.

"Ditch him before he thinks he's made a conquest," mike urges. "Don't even look in their direction, don't encourage them," jen pleads. Eye contact, all of you concur, is the key to scoring parents or avoiding them. Look at anyone instead, even at the two adults stooped under the weight of the heavy aquarium—the extension cord attached to it tripping parental pedestrians right and left, who in turn accuse the bearers of ill intent, for a parent competing on crutches must obviously carry less—as the tank's darting shimmery occupants negotiate the murky sloshing waters, appearing to all who view them, even through the slime and algae'd sides, as if they'd have been better left at home.

Look at any of the burdened parents who trail behind them tricycles, dirt bikes and bicycles, every so often a unicycle, cross-country skis, poles and rollers blades—for it's common knowldege that the coup for all parents is to be the chosen one the day those training wheels come off, to have been the transitional couple in witness of that first liberating albeit still tentative glide down the block upon the single unsupported slender tread, one front and one behind, no unsightly anchored sides, two instead of four; they'll document in every medium available, boast eternally of this moment to their friends and share it with you again and again (and again and again) in the family room, on video, and as far as you're concerned, and tim and tom and jeff and mike and megan, jen and debbie, you ought to make them *work* for it. It isn't something any family should be allowed to take for granted. How many milestones in one childtime are available for distribution, with so few unequivocally triumphant feats among the trial-and-error cumulative skills or less than glamorous exigencies, once one traces the trajectory from teething, speaking, crawling, sitting, shitting unassisted, walking, shoelace-tying, standing on one's head, masticating solid food, carving, spearing, scooping with utensils powered by oneself and so forth, so on, on and on to the ceremonious if anxious acquisition and subsequent removal of braces, jock straps and brassieres.

An enterprising couple flick a plastic orthodontic retainer tentatively, then get carried away and fling it back and forth as if it were a frisbee, from ever greater distances, until one fails to catch it and the now soiled, even more unsightly item is retrieved, brushed off furtively on a sleeve and returned sheepishly to the woman's pocket. "EEUUWW," says jen. "Who knows where it's been—how gross!" And debbie adds, "We know that it's been on the ground, for one." But no child is ignorant of the retainer's ramifications, i.e. who among the array of candidates assembled before them will pay for braces, glasses, ice cream, pets, karate, circus expeditions, laptops, let alone the *pièce de résistance*, college! Who can be persuaded NOT to pay for violin, piano lessons, sewing, boxing, Sunday School, ballet…? Your friends trade endless interpretations of computer equipment: "It means you'll never see them, they'll be at the screen all evening." "Yea, what's wrong with that? The perfect setup." "What's the point of choosing them then?" "That's the point, you jerk. You never have to deal." "No, it means you move in and it's yours; *you're* at the screen all week!"

Endless ambiguities, endless predictions, suppositions, intuitions, concerning the wielding of razors, insertion of tampons, sizing of brassieres. (Parents' magazines now disrecommend bras as props precisely because of ambiguity. The interpretation "We won't procrastinate, won't hinder your entry into womanhood" is as easily read as "You had better keep your breasts confined. Your body's freedom is your parents' jurisdiction." Not for long, of course.)

Just because they enter the arena with an arsenal of shuttlecocks, sailboats and soccer balls, frisbees, action figures, dolls and teddy bears and pop-up books and rollerblades, walkmans, running shoes dresses tee shirts levis; croquet mallets wickets leggos minibikes and nautilus equipment—"Look," says jen, "today the caboose is an iguana!"—does that entitle them to trophies gratis? You want to insinuate subliminally from a loudspeaker hidden in the park's tallest tree, you

213

want to bellow in shrill chorus with all of your accomplices, "There's no such thing, dear mom, dear dad, as a free child!"

Chant it daily and don't give in. Don't get soft. Never play other than hard to get. On the other hand, remember that once you're entangled you cannot truly extricate yourself; you're in the clutches of a gradual suffocation, this one that one no one with the right to say "stay here" and so you're free to go from house to house but driven to keep looking to avoid the unbearable realization that it might very well have been better—certainly simpler—never to be born.

VI

duck duck duck duck GOOSE! You have no hiding place. Accept your crowning syllable with dignity. Don't squawk with indignation at the unexpected sentence levied by a gleeful, careless palm. The crude, unsavory cadence that seals your fate at playtime becomes in dream an absurd noise that issues from the throat of the void. Is that what you want, say the nightmares that wake you gasping, your torso at a sudden right angle to the cot in your current parents' den, never to be born? Not to have been born? "Yes, just bad dream," she coos, the new one soothing you, cradling your head in her arms, while your nose is scrunched against the very breast that could as easily have been nurturing another, its stiffened tip wedged into the mouth of itty bitty bald and pudgy toothless Pooky, had the bar stools been differently arranged, had the times been slightly skewed, had your eyes followed a different route— AND YET IT DID NOT, they were not, things are as they are: you two ensconced as if you'd formed yourself this way night after night, since time began, as if the rhythm of your fear were all moments pulsing in her being.

"My silly goose," she says, when you without defenses yet, in hypnopompic haze, confess the title of your fright from which she fortunately dares not extrapolate. "You're not in trouble, silly goose," she soothes, "You're in a cozy quiet safe red room, with nothing to be frightened of." (What won't allow this to be true? Her soft strong arms and tenderness almost break through something even stronger in you. Where is its release?) Concerned that she has been dismissive of the shadow that still folds you, yet emboldened nonetheless, her tenderness augments, ends in a sibilance far more solicitous than the bird's name that assaulted you, then pierced your sleep and bid you scream.

You dare not disappoint her, dare not shatter her illusions, with the weighted truth that is your private grief. It must be so that every child who stayed here had the same disease. The sheets are fresh, the mattress not infested; something subtler even than the air and as pervasive bears the spores of your malaise. Such is your fate: to know the sheets will be forever fresh, the bed only almost familiar, the parent in her earnest nurture unable to reverse your unrelenting inquiry as to whether it might be better had you never....

VII

"O.K. Try not to think of a pink elephant," father says to this week's daughter, a mischievous gleam in his eye. He is impressed with his playful challenge. What better way to break the ice than with a harmless inexpensive game whose sole equipment is imagination? As for the girl, her room is pink as is the dress laid out for someone's party, and the sheets and quilt as well so it's even more difficult not to capitulate. The forbidden lures, a vast pink magnet.

"GOTCHA," Papa says, "I bet that guy got in your head!" "Yes, Papa," she replies. "Did you put him there?" Every five seconds thereafter, he puts his tongue against his teeth while pursing lips to simulate a buzzer (like a game show blooper sound) and presses index finger to her belly, then her upper arm like a pretend inoculation. "You thought of a pink elephant, didn't you?"

Indeed, she now can think of nothing else, even after perky daddy departs and shuts the door behind him. And the more she tries the more its weight crushes, its trunk begins to wrap around her neck, a scarf of pure muscle, its tusks indent her shoulders. The landscape of not being born should be spacious and weightless, she considers, so why has it taken this form? Besides, isn't this what parents are supposed to protect you from?

Take off. This isn't working out. Stuff that dress in your Pocahontas knapsack and find another party. This papa is one busted prophylactic.

VIII

Why do you feel somehow akin to the pet who maneuvers predictably on his tiny wheel, despite the fact you've seen a hundred hamsters, just as many gerbils, toucans, parakeets, canaries, goldfish, finches, silver dollars, wooden nickels, stamp collections, comic books with every single superhero and just when you're thinking it's been a while since you've seen—an iguana? By now pam and heather and debbie can be relied upon to roll their eyes whenever you spy a cage. "What a cliche!" megan complains. Yet these reluctant affinities persist. You feel more kindred to the furry creature than you do to jeff and mike, even as you scoff with them, for there's neither urge nor opportunity to confide in them, what's mingled is not feeling, it is circumstance, they're only friends, you didn't choose them, after all.

Fate was your engineer. You stood unwittingly on one site, they on another, and from that moment on it was clear you would be cruising together. Your relation remains the product of who stood where when. Based on this alone, you are destined to watch each other grow stubble and muscle and over time deepen the timbre of your speech, just as megan and debbie and heather will swell at hip and chest, as you discuss in exactly the same mode and manner each week the vicissitudes of family planning. Every one of you holds selective standards, but in the end, you can't afford to look down on anyone, can you? No one dares linger too long unattached.

When old-fashioned parents cajole you into playing hot potato, you find yourself uneasy, determined to win. You can't bear to be caught at game's end with the spud in your hand. "What's wrong, howard? It's a harmless root vegetable;

215

it isn't old, it isn't growing eyes yet." Yet through it, you can't help but see the prospect of annihilation. You flee to your familiar cluster and commence preaching at them in a most uncharacteristic manner.

"We call them pathetic," you begin, "the parents who are the object of our never-ending search." You find yourself projecting like a child possessed, to a congregation comprised of an unwilling tim and tom and debbie, heather, jen and mike. "But are we any less? Perhaps we only appear to have the upper hand!" "Oh, lay off, howard, find a family," heather retorts. Disgusted, tim and tom add, "Yea, how, go get homed."

IX

So home you go, and get there just in time for a piano lesson, on the magnificent instrument that lured you to this house in the first place, despite its wretched name. Baby grand. If you could learn just one tune, you might console yourself with it on any spinet, any upright in a hallway or a basement of the houses yet to come. EVERY GOOD BOY DOES FINE, writes Mr. Pultney, for probably the hundredth time this month. If only life were so simple as the lines on the staff paper claim. The bass cleff's letters tells you nothing new, just makes the treble's message plural—in case you forgot, between the staves, what good boys do. And furthermore, they do it into perpetuity.

The only trouble is, when Mr. Pultney drills you in the basics, demonstrating that the half steps E to F and B to C break up the pattern of the C Major scale, you can't persuade your fingers to make the leap from 3 to 4 and 7 to 8; you want to seal those vast white spaces up, or stick a sharp or flat in there. "It's just a half step, howard," he assures you, "like the others," but it's too late. The keyboard you had hoped to conquer in one afternoon has become an ivory sea expanding asymmetrically. You can't tell Mr. Pultney that the structure of the music keeps reminding you to wonder whether you were ever born.

X

You'll never have a song; you should have known. Even when Mr. Pultney made a whole note cord to fill in every space of the treble staff and called it FACE, you saw instead a stack of bald heads from the back that could belong only to the competitor: that baby, with his mindless smile. What a cheap come-on; he'll favor anyone who shoves a toothy grin under the decadent awning of his imported collapsible stroller. Those sounds out of his mouth: a gooey syrup any kid would be ashamed to ooze. As if to give a clue, his mouth often shapes itself into a tiny 'o.' But a parent, shameless, oozes even more unctuously than an infant. See how the latter is fondled by the former with exotic unguents for his belly button, as if a tree above his groin had got uprooted, and now they have to fertilize the soil with utmost care. Further down grows a sapling newly peeled of bark, likewise tended to alleviate rawness, and then, as if that weren't enough, they flip him over on his painstakingly assembled changing table to assuage his chafed buttocks? Why not a kiss for each cheek while they're at it?

Cream him till he heals, the lucky dog. Tend his tiny pecker day and night. You envy those transient wounds less for the nurture they elicit than for the badge they make, for no scraped knee or bandaid; no slinged arm or cast or crutch could ever provoke the slavish fascination that baby's wounds command.

These sites upon his flesh are semaphores. See how they demarcate what time's compulsive healing will dissemble: the choice to barter doubt for an assumption that it's better to be born. (Oh if only you too could participate, could surrender doubt. What went awry with you?) Once these decorations are, by time, removed, the option of imagining an alternate to what apparently exists is rubbed away as well. (Yes, soon the wound will be invisible; you'll search in vain as for a contact lens on carpet or an earring in the yard or a tarnished key in soft new-fallen snow over an unlit driveway; you'll search each inch of baby-skin to find only an unmarred perfect surface, no residue of trauma, no souvenir of the potential superiority of avoiding being born.)

Of course the parents yearn to be the ones erasing. Or else they stand themselves to be erased! (And he, beloved babe, as ignorant as his admirers, will be duped. Who will correct him?) A flash of inspiration. Simple as that, the formulation comes to you: a baby is favored for being contiguous to nothingness. A baby is obsessively attended so that what most profoundly marks him can be all the more expediently hidden for posterity.

Is the glass half-empty or half-full? (A parent's favorite trick-question.) Is the baby in his almostness a catalyst for despair or celebration? Depends on whom you ask. You would undoubtedly be crowned the pessimist, given your intuitions, which might be formulated as follows: If jen and tim and mike and debbie, heather, tom and you could nonchalantly lift your shirts or tug your waistbands that crucial inch to unveil a pride of belly buttons, and in so doing manifest a scar commemorating entry into this preposterous theater, you'd none of you have need to flip through pages of arresting if occasionally off-putting images or to gossip or to gamble for your immediate futures or patrol, as if a predator, the public places that are closer, in a real sense, than any house you've ever shacked-up in, to home.

XI

Meanwhile in the Bar, in the Park, in the Mall, the cliched questions persist. You supply your share, because you know you can't be more original yourself, a slave to habits, patterns every child inherits. How many have you had? (A question uttered as if it hadn't been a thousand times already.) For some the higher number is the greater swagger; others, more mature, honor the lowest integer with a whistle of awe, as if to say, you must be doing something right. You all, in theory anyway (in speech at least) abjure the bars, but continue to populate them night after night day after day with heads bowed or eyes lowered in shame, (averting each other's gazes) but never failing to note an exit. It isn't merely gossip-lust; it's a pragmatic way of keeping track, since updating an address book is a futile task. The next day, gossip will proliferate: who bought whom a glass of milk? Was skim or 2% on tap? " But what a tap at home!" shane nudges you, and gestures toward the baby who, in view of all, roots at a woman's barely covered breast before they're even out the door.

Or was that the night—or week—before? Well that's shane, ever-immature. You can't do more than roll your eyes at him, even though he's in a different clique; for that matter you can't do more for tim and tom and jen and debbie, that's how it goes with friends, it's not as if you choose them. shane's still in the inchoate stage, he reads the juvenile magazines; he isn't weaned off Playmom yet, for child's sake. You'd just as soon avoid him but of course, he's in the same rat-race; you have no choice, fate put you in that same spot side by side at the bar to endure the tedious gossip while you sip your sixteenth Shirley Temple. Who went where with whom for one night one week surreptitiously or proud enthusiastic or indifferent but in all cases advising each other, as if advice were not irrelevant, as if advice could make a difference, warn against, for instance, the tendency to succumb to TOYS-B-US, to glaze over at the glitz of a beach ball or stroller or swing.

Don't think no strings attach, that non-existent voice will never say, to your new gift, you're going home with them to try it out, together, for the camera, for posterity. Watch them assemble it, poking holes in the ground to secure the poles, attaching the cross bar to secure your weight. Hear their squeals of delight as you seat yourself, receive their push, and then pump dutifully, dispassionately, perfunctorily; if enough momentum accumulates to raise you parallel to earth they clutch each other's waists in glee, but if you carry on too vigorously they'll be alarmed. After a spate of families, going through the motions is like second nature, though admittedly an enervated nature. You'll swing for your supper tonight, for tomorrow's you'll pitch, play parcheesie, or poker, charades, guide them through the CD ROM inherited from your predecessor without the least awkwardness to taint your enthusiasm and of course the old standby the tube, the cave into which the whole family can climb without any exertion, still attached to the couch.

"And how many times during that week," they'll ask you next time in the park (mike, megan, heather, debbie, tim and tom) "did you watch TV together, and what was the size of the set, how many controls on the panel and where, and who was in what position on the couch, were you between them?" Most crucial question: "who held the remote? Was it you who chose the program every time?" (It's always that way at first, some say.)

And who can say what intangible ennui impels you to go on and seek the next set, next sofa, the next ping pong table—whose paddles can double as both punitive and recreative objects, so certain families, you notice, in the park, have stopped using them as props. "The cowardice of exploiting ambiguity," say debbie, jen and heather (recently obsessed with ethics), for instance, when couples flash them in the park to double their yield among those who crave discipline (after several lax situations) and those who read their presence as promise of endless play.

"Is every toy an oxymoron?" megan asks. "Save that for school, O.K.?" says tim. tom nods. "So what, though," you propose, "if parents send mixed signals or if children misinterpret? Every family is a gamble; don't you get it? Next week always brings another chance. They're playing poker up the block tonight; scrabble across the street. It's less exciting in the place where I crashed yesterday; would you believe—don't laugh—Old Maid? The stakes are just as high though." The only tragedy would be to sit too long at the table with that hag or that fool in your hand; just deal again, my friend, just deal again, get to the next game, at the next house, before you start to question were you ever born.

XII

Every child needs respite. Go on. Lay your body across the beat-up billiard table; don't bother about the small damp spot your cheek leaves on the worn felt. Go ahead, roll the ball down the length of the table just to hear it thud into a corner pocket, just to feel release from the exertion and the sound. You're doing it again, you're doing it again, and what other choice is there but to carry on, unless you elect to cease to be.

At the end of a long chain of effort and experiment might you surrender to the unbearable simplicity of never having been born? Anything's possible. But in the meantime, you will share the house-wise smarts each of you have acquired through trial and error. At thirteen, for instance, declare you must go to a small prestigious liberal arts college, if not an Ivy League University. You're hot. At seventeen aver that a state school or vocational institution are the only possibilities. Again you've got your pick of parents. Because if you don't shed your Ivy League fantasy by the time the funds are required, you're not just hot, pal, you're a hot potato! When tuition time looms, their pride succumbs to penny pinching. Just as scissors cut paper and paper covers rock, frugality eclipses pride.

XIII

Why even complain to them, your friends? They won't understand. And nonetheless, too bored to sip your sixtieth Shirley Temple without some—even lame—conversation, you entertain your peer's complaint.

"Can you believe she used the same pet names for him as for me? I even overheard her cooing in the new one's ear, 'my precious.' Then she had the gall to suggest we take our bath together, placated by a stupid squeaking duck, while she put these dumb plastic haloes on both our heads. 'See how fond I am of both of you,' she crooned, 'I buy the product guaranteed to keep away tears!'" (He bawls as he relates the irony.) "As if she hadn't made me cry in every other way."

"Chill, jamie. Don't take it so hard, huh? It's just one incident. One mom. Don't take it personally. You'll get a better set-up next time. We all get burned."

And then, oh dear, the object of his misery appears, and the scene begins. These occasional public confrontations do add drama to routine but hardly seem worth the humiliation. Familiar trepidation. Milk splashed in the woman's face. Then she reciprocates. Before you know it, jamie has raided your Shirley Temple, both his and your cherries dropped down her dress. He gets his wish: her tears. He loses patience, screams at her, "Go bear your breasts in sight of someone new, since you're so greedy as to want two. Most parents count themselves blessed to have one and then one and then one! Why not go for twins?"—it's getting ugly now. You move away instinctively. "How about those infants in the corner? Hey everybody, watch and let us know when they cry or yawn at the same time so my x-mother gets

219

to stick both nipples in, two for the price of one." Turns back to her. The slap. You saw it getting out of hand. What could you do? You're getting out of here.

It's time to go home, not a new one either, not tonight, no energy left to be on the rent. A finished basement is a special prize, hard to leave behind. Enjoy it while you can. Lie there again, in the cool dark, your cheek against the newly damp green felt. The parents upstairs would no doubt be honored to witness, in fact would lust to console, your rare tears, but what consolation is there for the realization that this wood, this floor, these posters—props they selected to please you—make you feel in fact more bleak? You'd rather turn your head or close your eyes or even cry than see through the awkward guesswork, to know these are the vestiges of children who preceded you: effluvia that embody their proclivities, their fantasies, all of which by definition must be transitory.

Suddenly you feel compelled to seize the unmarked white ball and hurl it against the cushioned side of the table in fury and sorrow, so vehemently that it skips off the ridge and drops with a crack to the floor. That is why you are here: whatever that null sphere stands for; not because of the table or the TV or her nipples (which admittedly have a nostalgia you cannot ignore or erase) or their eager faces or their hearts or good intentions, or for that matter their desperation. It is only as antidote to this void that you chalk the cue, twisting clockwise, counter, clockwise, the tip of the stick into the hollowed chalky center of the paper-covered cube until the blue dust makes you choke, then in frustration aim only at what will yield the most noise, as if you could crack open emptiness.

Soon enough their concerned voices echo in the basement stairwell? "Is everything alright? Is it too cold down there, howard? Should we turn up the heat, dear?" Why bring them into it? Shame is the least of it. What consolation could they offer, trapped as they are in the same situation, destined to go forward unceasingly into one illusion after another. In the subsequent silence echoing your own, you infer their reevaluation of explicit endearment. Was it premature, they're wondering. One simple syllable. Should they have uttered it instead tomorrow? Between today and tomorrow is an incalculable difference.

XIV

You remember a past time when the hint of that nipple, the sight of that dip at the bodice of her dress would have been like a magnet, as it must be for all the current babies. If you were once one, why is there no sympathy forthcoming? Why do you resent that they are less discriminating? Why do you so envy that soft-bodied baldie who'll put his tiny chubby hands out to anyone who pokes a face into his basinet? He is the root, or is what was the root, the closest to it. He is the...oh forget it, who can stand to think about it?

XV

Alone among the blades of grass and dandelions, a decent yard, (a good catch, pam or jeff would say), you feel consoled; perhaps you'll park with these rents for a while. Their property, at least, is soothing—and then suddenly she

220

comes to fetch you in, claiming ticks hidden there between the blades can make you sick. "Oh, for child's sake," you tacitly implore, "let me pretend the grass at least is innocent." Nothing is simple any more. You can't even enjoy the consolation of this classic childical gesture. "See me," you want to say, "the boy. See boy do simple thing."

But instead you see yourself blowing the delicate threads of the dandelion's head to denude its thereafter useless stem with far more emotional investment than you possessed as a toddler, an infant, a pathetic toothless Pooky, if ever you were such. You'd just as soon scrape off his navel crust, rather than watch them fawn over his mound of earth, the venerated *mons umbilicum*. The tree that fell there can't be heard except in the bleak, silent night of a helpless child desperately scanning the broadest band of universal doubt, only to discover a low rumbling or high-pitched scream: a frequency audible only to you, only to you and to whomever wonders whether this can pass for being born. That stem once bound to earth, now wrenched, divested of its gossamer head, has no function and no place.

Find another flower then. Pluck one petal, then another, until the daisy is mere button and you, the victim of your new toy's arbitrary starting point, do willingly consent to have this hitherto harmless lovely growing thing be arbiter of your fate: Move on. Don't move on yet. Move on. Don't move on yet. Was born, was never born. (Get reckless now: Eight petals left.) BORN. BETTER NEVER BORN. BORN. BETTER NEVER BORN. BORN. BETTER. NEVER.

XVI

How does she know the candle's count is accurate? No matter. Don't think. Blow! Keep blowing, until all flame is extinguished. Then the games begin! Pin the tail on the donkey. Whoever is the birthday boy or girl goes blind for the occasion. Stands passive as the white cloth is tied around her head over her eyes. How does it fit? her mother asks. You want to answer, all too well! There is a clown providing entertainment, but even his painted nose and goofy orange hair and bright billowing overalls cannot temper the suspicion that all of this festivity is just as much disguise.

Well, this is something novel. The parent has assembled a birthday band to provide live accompaniment for the game of musical chairs. He must have scoured the neighborhood for this orchestra of children who have somehow managed a botched continuity of lessons. Even learning "Happy Birthday" can take more than a week, and despite a probable parental conspiracy demanding all instrumental teachers include it as their first assignment, a child on trombone might have played violin last month, and the flautist hasn't practiced since she left the house in which the music stand is a permanent fixture.

Who can blame her? (Your only lesson ended dismally when Mr. Pultney couldn't help but notice that the open sound of the perfect fourths and fifths he played to soothe you, on the contrary, exacerbated your anxiety.) Dutifully—or perversely?—the players accompany the other children's instinctive choreography: anxious pacing in a circle, like the gerbil in his cage or rat-in-a-maze. Round and round and round. It would be too rude to put your hands over your poor assaulted ears. Each child plays in a different key, it seems, as the clown conducts with the long slender balloon he has blown up for the occasion. Your relief at the periodic cessation of cacophony is thwarted by the anxiety of knowing fewer and fewer chairs remain each time they pause. Can it be coincidence, you wonder, that the birthday girl or boy at every party is the first to be without a chair?

Yes, with babies it's simple: whichever parent inserts the pacifier first wins! So little nuance, scant discrimination. Even so, sometimes there are arguments about who got there first and you want to say when you witness these squabbles, "why bother to argue? Why be competetive? Possessive for what? He'll be at your house in a week—or three months or a year, for rent's sake! Leave yourself something to look forward to." As with your friends, your so-called peers, who on occasion land together at the same house, and don't exercise the courtesy of insisting 'after you.' "Can we afford this petty squabbling?" you demand of them.

Why do you play this role so often? Why can't they put their ears en masse to all the ticking toys surrounding them, why can't they hear the deafening song, why do you have to spell it out for EVERYone? Sometimes there are seasons in sequence to boast of, but how often is that? Everyone knows that family photo albums don't even leave a discreet blank page between the children anymore. No kid gets all indignant even if she finds her photo smack against her predecessor's, on the same page. No kid who knows the score. No way! You don't stand on ceremony, you do your best to face the facts, but the one fact some can't seem to face is all the more elusive for its hypothetical status.

The sweet doughy face of a baby, for instance, insulates fact. Oh let them have *their* pacifier then. They'll see a new face when he wakes them every other hour, that sweet yeasty mass contorted, scruched in agony of lacto-lust or colic or teething or needing to be changed: an inchoate protest, and yet incipient acceptance of the realization that it would likely have been better never to be born.

XVII

A father stands on line with an infant strapped into his kiddysack—the kind designed for frontal carrying, of course. Easier to supervise that way; nothing can take place behind his back. Too many stories of returning from the mall with one family in excess and another minus one. (Only even exchanges are desired.) The father bobs up and down to keep his passenger amused, content. Hear the responsive gurgling: index of success. In front of him on line a mother struggles with her first-grader who insists on one more game, another toy, more time to look around. All parents know that shopping only between kids is ideal but sometimes just not feasible. And conscientious parents who aim for early Christmas shopping are inevitably thwarted. The item they pluck from the shelf will very likely have, at home, a longer shelf-life than the child for whom they're buying it.

"It's been years since I rocked a baby in my arms," the mother says, to her surprise, out loud, as she observes the father/baby interaction. Already her daughter's getting nervous—she thought she'd get at least a week out of this cushy situation. Even the baby seems to see what's coming. "Funny," muses father, "I was just wondering how it would be when junior here is on his feet and filled with speech and toilet-trained and…"—cuts himself off—"of course, I'll never get that far…unless by some coincidence he returns to me years from now, but with so many in between, how could one recognize…? I don't know that it's ever happened, have you ever heard…?"

Impulsively, she interrupts his incoherent rumination, looks him urgently in the eye, angling her head ever-so-slightly toward her collateral. Into his ear she whispers, "Shall we just do it? Right here? Now?" The girl, who doesn't need to overhear to sense that something is amiss, blurts out, "Hey, what's going on? I'll find my own parents, thank you!" as the childsack is lifted over her new father's head onto the former mother's shoulders, and the girl's hand is transferred to his with no salespersons or customers the wiser. "If you're really that unhappy, kaitlin, ditch him in the parking lot. Watch out for cars, though," she calls out as she hastens away with her new charge. "Hey, what about my stuff?" "Now, that, dear, is a stupid question."

XVIII

But shopping for candy breeds almost as much anxiety as shopping for toys because the most alarming evening for the rents is Halloween, a sanctioned cruising holiday—its emblem the shameless glance over the shoulder of the candy giver to assess his, her, or their abode's interior. The gum drops, candy corns, mars bars and hershey kisses are excuses, ruses, confectionary decoys; in other words, for trick or treat, read, take me in. This method furnishes a process of elimination far more expedient than without these glimpses; children can cross off the list a house in which they may have otherwise had to spend an entire day!

Will they open up the door for you and *leave* it propped? That's what you wonder, what you hope. The trouble is that then it's open for the next kid in line as well, with his scary mask or silly hat that fools no one, open for the veritable assembly line of pirates and goblins and witches and wolves, ghosts, skeletons and princesses and ladies of the evening. Go ahead. Hold out your gaping candy bag. Wear your emptiness on your sleeve. For isn't this just a stylized version of your lives? Ding and you're here, dong and the next one arrives to take your place, grabs a handful of candy, and moves on. So tiresome, so inconsolably predictable, so much so that you wonder if it might be better never to have been born.

XIX

Fire, fire everywhere. The red truck she hoped for under the tree, from which the color derives its name, is now life-size and multiplied, as the men in slickers and helmets aim their hoses everywhere that says flame. To you it's one big birthday cake that blazes forth the sum of all collective child years. A conflagration composed of a million candles standing for an exponential lie, or an incendiary veil both cloaking and exposing annihilation. Even the ghosts that congregate this night in the village cemetery have something more concrete than any kid; they have dates etched in stone, a tomb to anchor them like a steady wrist tied to a recalcitrant rising balloon.

No matter. The funny hoses blow with water instead of breath, but the party's over anyway. It's just for kicks, each year, a kind of punctuation to the antics of the night before. "It says that we mean business," jen proclaims. "A statement: we're in charge," adds mike. "A little acting out is all." That's tim's interpretation, added to by tom: "You, know, against routine." "In any case," debbie concludes, "we always make sure they remember All Saints' Day." "All Souls," corrects heather. "All kids," the sweating fireman says, "should be sent back to where they came from." Then back to normal. Everybody scramble. Pick a new house.

XX

How mortifying when, as you gather round the tube, the fateing game comes on. Is it already seven-thirty? The show is on hiatus, they are playing reruns, and who should one of the three couples behind the partition be but—yes, you guessed—your current parents! Oh, the shame! For whom? You? Them? They turn the sound off furtively as soon as the gawky blonde girl asks the opening question. Thus the young contestant who has her way with them communicates only motion after her mouth inquires coyly, "What would you consider the ideal family evening at home?"

Your parents are playing every card they've got; you see it in their faces, even in the few pans allotted by the camera among the other couples competing. You feel how much they want to take her home and at the same time you feel, somehow, soiled. They scan your eyes for permission to turn it off—it's you who hold the magic wand—in order to let your mutual humiliation find surcease, as if they feared your very presence in their living room were rendered null and void by its convergence with the drama implicit behind the scenes, or between the lines, as it were, of the screen. Thus the ideal evening at home, ostensibly come true for them, through you, turns out to be, through the exposure of their WISHING it, or more correctly *having* wished, a travesty.

"Oh hey," you say, "who are we kidding anyway? Nobody's pure in this. We've all already been around the block." (Later their eyes stare through the picture window as if to itemize their neighbors.) "I'll admit I've sat on other sofas, just as other kids have sat here. So what? The stuff on TV or at the Bar or Park or Mall—what difference does it make? We're all out hustling in our way. Don't sweat it, folks. Don't take it personally. I won't."

XXI

What is it about you anyway? Somehow you're demographically the perfect child: just the right mix of goofy and sweet, courteous smart-ass, precocious, sensitive, and edging with endearing awkwardness toward adolescence. You don't threaten, neither do you bore; the many parents you have sampled seem engaged by you. Maybe it's because you're not as put-off by the corny stuff as your peers are. The birth-certificate ritual, for example. When they leave the xerox on the coffee table with fresh bottle of white-out, you don't see the harm in humoring them by letting your name lie upon the line provided, for the night or fortnight you lie in the bed upstairs (although increasingly you feel it a matter of integrity to leave the space at date unfilled.) Sometimes you'd like a moment to reflect amid the cumulative onslaught of embrace. You know how fortunate you are, but all the overwhelming change—and yet a moment's contemplation would be enough to send you reeling into the void and you can't afford right now to calculate the relative merits of never having been born.

XXII

ARE THEY IN THE DRAWER? Under the bed? Inside the under-bed storage unit? In the furthest corner of the closet floor or way back on the closet shelf? Under the stereo? Where has your predecessor hidden her or his stash? No, not under the pillow; anyone could find them there. Every child, whether genius or dork, confident, awkward or arrogant, participates unanimously in one particular rite of passage, which evolves into routine. She or he must have been a genius, to hide them so well. And you'd best be one yourself, to find them. For child's sake, isn't there even one issue? Maybe the toy chest? Yes! O damn! To go through all that searching and discover PLAYMOM! This confirms, a toddler was your predecessor. The cleavage contest issue; give me strength, you groan. It's embarrassing is what it is, to be reminded of your earliest inexperienced years. Memory can no longer supply to you the plethora of tastes you acquired, each mother's milk a new delicacy, some sweeter, some thicker, some richer, all wholesome, all hitting the spot, all right on the money (O Breast!) when you possessed a crude articulation that was itself volition: Mama Mama and it swelled for you, your wails its reveille; even before your eyes could see that far you'd *sense* it rise to you, your call, the nipple puckering in tandem with YOUR tiny lips.

Alas, you're past that now, it's all outgrown; you want as any self-respecting adolescent does, the clothed centerfold for over three, preferably over thirteen. You'd recognize it instantly, the issue of PLAYRENT you most prize, with both parents standing regally, arms outstretched, their eyes imploring you. It's the magazine that features words as well, articles and interviews on how to manage the frantic pace and how to keep your cool, although no article ever addresses that white noise of evaluating whether it would be better never to have been born.

Even now you see the father's strong white teeth, gleaming with a lustre greater than all cumulative color. His shoulders, were they hunched or straight? mike and tim and tom and jeff all say straight shoulders in a dad is key, is primary, but hell, maybe the slouching guy just had a bad day. Who wants to pose for this shit anyway? Debates among your friends abound: are the posers proud to set the standard? Or desperate since they can't find a connection any other way, than putting themselves—standing in as it were, for their toys—on display?

The smiles invariably get the most attention. The mouth is scrutinized for evidence of earnestness or ambivalence. Posture is a high priority as well. Stooped shoulders, slouching: notorious signs of weariness, the side effects of carrying too many aquariums. The judgments are for the most part instant and irrevocable. One child learns from another how to fashion them and levy them. Hours are spent distinguishing a genuine from a fake. See the seemingly flawless curve of that mouth with its perfect proportion of upper to lower lip, enhanced by dimples, no less; it makes an irresistible affectionate smile.

Now, imagine that smile greeting you each morning. You do, over and over, imagine it, and achieve a species of catharsis in this fashion; in fact you would not dare disclose to tim and tom how fervently you carry in your mind the image of that tender beckoning crescent, a haven you drift toward in moments of distress or inattention or confusion. You remember your shock and feeling of betrayal when tom informed you that those images were not entirely authentic. "It's doctored," was the way jeff put it. Ever since that incident, your friends have lost no opportunity to assess your progress, test your powers of discernment. Each time you're taken with an image, each time you skate on the periphery of revery, they jerk you back to earth: "Can't you tell it's airbrushing?" And if you hesitate a second, the nya-nya-nya-nya-nya-nya commences: "howie doesn't get it; howie doesn't get it!"

"Well what, in that case," you protest—refusing to capitulate or mimic their immaturity— "is wishing for? Why have these lures at all? Is it considered consolation, when the postures, when the parents' very bearing is leading us toward what can never be attained? I mean, for parents sake, why stock the bait if all the fish are fake?"

"Get real, howard," debbie says. "Yea, he's real," chimes in tim, "a real party pooper." "You know, I just don't give a toy," says jeff, exasperated. "Will everyone shut up so I can read?" "You call this reading?" megan challenges. "It's howie's house, remember?" mike interjects to your relief. "He asked us over. Don't give him such a hard time."

And they comply, though inadvertently, mutating from abusive to dismissive to preoccupied. jeff and jen and debbie eventually glaze over in front of the October issue. You know the image: ingeniously simple: a man and woman's face in profile with a seductive child-sized space between them. They'll hover over it for hours. Meanwhile, tim and tom are ticked off by the farm scene in the month before. "Give me a break, what do they take us for?" one asks the other. "They've got some nerve to print this!…it's so…fakey."

And indeed, they have a point; a lapse in judgment may be the best explanation for the close-up of a father's hand around a child's around the udder of a cow, conveying the jubilant, triumpant sensation of the squeeze. Strange though, to see an actual child explicitly included. "megan, isn't that illegal?" you call over. Incensed, they tear it out and toss it in the trash.

As for RENTS HOUSE, at one time, censors allowed only the exteriors to be displayed, leaving inside to the imagination. All viewers had abundant two-dimensional access to wood, stucco, brick, or cobblestone. But now, of course, interiors are standard fare, nothing too precious for the page, even the fluffy canopy bed that jeff says is sissy stuff. You're inclined to agree, as it reminds you of the fabric awning vigilantly shading the precious hairless noggin of the itty-bitty one inside his imported collapsible stroller. For child's sake, his whole head's a bald spot. What's so adorable?

But the question on every kid's mind, no matter what the season, is, what will be featured this month? You've placed a bet with mike that this time it will be the king-size bathroom with shower-massager and jacuzzi, three heads bobbing above the foam, two fully articulated in their features but one vacant oval to FILL IN THE BLANK of, and every child cuts his or her little photo-face and pastes it to the vacant space, even if another child's head got there first.

"But once you get there," proposes debbie, "once you're there a week? Whose hot tub is it gonna be?" "Oh, come on," heather says. "They know if they turn off the jets, you blow the joint. What parent will dare say, O.K., jacuzzi is off-limits now?" "It's all irrelevant," you intervene, "since no one stays a week. Well, almost no one." "You've got a point there, howard." Your banal discussion is interrupted by tim and tom shouting, in stereo, at all of you to come look. "megan fished the farm scene out of the tra-ash! megan fished the farm scene out of the tra-ash! Look, she's getting off on it!" Again, you feel compelled to clarify, "She's checking it because I asked her if it was illegal to use a kid like that, remember?" tom won't relent. "Yea, sure, howard. Is that why she's crying then?" megan tries to shield her face but the tear has already been perceived. Caught in the act of wishing: the worst vulnerability to suffer amid peers. "megan's wishing! megan's wishing! Off a jerky picture!"

"So what's the use of wishing then?" you carry on, running interference in the hope of mitigating megan's torture, although your question is, as ever, genuine, not at all rhetorical despite its form, and yet it might as well be for the paucity of response. Accept that there's no answer here. Nor is there answer to the larger question that pervades your private meditations. Those to whom you sometimes wake cannot abide to contemplate the answer either, because they stand as alternate, thus seek instinctively to block your option to not being born, and to imagining not being born.

XXIII

As if there weren't enough to make one anxious, you have to be alert to a signal in yourself that it is time. You must eventually step over to the other side. You will be required to find, quickly, a teammate and to look through the list of vacant houses and to accrue the enormous expenses of soliciting the class of individuals who until yesterday would have included you. It will be particularly awkward if it happens before, say, megan, mike and jeff and debbie's change; they'll look across the park at you as if you were a traitor or a square, as if these transmutations were within a person's power to schedule, but soon enough, soon enough, you'll find them in the house next door, and even in competition. Perhaps megan would team up with you if not she, heather? It's not as if there's any choice in it. Whoever is available will show up in the kitchen or the basement or the bath. There's no time for discriminating in these partnerships when all your energy is taken up in trying to score. And if you execute a smooth transition and make a seamless team, then all the better, to facilitate your being chosen. No manual is required, or rather, none is offered. Just sign the lease. Amass and divvy up the goods. That's all you'll have to do.

It should be better. At last the weight of childhood brooding will be lifted. The stress of scoring prime child cannot help but tax you less than your habitual concerns.

Once maturation brings you to the fence's other side, you might well shed the questioning, might leave your skepticism at the door, since when you're hustling, surely you cannot afford to ponder whether it were better never to be born.

Accept your lot, get on with it, stiff upper lip, and don't indulge yourself, except for child's sake, i.e. at TOYS-Q-US. "How adolescent!" jeff, mike, debbie, heather, tim and tom will eventually complain if you submit for discussion an existential dilemma. "I don't remember ever wondering that," they'll insist. "And isn't that irrelevant? Besides, howard, it's almost dark. Dig up some batteries. Clean out this old aquarium! Parade's about to start. For rent's sake, howie, don't slouch!"

The prospect alone is enough to send you pouring over Rents house, even Playmom, as a tonic, no, a life-preserver. There is a guaranteed release in the familiar arc that starts at stimulation and concludes with soothing. What's your pleasure? Which one will it be? No hesitation: the close-up sequence of a tender waving hand behind a windowpane, the glass so clear. Five glossy pages; they fold out almost like a flip book to insure you can create the motion in your mind, like a pendulum that speeds and slows according to your needs, goes right to left and back again, for as long as you desire. You trace the life-lines in the palm with your own fingertip, then, knowing privacy is for the moment assured, your tongue.

You have no idea how to read a palm or prophesy the future but you sense if this were actual flesh before your eyes right now, it might somehow reveal the past. You might be able, through a scrutiny of the uniquely etched configuration, its rivulets and deltas, its forked or braided paths, to glean essential information: were you born and were you better never born?

"Why won't you come out of your room tonight, howard?"

You can't confess, "to delay as long as possible becoming you."

XXIV

Carpe diem. Something that the teacher said, in passing, lodged inside your head. If whatever this has been is soon to be surrendered, or transformed, make the most of it. And what better opportunity than the most anxious day of the year? The electricity in the air on this late December morning is not to be attributed exclusively to the strings of lights twined over branches, hedges, houses, doorways. No household is exempt from this ritual: the culmination, in a sense, of everyday giving.

Keeping up with the Joneses is all the more the order of this day, and on this day particularly, a daunting agenda. In many houses, ladders are set up to permit children access to the piles of presents reaching as high as the star on the tree's tippy-top, and it is not unusual for children to wave to each other through the house's highest windows, from their respective perches, when parents are distracted. Unwrapping is precarious and exhausting; children whose agility has been facilitated by sports participation and informal athletic activities now benefit. Autumn gym classes at school traditionally devote one session per week to the game of "reach for the star," during which the basketball hoop is supplanted by a facsimile of what will cap the tree on Christmas Eve. The trampoline is employed for developing height and balance. Shop classes occasionally implement student suggestions to design a ladder with padded rungs.

It is considered common courtesy to linger over every gift, regardless of their number and regardless of the unremarkable nature of the practice of receiving. Today is distinct from other days only in that a layer of surprise surrounds each present, and in that these objects are guaranteed hot-off-the-shelf, i.e. NOT yet used: one hundred percent NEW.

That distinction merits fawning over, does it not? You oohh and aahhh on cue and daintily as possible remove, then fold the pretty crinkly paper while suspended from the chandelier or skylight, or while clinging to the ladder's second-highest rung, or else thrusting out your arms from an excavated pit within the mountainous conglomerate, all the while taking care not to displace ornaments or lose your concentration—or worse yet, balance—due to an unsuppressable sneeze. If only the tinsel (whose interminable meticulous dissemination gave you a headache in the first place) did not tickle so. Even if it wasn't this tree in this house whose decoration included your participation, it was one just like it.

No matter. This is where you spent the much-coveted night of Christmas Eve. It was not snow that woke you, nor the shadow of an obese, bearded man, nor the muted tympani of his primitive transport, whose antlers might scrape against chimney, roof and walls, suggesting squirrels or vermin. Pretend for them (i.e. your parents) it was excitement that inspired you to rise at dawn, rather than the literal alarm clock in your heart or head. Pretend, again for them, you would be delighted to attend a post-toy-getting service—if this is their custom—in that special breed of house whose stained glass and distinctively set table has yet to be exposed in Rents House. Don't let on that even the awkward, chipped clay figurines, conspicuously NOT new, nestled under the burdened pine-tree's lowest branch, make you uneasy. You notice that their little wooden house, although it has a sort of roof, is open-faced: a gallery of simplicity. It's like a farm too, though you don't know what the animals are really doing there. The donkey, for example, seems too close a relative of the image on which you pin the tail at other parties. As for the humans, the kings seem ostentatiously archaic, and the man and woman equally unconvincing in their humility. Come on, who lives like that?

Thanks to megan, you detect the oxymoron. Thanks to you, you recognize it as contrived. Meanwhile, the baby lying complacent on his erzatz straw commands—does it surprise you?—everyone's attention. You've heard of him yourself, seen him somewhere. Or maybe everywhere. He didn't come from TOYS-Y-US, although almost every other object on the floor did, and even now encroach upon his trademark village. The whole scene reinforces only your uncertainty as to whether he, if able to foresee the hyperbolic distortions in the legacy of frankincense and myrrh, would ever have elected to be born.

His story is so strange. Did it create this day, or did this day create him? The lucky lamb; at least he has a narrative of being born. For child's sake, time is split along the seam of his supposed birth. He is the fundament for all the history you learn in school, and lots of people think he isn't even real. Go figure!

Yet there his little manger sits, wedged between two segments of conveniently initialed time, for what would otherwise provide a reference? How would one demarcate the condition of never having been born? What acronym could do it justice, or for that matter, not glut the tongue with consonants? B.N.B? A.N.B.? P.N.B? Before or after or perhaps or better never born? Or would an image be more accurate? A volleyball suspended in glorious momentary spin—perhaps its blur alone to represent this modest, suspect fulcrum for an oblivious, compulsive, turning earth. All time leads up to or away from him, and by extension to the props of this most familiar stage set. How right it seems, though corny, that the kings are bearing gifts—even if one has a gauge in it—this baby's power is no secret.

He's got it made. Even those who don't buy him acknowledge him; they buy around him, and indirectly, at least celebrate him. The music pumped into the mall during holiday season would be full of holes without his name, holes to take the place of the implicit wounds that make him, even prior to receiving them, a star. "What is your deal?" you want to shout at him. "You've got it both ways! You're on the top; you're at the base. A bleating sheep, a shining star, an oozing wound!"

"You lucky duck, you schmuck, you superhero! You don't even need a cape, your blazing insignia worn across your skin, insuring you will never wake from nightmares dubbed a goose. You play it every way. You've got your cake, they eat out of your hand, they lick your wounds, your heart's a flaming candle dripping wax, they spit at you to try to blow it out, and yet they bow to you as well, they try to rip you from the picture only to find you leave a big, fat hole."

He's got a story any kid would be sent home a liar for telling, but somehow this big baby stands for what is brave and true. The common sense prized by parents suggests he would have better missed his grand debut as THE SCAPEGOAT, THE PINNED DONKEY, THE SLAUGHTERED LAMB, but whoever wrote his script made sure that no one could conceive of his not being born. After all, who needs a house when his story is completely furnished? Who needs a parent when his father is built-in? Why bother envying a baby when you stay one for two thousand years?

For child's sake, who can stand to think about it? (If only you could have a story too, a story that compelling, straining credibility yet curiously persuasive.) It makes your head swim. Makes your heart race. Just push that creche way back against the trunk, why don't you? Let it lie under the harmless paper avalanche until tomorrow, or till twelve days from now, or until you too can conjure up a story that would, by ingenious or outrageous means, arrest your chronic visitation to the house of never being born.

Billy Childish

The Medway Bog Man
from *Notebooks of a Naked Youth*

I narrow my shoulders and looking only at the pavement and passing feet, pull my hat down over my eyes and quickening my pace, pass her, feeling positive that she is indeed the most spiteful and persistent old bag I have ever encountered. When I next look up I have evidently re-crossed Star Hill, for I am standing outside The Andy Snacks.

I push inside, go straight to the counter, and order egg and chips. The lady who takes my order has a large drip hanging from the end of her nose and I have to use all of my self-control not to reprimand her on the spot. Something of course, which I would never do. Instead, I smile weakly and ask her for my eating irons. She picks my coppers from the counter and counting them out into the palm of her hand, sniffs and hands me a cloakroom ticket.

"We'll call your number when it's ready, love."

She flings my knife and fork down on the counter and they clang and bounce in front of me, probably more out of slovenliness than any show of contempt. But I still decide to take offense and think peevishly that she has decided not to like me, maybe on account of the cut of my jib, or perhaps just because I have neglected to comb my hair, which apparently stands up on end like a lot of porcupine quills.

She points me towards an empty table. I stride over, pull out the plastic seat and sit resting my elbows on the yellow formica table top. I pick up a paper napkin and stuff it inside my open shirt front and play chess with the salt and pepper pots.

A man with startling white eyebrows comes clinking his cup and saucer at me, sits himself down with a groan and empties his tea into his saucer. He bunches his lips together like a dog's arse and sucks on it loudly, licks his lips, looks at me with his insolent eyebrows and winks. I look down and study my ticket: number 146.

"What you got there?" He speaks at me. I pretend to be so deep in thought that I haven't heard him, and scrunch up my brows and stroke my chin as if on the verge of solving some impossible mathematical equation.

"I bet you're having egg and chips ain'tcha?"

I realised that yet again it had happened to me, that I must after all carry an invisible sign round my neck welcoming all the disadvantaged, the shambling and the lost, to come barging in and harass me with their impudent and pointless questions.

I twist in my seat and look over my shoulder, purposely ignoring him.

"I knew it! Egg and chips!"

Exasperated by his inquisitiveness I turn on him roughly.

"Evidently you were standing behind me and heard the lady take my order!"

"That's right, I did."

I was counting on him contradicting me and am forced into silence by his joyful admittal.

"Got any work?" he asks.

"No," I reply, then feeling the still unposted envelope in my inside pocket, I add mysteriously, "yes and no."

"That's interesting," he says pleasantly.

"Interesting and not so interesting, depending..." and I look at him mischievously, egging him on into heaven only knows what nonsense.

"I suspect you're a student?" he enquires.

"Not at all," I lie. Just then the lady calls out my number. I lift my ticket and wave it above my head and she creeps painfully over in her worn carpet slippers, the drip on her nose extending down into somebody's rice pudding. She bangs my plate down in front of me and lets out a tired sigh.

The old crust wiggles his eyebrows at me as if they are a pair of snow-white badgers romping over his forehead in search of their dinner. Ignoring this tiresome oaf I start right off scoffing the food into my face.

"You'll get indigestion," he volunteers hopefully.

I grunt, stuffing the chips into the egg and into my mouth with my bare hands. Quickly, I clear the plate and sit back. All that remains is my white of egg, lying there like piece of vile jelly floating in a sea of grease.

"Are you not going to eat that?" He nods towards my egg white.

I push the plate across the table towards him and watch disgusted as he picks up my unused knife and fork and proceeds to cut the egg white up into elegant little strips. The, folding them into neat parcels he transports them to his waiting gob, where he pecks at them like a small bird eating nuts through a wire basket.

The finickety nature of this old crust's manners makes my teeth itch. I lean over the table towards him and shout in his ear.

"I'm writing a paper on the legend of the Medway Bog Man!"

He stops mid-peck and raises his eyebrows, which gives the impression of a wise old monkey.

"The Medway Bog Man?" he says, nodding slowly, and then carries on eating.

I am outraged that this stupid old man sat pecking at my white of egg like a half-starved gannet should utter the name of the Medway Bog Man so casually.

"Yes, the Medway Bog Man!" I shout at him again. The people on the next table turn to look at me but quite frankly I am oblivious.

"It's a very unique case," I carry on emphatically, "and one that science has largely ignored."

"I thought these mummified bog people were quite a common phenomenon."

"I can assure you, sir, that there is nothing in the least bit common about the Medway Bog Man...but I suppose you know the whole story back to front!" I spit at him sarcastically.

"I remember some of it from school and some of what folks have told me since," he replies mildly.

I unplug my ears and stare at him totally gob-smacked. He carries on chewing on his final and most disgusting mouthful, swallows, and arranges the knife and fork neatly on the plate in front of him. He loosens his collar, coughs, sticks his greasy finger into his vile gob, withdraws it, studies his filthy nail and dries it carefully on the leg of his blue overalls.

I peer for any trace of humour on his wrinkly old mug but there is none. He really does believe that he has heard of the Medway Bog Man, and that he even studied the subject at school.

"You must have gone to a very advanced and forward thinking academy."

"No, not at all," he replies, "actually, I left school when I was only thirteen."

"But it seems that you've studied local history in quite some depth?" I add bitterly.

He waves his hand dismissively, completely ignoring my caustic tone.

"No, no, I just like to keep abreast of local issues. It doesn't do to keep your head buried in the sand does it?…Now, this Bog Man," he carries on, "weren't his legs lost whilst they were excavating him?"

I look him up and down. "No," I shout, "you must be thinking of an all together different Bog Man, probably his Russian cousin or something."

"I'm sure I remember reading that the excavator took off his legs, just below the knees, before they quite realised what they'd found."

"Absolutely not! The Medway Bog Man is an altogether different kettle of fish! He was found at Upchurch, perfectly preserved, clasping a twentieth century school girl's shoe in his leathery grasp!"

"Is that so?" he says thoughtfully.

"What's more, the pathologist had to break his fingers to retrieve it!" I add ghoulishly.

The man strokes his chin, takes out his tobacco pouch, rolls a cigarette, lights it and sits there puffing out the blue smoke, totally unruffled.

I stare at him gloweringly, studying him for some glimmer of doubt. He taps the ash off of his cigarette and clears his throat.

"He was quite some age this Bog Man wasn't he? Two thousand years was it…?"

I narrow my eyes.

"They actually estimated his age to be some seven thousand years old…" I stare at him, "preserved in a freak fermentation at the bottom of a silted-in creek, or palaeo channel, to use the full archaeological term."

He nods knowingly and coughs again slightly. I see that I will have to come up with something truly spectacular to ruffle this old coot's feathers.

"Despite it being highly unusual," I continue, "to find a peat layer with a pH level suitable for preserving the living flesh of a Bog Man in an intertidal marshland, by a fluke of nature, or perhaps by the devil's own design, every single pore of his body was perfectly preserved! It was evident from the stubble on his chin that he hadn't shaved for several days. There was even a tattoo of what appeared to be a crude Mesolithic gallows still clearly visible on his upper arm, and the remains of his last meal, a form of Stone Age muesli, still lay partially undigested in his lower gut. His neck had been snapped and he was pushed into the creek and evidently left to drown."

The old crust merely nods and seems to be quite at home with my description.

"You do understand the ramifications of this discovery?" I hiss at him, "we're not just talking about any run of the mill old corpse here, we're talking about the living flesh of a Mesolithic Man, equipped with hunting bow and two mud-encrusted hell hounds!"

"Oh, the dogs…" he muses.

I can't believe my ears…that he just sits there and hasn't questioned one single jot of my story, and hate him all the more for his naivity and gullibility. I can no longer tolerate this sinewy old crust believing a word of what I say and decide to force him, by hook or by crook, into denouncing me as a liar.

"The Bog Man, or Thee Medway Bog Man to give him his full title, was unearthed in 1936 whilst the police were searching Upnor Marshes for the missing school girl Kursty Morgan. Her body was eventually found some fifteen years later, after the death of one James Lovecroft, game keeper and armchair archaeologist, who was coincidentally a tireless campaigner to keep Thee Medway Bog Man in North Kent. Kursty's perfectly preserved body was discovered still fully clothed in a sealed cot in Lovecroft's attic. The only item of clothing that was missing was her left shoe." I look at him pointedly. "The mystery was further compounded by the nature of Lovecroft's demise, namely that his death had been brought about by the forced ingestion of the toadstool Amanita Virosa, more commonly known as the Destroying Angel. No one was ever convicted of Lovecroft's murder, though rumour has it that his housekeeper and cook Patricia Coltsworth was in fact none other than Kursty Morgan's great aunt."

My wise old monkey narrows his eyes.

"That's right," he agrees, "I remember it now. Fungus poisoning." And he puffs out another bitter mouthful.

I feel a tickling sensation somewhere in between the back of my throat and the depths of my right ear and bang myself on the side of the head with my fist. The nonchalance and unshakability of this old crust completely outrages me and I decide to drown him in dates and fabrications, to see just how deeply this vile rascal can be drawn in. I place my elbows on the table top and lean my face into his.

"I suppose you think that I've made this whole story up from start to finish don't you? I suppose you think that there never was a Medway Bog Man and that I've just been sitting here stringing you a line for my own entertainment…? This is not just hogwash or hearsay!" I yell at him, "there were reports in all the leading journals of the time, he was running around naked with his neck snapped and his head on backwards for God sake! Go and read them for yourself if you don't believe me!"

He sits back with a look of bewilderment in his eyes.

"No, I believe you," he implores me, "I can even remember going to see the body with my father before the last war. I was just a boy. I must of only been about—what—eight or nine. He was on display at the old museum at East Gate House, before they moved it to the Guild Hall. Then the war came and I don't know what became of him…I believe he was put into storage in case of an invasion or incendiary damage I suppose."

I stare at him, completely floored by this fantastic new revelation. Incendiary damage my foot! This spiteful old crust is intent on stealing my creation away from me—from right under my own nose, so to speak.

"I think I might still even have a postcard of him indoors. I could look it out for you if you like, do you come in here often?"

I realise that I will have to muster up all of my powers of invention to snatch my Bog Man back from the thieving grasp of this unscrupulous individual.

"You seem to know an awful lot about this Bog Man," I humour him, "so I presume that you are familiar with the incident when he escaped?"

"He escaped?" The old crust pinches his furry brows together, looks sulkily out at me and scratches at a gravy spot on the table top in front of him.

"Yes," I rush on excitedly, "on the night of the 14th of April, 1942, on the seventh anniversary of his discovery, during an air raid. When the guard returned from the corporation shelter, he discovered that the Bog Man's glass case had been smashed open and his muddy foot prints and those of his two hunting dogs lead out onto the main stairway, down the hallway and out through the front door."

"Surely you mean he was stolen," reasons the old crust.

"No!" I shout triumphantly and smash my fist down onto the table, "if you remember, the police report stated quite clearly that the cabinet had been smashed from the inside, the glass splinters covered the whole room. The bolts on the front door were thrown and the latch lifted from the inside. No traces of a break-in were ever found!"

The wise old monkey leans forward thoughtfully and shakes his head. I fold my arms, puff out my chest and stare intently at him, daring him to contradict me. He looks down at my empty plate.

"It's true," he mutters to himself at last, then turns to the next table, "I remember it all now, the whole mysterious incident." An old lady and her little white dog nod to him consolingly.

"But the story didn't end there," I cry maliciously, "not by a long chalk it didn't."

I decide to teach this old rascal a lesson he won't forget in a hurry, to smash him once and for all, for having the nerve, the audacity to try and steal my Bog Man. I rub my hands together and my victim smiles up at me timidly.

"Shortly after the Bog Man's escape," I elaborate, "various incidences came to light to suggest that the Bog Man hadn't returned to haunt the marshes as the authorities had originally hoped, but that he was in fact living in the vast labyrinth of tunnels that criss-cross beneath these very streets, and that he was intent on causing as much mischief as was ghoulishly possible within these very city walls!"

"Now that, I know, is fact!" pipes up the dry old crust. He speaks to the whole room, still greedily intent on stealing the mummified ghoul of the marshes. "All the forts are linked by tunnels, from here to the dockyard, some say there's even one that runs clean under the river!"

I glare at him, forcing him to shut up, then carry on with my magical story.

"His first hide-out is now known to have been in the caves under Amhurst redoubt. At night he would re-enter the city via Fort Pitt and the Delce Tower. Fantastic rumours started spreading of a mud-covered ghoul seen accosting school girls on their way to and from school. There was even one report of a twelve year old child having her school shoe fondled in broad daylight!" I pause and tear at my thumb nail. "In an entirely separate and unrelated incident, the original guard from the East Gate

Museum saw the mud-bedecked ghoul cunningly disguised as the town crier. After trying to tear off the ghoul's whiskers, he was beaten, kicked and chased by the ghoul, roaring and spitting fire down the length and breadth of the high street. Fearing for his life the guard ran into the Two Brewers, where he insisted that the landlord double bolt all the doors whilst he relaxed in the bar. Wherein he remained ensconced until morning. Several Officers of the Law were in attendance and vouched for the sobriety of the witness. And he later attested on oath that it was indeed the very same Medway Bog Man, and not an impostor as some sceptics had suggested."

The old man shrinks smaller and smaller with each new revelation I make, and whereas before he had had an air of amenable friendliness, now all he can muster up is a bitter smile. I stare at him daring him to refute me.

"Reports and sightings of the Bog Man continued right up until the 1950s," I gloat, "even the church became involved and the Cathedral employed the services of one Reverend Arnold Trescot, pot-holer and professional exorcist, aided and abetted by his three accomplices, the Bunion Triplets. They were given strict instructions by the Mayor and City Council to recapture the Bog Man dead or alive and return him forthwith to his display cabinet, along with the museum's missing collection of Iron Age pottery and artifacts."

By now the whole cafe has grown hushed and turns to listen to my wonderful tale. I grow more and more exuberant in my descriptions, until my friend, the thief with his snowy-white eyebrows, slides from behind his table and runs towards the door.

"This they almost succeeded in doing on the 5th of November, Guy Fawkes night 1956!" I scream after him, "listen to me!" I gasp, "listen to me you damned thief!" I yell at him shaking my fist, and the poor wretch stands there dithering in the doorway, neither coming nor going, explaining himself to anybody who will listen.

One of the serving ladies comes over and tells me to sit down and quieten myself. She touches my arm very lightly and it is as if a bolt of electricity shoots through me. I collapse to my chair, hold my head in my hands and rock back and forth, sobbing uncontrollably for the loss of my youth, at the theft of my marvellous creation.

That my nerves were completely shot through was obvious. It now became clear to me that protein was what was at fault, the yellow of egg was evidently too rich for my liver.

The serving lady leads me from my table and takes me out back. My whole frame is wracked with cold chills and I sit there trembling for what seems like hours.

She tells me not to be a silly boy and that her name is Dot. She brings me a large mug of hot sweet tea, but rather than helping me dry up, her kindness sets me off on another weeping fit and I cry so pitifully that she holds my head in her lap and my tears wet her apron.

"The Reverend Trescott was lucky to escape with only a severe mauling," I blather, "the Bunion Triplets are still in the madhouse to this day!"

"Yes dear…I know dear, it's shocking, shocking…"

She stroked my head and I erupt into another torrent of self-loathing, berating myself and apologising for crying…that I don't know what's come over me.

My eyes are blinded…great strings of snot cascading from my nose. I stand and she takes my hand and shows me to the toilets, where I sit shivering for half an hour blowing my nose like a bugle.

Julia Duncan

Ghost in a Glass House

I met Simon at Under the Bridge, at a commitment party for Soho and Lisa. Commitment as in lesbian marriage, not mental hospital, though their friends thought the latter more appropriate. Soho was crazy, and Lisa was crazy for marrying her. Most of us were not what you would call completely sane, but that never stopped us from throwing stones.

I sat at the bar, doing a leather-cool, half-lidded stare over beer after beer, thinking about killing myself, talking about Denny whenever one of my friends would sit next to me for more than a minute. Two weeks since she'd dropped her bombshell and left town, enough time for my friends to move on. Barely enough time for me to grasp that there'd been an explosion.

"Two years," I complained to Gem, one of the bartenders. "She was with me for two years. And she told me two hours before their train left."

Gem had heard it before. He fixed me with his big blue eyes and said, "Well, Rena, what do you want?"

"I want her back."

"Honey," he said, "that's not love. Letting her go is love."

I hated Gem. I hated the truth, which was that I would have done anything to get Denny back. "You just want me to keep drinking," I accused him. Despite my tough wardrobe, I was a big tipper when I got drunk, which was a lot lately.

I was drunk when I met Simon. Not quite falling-off-the-barstool stage but on that road. I noticed this man in the crowd, with gray hair and a trim gray beard, green eyes, and old-fashioned clothes, a dark gray suit that looked like it came from the vintage store on Grace Street. Turns out it did. Simon has a taste for the old—if it lasts, he says, it was made to last. That kind of quality means something to him. Most of what he owns comes from estate sales and vintage stores.

Simon looked so out of place, he fit in. Amused with that thought, and ready to seize any excuse, however slim, I turned around and raised my hand to signal Gem for another beer. "Who's that guy?" I asked when he finally got to me with a bottle. I tossed him a five. "The old guy."

"He's not old; that's Professor Dorcy. Philosopher. Everybody knows him."

I didn't, but Gem knew I dropped out of college in my sophomore year, worked night-shift in a darkroom, didn't know a lot of people called "Professor." Sweetheart, Gem was. I waved him back my change. "What's he doing here?"

"One of Soho's stable of writers," Gem said. "He wrote that piece last month about art and death. Fantastic mind." Didn't thank me for the tip, as usual.

I nursed this beer hunched against the bar, shoulders stiff to protect my little world. Didn't work. I'd barely finished off the bottle when a new one arrived, escorted by a clear drink over ice in a cocktail glass, and met by a hand offering bills before I could reach into my pocket.

Turning my head, I was careful to remain stable, anchored against the bar with my arms. It was Professor Dorcy, standing next to me in the space where someone had borrowed a stool. "I'm Simon," he said, not offering to shake hands. "Nice to meet you."

"Rena," I said. "Thanks for the beer, but I'm queer."

"Drink it anyway," he said. "I'm not asking you out on a date."

"Good," I said, or something equally brilliant.

He didn't leave. "Is Rena from Irene?" he asked me.

"Sure is," I answered, drinking.

"Irene means peace; do you know that? It does not suit you," he said, casually. "I would think something like Ireta—angry one. You are very young to look so angry."

I looked down at my bottle of beer, realizing I would look ridiculous trying to toss it on him. He had one hand wrapped around his own drink, protecting it. I shrugged my tense shoulders and told him, "I'm twenty-one."

"How long have you been thinking about killing yourself?"

I turned my head toward him again, still careful to move slowly. "How the hell do you know that?" I asked, thinking one of my stupid friends must have… but who had I told? I racked my brain. Must have been drunk. Don't remember saying it to anyone.

"Hobby of mine," he answered, just as smooth as before. "So I am correct. How long?"

I considered that. Simon had an older man sexiness, a trim body, every hair in place, clothes bespeaking exquisite taste even if they were straight out of the fifties, a clean cologne smell. His accent was Boston, I thought. Money, I thought. Reminded me strongly of my parents' country club set. He should have been on the board of the university, not teaching there.

"Since I discovered death existed," I answered him, pulling the collar of my shirt aside and turning slightly so that he could see the small black skull and the word "Hellbound" tattooed on my chest.

He didn't even flinch. "How are you thinking of doing it?"

I stared at him. His eyes were a strange sea-green, with a hint of gold in the bright fluorescent light from over the bar. I thought it was an amazingly stupid conversation to be having with a stranger, so I gestured with one hand, thumb up, toward the bridge.

He nodded slightly. "A classic," he said and drained his drink. "From this bridge, you'll probably die or pass out when you hit the water. If not, drowning is said to be an easy way to go. Not much of a mess either, at least until your body washes ashore."

"Jesus Christ, what are you drinking?" I asked, shaking my head. That was a mistake, but his comments were so bizarre. What kind of twisted philosophy professor was this guy? I wondered.

"Hoover Dam," he said.

"No, I probably couldn't get up there to jump off."

He smiled, raising his glass. "Water on the rocks."

"Oh."

"Mind if I ask you why now?"

I was still looking right at him. Even through the beer haze, I knew what he meant. "Just found out," I told him, "I'm not a very nice person."

"Weak," he said. "If that were a good reason, the river would be clogged with corpses."

I turned back to my beer, carefully raised it, and took a swallow.

"Must be love," he said. "What did you think of the ceremony?"

Ten minutes into the bonding ceremony earlier that evening, I'd decided killing myself was the only thing left to do.

"I think Soho is certifiable, and she's going to make Lisa even more miserable now. What do you think?"

He chuckled low. "People who live in glass houses shouldn't throw stones," he said.

"People who drive in glass cars shouldn't have bones," I replied.

He laughed, this time a dry and humorless sound.

I said, "Lisa will never be careful enough to avoid getting hurt."

"Love must be a glass car."

"Is love a good reason?" I asked.

"Rarely."

"Are you some kind of expert?"

"I've considered the topic." When I did not respond, he asked, "May I buy you a cup of coffee, Rena?"

We made an odd couple at the bright diner up the street, but not one worth a second glance from a staff used to all kinds. Seat the distinguished gentleman and his crewcut, tattooed, leather butch escort in a booth toward the back, OK?

Simon didn't tell me shit about suicide, or what would be a good reason. He bought me coffee and a bran muffin and he listened so hard I had to talk, as if his listening was a vacuum cleaner pulling the dust out of my mind.

I must have told him everything. How I came out and my entire family disowned me, down to great-aunt Ethel, who wasn't sure what lesbianism meant but was fairly sure it had something to do with communism. How I haven't spoken to any of them in four years. How my lover before Denny left me for a guy and was married and pregnant within two months. How my best friend, River, died of AIDS. How I dropped out of school because of soaring debt and my full-time job hadn't slowed the soar one bit, and wouldn't as long as I kept tipping bartenders like a maniac. How the love of my life professed undying love continually while she had her fingers in another pie so deep that they'd already rented an apartment together in a different city, and how the stupidest thing of all, the thing I just could not stand much longer, was the overwhelming need to have Denny back, not to see her happy, but to have her. In my bed, in my arms, mine alone. My possession.

How it made me loathe myself.

When I was done, Simon didn't speak. He looked at me for a long, long time without opening his mouth, until finally I said, "So aren't you going to try to talk me out of it?"

"No," he said.

"Why not?"

He sighed and picked up his coffee cup to blow on the liquid. "Most of the people I talk to change their minds while they are telling me about themselves. They decide that they want to live, glass houses and all. They find sympathy for themselves."

"Not me," I said.

"Yes, I sense that about you. I think that you are mentally ill."

He said it in all seriousness, as if it needed saying—was it not obvious from the topic we'd been discussing since he walked up to me at the bar that I was mentally ill?

I played along, toying with one of my skull earrings. "Really? Why is that?" I asked.

"Because you don't value your life."

I answered him, "What value? How do I know that, if I don't jump off the bridge tonight, I won't get hit by a bus tomorrow? Or that I won't get drunk some night, get in my car, and kill someone? Here it is after all, ho-hum, the your-whole-life-ahead-of-you bit."

"Hm? No. Quite the contrary, I'll walk you to the bridge if you're serious."

He was, to judge by his cold eyes, quite serious. It took me a minute. I sipped coffee. I ran through my possibles, my limits, my sore spots. I even thought about those few seconds of flight, and then…pain over. Done. Oblivion.

"You're on," I said.

Rain drizzled down steadily, but we walked slowly to the bridge. For once I was free from caring how wet my carefully preserved leather jacket was getting. Simon didn't seem to even notice the rain.

We didn't speak until we got halfway across on the walkway, on the east span. I looked down at the water for a minute. It looked dark and cold and disturbed in the rain. The cars going over the bridge made a sound like ghosts in a tunnel. I shrugged out of my jacket and handed it to Simon. He took it. Then I thought it might be nice to wear it down, and if I didn't die when I hit the water, my old companion would help me sink to the depths. But I couldn't bring myself to reach for it back.

"Denny," I said to him. "Denise Applewaithe. In Norfolk. Call her?"

He didn't nod, but I figured he would do it. I turned and climbed the railing, crawled across the beams, threw my legs over the other side, and twisted to catch the edge with my feet. It was easy to hang on there, and I did for a moment, watching Simon's eyes darkly assessing me. I let go, bending my knees and shoving myself away.

I fell backward, with the rain, out of the sky, and though I couldn't see it, I sensed the river waiting to embrace me and carry me away. With a great sense of relief, I watched Simon and the bridge recede against the flat, dark gray sky. I surrendered to the coming embrace.

I spun and twisted, my head reeled, I couldn't breathe, I was blind. There was no pain, only confusion and heat.

I heard squealing brakes, shouting, footsteps on metal decking, ghosts in a tunnel. I felt drops of water hitting my head.

Simon held me.

For an instant, against my cheek, I felt skin and muscle slide, hard and slick, pulsing with heat, and my mind was filled with the color of blood and the smell of oily yellow smoke.

Then I heard Simon speaking, the sounds of his words humming meaninglessly from his chest into the bones of my face crushed against his white cotton shirt. I smelled wet wool and wet leather and the undertone of rot from the river far below. My mind went blank in shock.

Simon took me home.

He gave me towels in a sumptuous half bathroom right off the foyer of his house, disappeared, and brought back a soft robe. He left me alone to change— my reflection in the mirror looked strange with this regal dark blue robe and all the rings and skulls and things in my ears—then he returned to escort me into a living room full of antique furniture and Persian rugs. He sat me down in front of a gas fireplace; I accepted brandy only because he placed it into my hands.

"Are you sorry you're not dead?" he asked very quietly, as though asking if my drink was acceptable.

I nodded.

He paced slowly around the room with his own small snifter of brandy. "May I ask you a few questions?"

I nodded again.

"Were your parents wealthy?"

I was confused. I nodded anyway.

"Can you tell Mozart from Bach?"

I nodded again.

"Do you know what *carpe diem* means?"

"Of course. Seize the day." At last my mind began to move again. "What are you?" I asked. "How did you...do what you did?"

He had stopped pacing and stood with his back to me for a moment. In front of him was a stand displaying a doll in a glass case; he may have been looking at it. I could see that it was in ornate ethnic Chinese costume. The case had carved black trim and a tassel of bright red serving as a doorpull.

Finally, Simon turned around. I found the strength to look at him; he had not grown horns or begun to breathe fire. He looked relaxed, though slightly eager, and he gestured vaguely with his snifter. "Don't you think *why* is a more important question?" he asked.

"What do you want from me?"

He smiled at me, for the first time a genuine smile, full of pleasure. His sea-green eyes glimmered in the false-fire light, green and black like the bottom of the river. "I want your life," he said.

I blinked. "What?"

He answered slowly and steadily. "Your life. What you threw into that river tonight. Say your life was that vase over there." He pointed to a beautiful vase enameled with red roses. "You throw it over the edge. I catch it. You owned it—you had the right and the power to destroy it. But now I have it in my hands, intact. Who owns the power to destroy it now?"

"Are you saying that you want to kill me?"

"Not right away."

Chills ran through me, deep into my gut, up the back of my scalp. Warmth followed. No fear, just that odd liquid excitement that happens half an instant before orgasm.

"You could be dead right now, free from pain," Simon said. "I'm offering you what you want, just in a different mode."

I looked around, reflex, checking for weapons. Death I did not fear, but more pain wasn't on my agenda. There was plenty of material at hand, from lamps to just-for-show fireplace tools. "What do you mean?" I asked.

He did not answer right away. Instead, he refreshed his drink, collected a cigarette from a box near the bar, and chose a chair. He lit the cigarette with a gold lighter from his pocket and savored the first puff. Then, looking into the fireplace, he elaborated.

"I offer what you want: freedom from pain. In exchange I wish to own the rest of your life. Your body and your mind, all that you are now, living, but as if you were that vase."

"Without pain."

"Without pain," he said, as serious as he'd been when he offered to walk me to the bridge. "An example. Think of your Denise."

I had to think of her as soon as he mentioned her name. And it was as if I was thinking of someone I didn't even know. I stared at Simon.

"Trade to me what you are willing to throw away—trade it for the loss of your pain. If I'm lying, you can always go leap off that bridge."

I finished the brandy sip by sip, also watching the fire. Twenty minutes went by according to the clock on the wall before I said, "And if not?"

"The bargain will hold," he answered without hesitation, softly, like a caress. "I will own your life."

"Not my soul?"

"Souls bore me," he answered, his eyes afire. "I desire other things."

"What are you?" I whispered.

"If I can give you what you want," he answered, "does it matter what I am?"

I let go for the second time that night. This time, I got what I wanted.

I never even went back to my apartment for my stuff. My landlord kept it for a while, then he gave it all away.

Word went around. Friends came to see me. Campus gossip said Professor Dorcy had acquired a sex slave, that he'd hypnotized me somehow and was holding me prisoner. My friends checked my arms for needle marks and my back for whip scars, and when there weren't any, they tried for an hour to pry something out of me or to get me to leave. Muir couldn't keep his eyes off Simon's things.

"This doll is exquisite," he said. "Look at her eyes." He made Sandy look at the doll's ink-black eyes.

Sandy said, "She looks like she's afraid of something."

"Where did he get all this stuff on a teacher's pay?" Muir muttered. "What a collection."

Sandy stared at my hair, growing out, and my ears, full of empty holes, and she couldn't help herself. "He can't be that fucking good," she told me. "Rena, you've sold your soul."

I told them I'd lost my bones. They went away muttering, "Certifiable."

What could I have told them? That a ghost in a glass house feels no pain?

I saw Denny one night, downtown. We'd eaten dinner at one of those gorgeous new restaurants opening up in the old warehouse district, and we were walking into a nearby hotel when Denny got out of a cab right in front of us. She looked just like always, slim legs in tight jeans, black car coat, red hair bright and teased, strong hands. I stopped and looked at her, interested. She glanced my way for a brief second, as people do on the street; I hadn't thought she would recognize me. My hair was curled; my dress was low cut; my heels were so high, I leaned on Simon's arm as we walked. The diamonds dangling from my ears were worth more than I made in a year when I lived with Denny.

Then her head whipped around, and she stared. Her face went dead pale and her mouth came open in a little "What?" motion. But she said nothing, and I felt nothing as we went on our way inside.

Simon did not lie. A property of his mind, I am like a vase, like a gas fireplace, pretty and warm but untouched by the flame. Another possession, his to enjoy, his to destroy. He did not lie. Sometimes I beg him to hurt me, but I never feel any pain. When he kills me, I will thank him; I died some time ago and am no longer throwing stones.

Mary Halnon

How It Seems in September

"How was your visit to Aunt Lil's?" his mother says as she leans over to open the door to the Plymouth. She has a new permanent, he notices, and she's wearing the sun dress striped like peppermint candy, the one he likes. He's been standing under the Greyhound sign for fifteen minutes beside a pyramid of luggage, counting spots of gum on the sidewalk. He's counting so he doesn't have to think about the knots in his stomach and the darkening sky. When she arrives, finally, he wants to hit her. How could she be late? Instead, he starts to cry. "David?" She knits her brows together.

He'd spent two months with his Aunt Lil and Uncle Vernon in Newark because his mother needed what she called a "mental hiatus." She'd been peevish with him since his father left eight months earlier. "Going out for cigarettes," Roy had called before he wheeled out the door, but apparently his cigarettes were difficult to locate because he wasn't back yet. The memory of his father was strong in him, but his secret fear was forgetting Roy, pieces of Roy floating off, so that one day when they met on the street—and they would meet—Roy would be unrecognizable, and the reunion missed.

He made a list in the back of his school notebook:

1. My father whistles, mainly "Take Me Out to the Ball Game."
2. My father drinks beer straight from the bottle.
3. He reads the funnies out loud, even when no one's listening.
4. His birthday is August 1.
5. My father takes me to the matinee every Saturday afternoon.

This last was a lie, but he wrote it anyway, just in case someone looked in his notebook. Sometimes when his mother was at work, he closed himself up in his father's closet and breathed deeply. Everything was just as Roy had left it; the small space was almost heady with Roy's full, slightly salty odor, the smell of men to David.

Since Roy left, his mother was on the phone to Aunt Lil all the time, it seemed. When David passed the open kitchen door, his mother started spelling: "that B-A-S-T-A-R-D," she said more than once. As if, David thought, I wasn't twelve. As if I didn't know who she was talking about. She smoked a lot and played WBAN as a constant background hum in the apartment. She sewed new curtains for the kitchen, yellow dotted swiss. He told her it was a perfect match to the roses on the wallpaper, but she put the old ones back up after only a week.

Worse, she didn't laugh anymore when he told her the *Reader's Digest* jokes he memorized at Stewart's house. He loved his mother's laugh. She had a long, fine neck and it was shown to advantage when she threw her head back. Her mouth turned up at one side when she smiled, and her hand fluttered to her collarbone. Sometimes she had to wipe her eyes and say, "Oh, me." Often he had heard her repeating his comments on the phone. "Alice, my David said the funniest thing to me last night." When she talked about him this way, it was as if her voice were a water glass held on a saucer, high and clear, about to spill over into laughter at any moment.

As he cries in the car, his mother's face draws up into a question mark. "Oh, honey, what's wrong? You weren't scared, were you?" She turns down the radio. He shakes his head and tries to stop the tears. He isn't sure why he is crying now. He begins to hiccup. An ice cream truck passes by.

His mother draws some spit onto her thumb and smooths his eyebrows. "Don't!" he shouts. He shrinks against the car door. He wants the plump of the inside of her arms around him; he wants the old, happy orbit around his mother's laughing face.

Aunt Lil had made him drink spoiled milk that morning. "After you go, no one will drink this. Vernon and I only use skim. It won't kill you. What do you think yoghurt is?" He found it difficult to argue with Aunt Lil's logic. She still served him in a Peter Rabbit spillproof tumbler. He almost gagged on the first sip, but she was watching with her hands on her hips. When he finished the milk he felt dizzy. "Good boy," Aunt Lil said, and she handed him a Fig Newton. The swirly design in the kitchen tabletop reminded him of the bacteria and parasites from science class last winter. After learning about the dangers of spoiled food and undercooked pork, he'd refused to eat anything besides saltines for a week. His mother eventually baked a chocolate cake and sat across from him in the kitchen after supper, spooning it into her mouth and rolling her eyes after each bite. "Mmm-boy!" she declared. When he could stand it no more, he ate three pieces, almost simultaneously. For the rest of the night he watched TV with his head in his mother's lap.

At Aunt Lil's he ate alone in the kitchen. Uncle Vernon had his Postum and toast at the dining room table while reading the paper. He liked to call David "Little Soldier." He said it so much David secretly believed his uncle didn't know his name. It seemed Aunt Lil never ate, but was a flurry of motion. She cleaned almost savagely, and in her leftover time she crocheted covers for the spare toilet paper rolls. To David they looked like little snow hats, but of course he would never say so to Aunt Lil. Every morning after breakfast she shooed him out the door and said, "Now scoot. I have cleaning to do. Lunch is at noon. You can bring Buster."

Buster was the only other child in Aunt Lil's neighborhood. Even though he was ten he was good company. His parents had a swimming pool that the boys weren't allowed in, but they could dangle their feet by the edge. Buster's mom bought them Coca-Cola and Buster had a dog, a chow named Buddy. One day David and Buster and Buddy were sitting by the shallow end of the pool; David watched the reflection of the clouds in the pool's surface. He followed the progress of one that looked like a giant cowboy astride a rearing horse as it travelled across the deep end of the water. Inside Buster's house his mother was doing the dishes from breakfast and singing along with Frank Sinatra. Buster was trying to teach Buddy how to pass gas on command. David turned to Buster and blurted out, "Do you ever feel like your life has a hole in its pocket?"

"Huh?"

"Like pieces of you are falling through as you walk." Buster looked blank. "Like coins or something." But of course Buster wouldn't understand, David thought; he was too young. "Let's go to the drugstore." Buster and Buddy could almost make him forget his mother's cooking, or her face across the table, or his father's smell.

His mother still faces him in the Plymouth with the engine running. He gathers all his parts again and stops crying. The line between her eyes is lengthening; she's upset, and he hates to make his mother upset.

"How was Aunt Lil's?" she repeats. "Was something wrong? Did something come up I should know about?"

"No, I—" he can't find the words for Lil and Vernon and himself and his mother. He tries to think of a joke, but Aunt Lil subscribes only to *Guideposts*, so he's out of new material. He feels queer and as quickly as the thought comes, he throws up the spoiled milk and Fig Newton on his mother's dress and across the green vinyl seat cover.

"Oh, dear God!" his mother cries, lifting her arms off her lap. "David!" She puts her hands on the steering wheel and looks helplessly around her.

For a moment she watches the traffic; David watches her. The laughter is slow to come, but it sparkles when it hits the surface, where David has been waiting.

Ken Hollings

I Am Singing

from *The Songs of Yma Sumac*

> "What monsters continue their lives in my depths?"
> – Jean Genet, *Our Lady of the Flowers*

I am Yma Sumac. I am singing.

A white Plymouth Fury bursts into flames at the American border, throwing out longs streaks of burning gasoline and fiery metal splinters. All across Madonna Negra I can hear mambo music in the hot night air. People are shouting, glasses are slammed down on bar counters and doors swing closed on tenement landings.

The wreckage of the car lies blazing at the end of the main drag, a few blocks down from the hotel where I live. Black smoke from burning pools of oil and melted rubber tyres billows out in dark sweltering waves. A group of small children in ragged clothes kneel together under a sodium street light beneath my window. They look deep into the fire and smile, their faces turned radiant and loveless in the heat.

As the sun went down this evening I met an old negress in the street. She walked up to me slowly, smoking a long cigar which she held between fingers that were worn and callused. Without looking at me, the old woman opened the greasy bag she had slung under her arm and pulled out a sheet of yellow paper which she pressed into my hand. I looked at what she gave me. It was a handbill printed in red ink, advertising a prayer meeting on the other side of town.

"The lesson for the day is written there," the old negress said, "that is, if you can read it. And if you can't, I'll tell you what it says, child. Follow the lines with your finger while I speak them out loud to you."

Then she made me point to each word as she slowly pronounced it:

"'The Spirit of the Life from God entered into them, and they stood upon their feet, and the Great Fear fell upon them, which saw them.'"

She looked hard at me.

"You know what that means, don't you? It means the year we're in is numbered 1949, girl, and the decade will soon be ended. All fear and strife goin' to end here, you know. This is the middle of the century, a thousand years will soon be passed, but I don't expect you to understand that. You too young, girl, and just like all the rest—negative, you know what I'm saying? Neg-a-tive."

The old negress didn't smile when she said that. She just nodded grimly, turned and walked away.

I said "thank you" as politely as I could, but she didn't even turn her head to look back.

Down in the street outside my window, the children put their arms around each other and huddle together. They still gaze into the fire that glows darkly at the bottom of the main drag. But their poor young faces have no life in them, no life at all.

The smallest child looks up at his sister.

"What we doin' here?" he asks.

"Watching that car burn."

"Why?"

" 'Cause we got to keep an eye on it."

"Why?"

"So we can find it again tomorrow, when the fire's out."

Flames dance and the black air ripples and billows around them. The whole of Madonna Negra is restless and on edge: a border town twitching in the heat, so close to America.

"Where did I come from?" the little boy suddenly asks.

His sister groans.

"Not that again."

"Please."

The other child, an ageless, sexless creature, leers down at the boy.

"You came from out of your mama's ass. I know, cause I was there. I saw it. She had you the same way animals have babies. I *saw* it."

"Shut up," the girl says. "Don't upset him again."

The boy wants to sneer and boast of how he has always known the truth about making babies; but he sees the look in his sister's eye and goes back to watching the burning car. The girl pulls her little brother closer to her. She tells him how he was planted in the ground like all the other children and how he grew there until the day came when their mother had a dream which showed her where to find him.

"And when mama woke up she seeks out the exact same spot and sees your face just breaking through the soil. Then all she had to do was dig you up and clean you off and take you home with her."

The little boy listens to his sister's voice with a rapt expression on his face. He has listened to the story a hundred times before, and will make his sister tell it to him again and again until he grows too old to hear it.

The wreckage of the burning car smolders in the hot gaudy night, and the music from across the street gets louder.

It always does when I sing.

A piano is playing by an open window above a crowded bar. The tune blends in with the sound of the flames. I can sing nearly every note that the piano can play: almost five of its octaves and beyond. The range of my voice is from darkness to darkness, from above to below. It is a great gift for which I must always give thanks.

I am the daughter of a high priest, one of the last true Incas, and my voice is unique.

When I sing everything comes crawling alive.

Embracing every note from the highest down to the lowest, my voice reaches deep into the ground where I can feel the desert bloom with life. Whole jungles of flowers are being born beneath the sand: thick green vines push upwards into the stifling air, their tendrils uncurling. The dark animals that live under the earth stretch themselves, their eyes gleaming and bright.

Lemurs turn their ageless dark faces towards me and stare out from their distant twilight world when they hear my voice. It spirals up high into the sky where the blue turns softly to black and I can see the curve of the world beneath me. Hummingbirds hover over the earth, their beaks pointing at the sunrise. They make the air vibrate around them; and the sun's first rays cast lines of shadow and light across their shimmering breasts.

In the darkness under the buildings I can feel insects moving through the dusty lifeless air, probing the black silence with their antennae. The spiders spin out webs where they hang motionless for hours, listening to my song and splitting open their skins to reveal shiny new bodies. Emerging into the night, the insects sprout wings and seek out the hearts of the flowering jungle vines that blindly feel their way out of the desert, towards the centre of this tiny border town.

And the lemurs throw back their long arms and call to one another with voices like tearing metal and flames.

The piano pounds out a dance rhythm. Its loud, sweating beat seethes around me: an open doorway from which dirty light and music stream out onto the dark streets of Madonna Negra, where an eternally injured night rolls about in its own blood.

A yanqui tourist in a white shirt gets rolled in an alleyway by two young Mexican youths in black leather jackets. He stumbles, savagely blinded by the red light. The darkness lies in the gutter with its face cut open and its pockets turned inside out. Children settle down to sleep in doorways, or in crowded rooms enveloped in the dry heat that rises from the desert. They dream of hungry animal spirits, come to carry them away. Cars are stolen and left as wrecks. Drunken soldiers topple over each other, their voices tumbling and sprawling:

"Devastating cunt around here."

"Carries a pipe wrench in her purse."

"Some fun tonight, right?"

"Heh heh."

"Haven't been in this fucking town since '42."

"Jesus, that's nearly eight fucking years ago."

"Don't fucking change much."

"Don't fucking change at all."

Madonna Negra never changes.

Not for any of us, soldiers, children, animals, however long we stay here. Somewhere the old negress is kneeling and praying in a storefront church. I can see the dishes of cornmeal and incense, the coloured powders, the bottles of cheap perfume and alcohol. In front of her, the walls are covered with an endless confusion of shelves packed with little statues of Mary, Jesus and Joseph standing beside plaster saints and the bloody pictures of martyrs, all of them draped in flowers, tinfoil stars, silver coins and pieces of turquoise. White candles flicker in every corner.

Deep in the night I dream that my voice has died in my throat, crushed there by an unseen hand.

I awake with a start.

In my sleep I had been beating my fists against the rough plaster wall above my bed.

It is early morning, and the air is still and cool.

The three children who had watched the fire last night have been joined in the street by a large group of boys and girls gathered around the burnt-out wreckage of the car. Some of them are already squatting down on the black charred surface of the road and have begun to trail their fingers through the ashes in search of spare change. All the children are silent. They work busily with their fingers, picking over the blackened remains, searching for coins, teazing out and rubbing down any piece of metal or melted plastic they might be able to sell or trade off later in the day. By sundown most of them will go back to begging on the streets.

An old drunk emerges from the shadowy entrance of an alleyway and wanders out into the sunlight. He shades his eyes to look more closely at the wrecked car.

"Finance companies," the drunk says. "How do you like those guys? Time was, when you got behind on your payments they just came and took your car away. But now, Jesus, they just don't know when to stop."

Then he wanders off, muttering words of disgust, and I try to clear the night from my mind in the bright early morning sunshine.

America seems so very far away today. It lies somewhere in the distance beyond the night clubs, bars and storefront churches, beyond the doorways and the empty hotel rooms. Far from the crowd of hungry children and the burnt-out wreckage of the white car.

I take a walk through town, along the main drag, away from the border; and Madonna Negra's walls close in around me. As I reach the edge of town, the brightness of the sun floods through my body. The light makes my head feel hollow. The desert lies ahead of me now.

The sky is motionless, and the clouds hang flat and distant along the horizon. I start to sing.

I can feel my voice rising from deep within me. The earth is moving beneath my feet, and the air trembles all around me. The song I sing grows in the darkening sky over the plains. I am still, and yet I can feel my body disappearing under the shadow of the earth.

I see the old negress walking slowly across the flat dry land. She looks down at the ground intently, holding her cigar clenched tight between dry lips. Her shadow stretches out before her, and white desert birds wheel and circle through the halo of light that surrounds her. She stops walking and kneels in front of the patch of dried clay which she has been searching for.

The old negress bends forward and starts tearing at the ground: she pulls back the hard crust of clay and scrapes away the earth. Slowly she pulls a baby out of the broken ground. Loose soil and pieces of dry mud flake off the newborn infant's skin, falling from its fat, slow-moving limbs. The baby works its body slowly into life.

A thin stream of wet sand dribbles from its mouth; and as the child starts to cry, the old woman enfolds it in her arms, hugging it to her breast.

I am Yma Sumac. I am singing.

My voice fills me with joy, and I fall to my knees to give thanks.

Stokes Howell

Just Drive

The fourth time my wife tried to kill herself I said "That's it. I'm leaving." I didn't say it out loud, no, I was too busy walking her around between her puking fits and trying to get some Pepto-Bismol down her to settle her stomach. It was only aspirin she had taken, unbuffered, and she'd thrown them up right away, but they had left a gassy burning feeling in her stomach that was the worst part of the whole thing.

"I'm sorry," she said. "I'm sorry." "I know you are," I said and kept on walking her around. But inside I was pissed off. She had called me over at Rudy's where I was playing poker and told me to come home because she had taken a bottle of pills and wanted to end it all, and I had to get up from the table without even cashing my chips and make some lame excuse to Rudy and the boys about the baby being sick and leave knowing they were back there talking about what a pussy-whipped son of a bitch I was, and maybe remembering the time I had told Lucy I was going to go fishing with them and us sitting at the filling station downtown filling up with gas and buying a couple of six-packs and she came driving by in her car and instead of waving to me she gave me the finger. It was embarrassing as hell, and Larry said, "Man, that's a bummer," and we didn't talk any more about it but it sure put a damper on that afternoon of fishing for me.

I wanted to ask her, "Didn't you think about the baby? Were you just going to kill yourself and leave it there alone until I got home?", but as soon as I thought it I answered it myself: "Of course she thought about the baby, that's why she took aspirin." She knew she wasn't going to croak. She was just expressing her frustration at being stuck married at sixteen in a ten by fifty foot trailer with a child she got from being knocked up by me who was older, nineteen, and should have known better, that's what her father said to me, that he thought I'd be more careful. And here I was working at the rake factory and hating it, and her not working at all except on her GED and staying home with the baby at her mother's in the daytime watching soap operas and watching her mother get sloshed on bourbon on the rocks at two in the afternoon because Lucy's brother had gotten killed in a car wreck, which I guess is as good a reason to get sloshed as any, I might do it myself if I lost a son in a car wreck.

And I wanted to say, "Why the hell didn't you tell me over the phone that you took aspirin?" Because the way she said it I thought she meant it was the sleeping pills, and even though the doctor had told me the time before that it was virtually impossible to kill yourself with librium I could imagine that with her it might be that one in a million shot and I had driven home like a maniac out Highway 72 four miles to the turnoff and nearly went into the ditch on the curve by the bridge. Now that would have been ironic, me clanging into that old iron bridge and flipping over the railing and drowning upside down in a drainage ditch full of pesticides and fertilizer run-off because I was hurrying home to keep my wife from killing herself for the fourth time.

But of course she wanted me to think it was the sleeping pills, that's why she hung up before I could question her. And she wanted me to rush out there like a bat out of hell to save her. And she might even have wanted me to drive over the rail of the bridge and land upside down in the ditch and drown, maybe she was that sick of me and of us. She had certainly acted like she wanted to kill me when she found out about me smooching on her friend Ruth that night on the trestle when I was supposed to be giving Ruth a driving lesson, the same night Lucy was in the hospital with stomach pains that she had assured her mother couldn't be from being pregnant and turned out to be just that. That whole deal was Rudy's fault because he was sweet on Lucy, and after the baby was born one of the times Lucy and I were split up Rudy thought he might get some off her and was sniffing around Lucy's mother's house all the time. He figured he might improve his chances if he told Lucy about me and Ruth, something I had been stupid enough to brag about to him when I was drunk and wanted to let him know that I could have had Ruth then if I had really wanted to, but all I did was feel her boobs a little and rub between her legs, and maybe it was guilt or the fact that her breath smelled like pickle brine that made me stop and say, "I'd better take you home now and call over to the hospital and see how Lucy is getting along." When I had to tell Lucy about it because Rudy was going to if I didn't she tried to hit me and I held her arms back until she got loose and grabbed her mother's sewing scissors and told me to get the hell out of the house and leave her alone. And I did leave her alone but only for a couple of days and we got back together for the thirtieth or fortieth time, back into the trailer with the baby. Her mother saw me uptown one day and said, "You're a son of a bitch," and I said, "I know it," and we stayed together then for a few more months.

But I don't really think she wanted me dead, or even herself dead, even with the fact that she was shooting up methedrine (she said) she was getting from a guy over at Garnersville. She wouldn't tell me who it was, but whenever she felt bad or if I wasn't around or was off playing cards I would come home and find her higher than a kite, but always after the baby was asleep. And even with all this turmoil only once did I see her do anything bad toward the baby, and that was when he was crawling around on the floor and bit her on the ankle and she kicked him with her other foot on the back. She said, "He bit me," and I told her, "He's just a baby. He doesn't know what he's doing," and the baby crying and crying and crying, and me thinking the worst things wondering what went on while I was at work, but I never saw another instance anything like that at all.

And I'm thinking, "I've got to get out of this thing or I'm going to die" while I'm walking her around, trying to think about where I can enough money to get the hell out and away to St. Louis or Kansas City or San Francisco, some place where they don't have rake factories or pre-fabricated home factories where I worked before and where Larry got a nail in his eye and where Rudy and I used to steal lumber and hide it in the grass behind the building to pick it up later so Rudy could

253

build the addition on his trailer that his wife wanted. And I'm wondering how the hell it happened that Rudy was trying to fuck my wife that time when I wasn't with her and he wasn't with his wife either, and yet here I am still playing cards at his house, and thinking that's just exactly what is wrong with this town, there is no other way to live here than the way that everyone is living and that's what makes it so crazy. And it's no wonder that the schoolteacher drank Drano and the farmer blew his brains out in the barn and the Sunday School teacher's husband pummelled the hell out of her and the kids until one day he walked in the house and she shot him right dead center in the heart with a shotgun and got off with probation because he deserved it.

And I'm wondering if it's always been this crazy and I think about the stories my grandfather told me about wife-swapping picnics out at Johnson's Gullies, not that he did it but his cousin Dan did and got Judge Malcolm's wife pregnant and had to pay him five thousand dollars and move to Texas, and it being so strange that Judge Malcolm's son also became a judge and became the judge that married Lucy and me in a civil ceremony at the courthouse, with me wondering the whole time if he knew we were related or did he think old Judge Malcolm was really his natural father. And I thought about Granddad having a stroke and then two more and getting so pathetic he just sat in his wheelchair looking out the window not saying a thing, but once turning to me and saying, "I just eat to stay alive," like he knew there wasn't any point to it and he would quit if he could and just be done with it. What a contrast it was with the days when he used to talk about the Girl's Drill Team over at the Junior College in Kilgore, the Rangerettes they were called, his eyes having a devilish glint in them as he told me over and over again how they all wore the same size bra, you had to fill a 'C' cup to be a Rangerette, and Grandmother seething in the kitchen because she was a Baptist the daughter of a minister and she didn't like hearing that kind of talk.

That's where we had gotten to, me and Lucy, from the spark of her bra size to just eating to stay alive, and I think she knew it and that's why she took the aspirin, and the librium the time before that, and the other tranquilizers the first two times, and she probably did wish she was dead but just couldn't make herself do it, I don't know why, because of me, or the baby, or her dead brother, or her sad mother, I really don't know what kept her going. But I walked her around and around and she was crying and hiccuping and apologizing and I was as tender as I could be with her while still feeling cold and detached inside and we lay down and talked and she cried some more and the baby woke up for a feeding and she gave him a bottle and the baby went back to sleep and we nestled in the bed and made love and made love again, and then the sun was starting to show red in the east and I was glad it was a Saturday so I wouldn't have to call in sick to that son of a bitch Howard at the rake factory, and I said, "One more week and I'm out of here." I said it to myself after she was already asleep, and it was the twentieth or thirtieth time I said it but that time by God it was the truth, I meant it, I was out of there, I was gone, done with all the crying and puking and card-playing, just get the hell out, I'd do it, come next Friday I'd pack a suitcase cash the paycheck and head west on the highway, to Denver, or Dallas, or Albuquerque, it didn't matter, just drive drive drive drive drive.

Kevin Jackson

Zembla

The first card said: "You saved my life". No name, no date, no return address, and the handwriting wasn't familiar. On the front was that terrible photograph from the First War of a skeleton in the uniform and steel helmet of the other side, lying back in a trench with a broken arm slung across the remains of its neck as if in grisly parody of a salute.

If I'd been less worn down by self-imposed overwork, or less bewildered by the final ruins of my marriage, I might have been able to see at once what it meant. Numbed as I was, though, I couldn't begin to guess who was playing the sick joke. No help from the postmark: illegible. The card rattled me, mildly, for about forty-eight hours, until I'd made good and sure that life was too busy again. But I kept it next to my wallet for a few days, and in the rare idle moments my work allowed me—I mean, that I allowed it to allow me—I'd take it out and try to see what associations I could trigger. Not many; none that made sense of the message.

The second card came a week later, and said: "You're responsible for it". That one spooked me a little more, especially when I'd looked more carefully at the picture on this one—a famous painting, by an old French artist, of a Roman general acting the Stoic on his deathbed. This time the postmark was legible. It was from a small town in the north I'd never visited, and knew almost nothing about. I pinned the two images up above my desk—the uniformed skeleton was heavily crumpled by now—and found myself staring at them and daydreaming even when my deadlines, real and artificial, were less than a couple of hours away.

The third card—a different postmark, of another unvisited, nondescript northern town—came a week later. No words this time, just two lines of numbers and letters written in the same loose, backward-sloping hand. It wasn't hard to make sense of the first line of numbers. Two figures, one figure, two figures: a date—the date of the summer solstice, just over six weeks away. The second line was harder to crack, though for some reason I couldn't puzzle out, it seemed to me that the pattern of letters and numbers was intended to be helpful rather than cryptic.

I copied them into a notebook and pinned the new picture up next to its forebears. This one was a painting of a cavalry charge, with horses galloping full pelt towards the viewer, their nostrils flared and ears flattened back in terror and excitment. It struck me that, set out from left to right in the reverse order of their arrival, the three cards in my miniature gallery now formed a kind of abstract narrative of a soldier's fate: the rush to battle; the lingering deathbed; the worm-raddled corpse. Hardly cheerful companions for my long working hours, though

I sensed that the reason they had begun to add new strata to my depression wasn't solely the result of their subject matter.

Throughout the evening after the third card came I was, as so often in those weeks, incapable of doing anything more purposeful than sprawling across my bed and idling in unfocussed gloom, trying to work up enough energy to go out to eat or drink, or simply to call one of the last few friends whose sympathies I hadn't completely exhausted over the past year or so.

I even thought about calling my wife, which shows how close I was to becoming divorced from common sense, too. It was while I was mentally turning over the details of our last major argument, honing and polishing the dazzling turns of sarcasm I wished I'd lashed her with at the time, that it struck me that I knew quite well what the letters and numbers meant; and, knowing as much, that I also had a fair idea who must have sent the cards. Far from disturbing me, the realization made me feel so smug at my own powers of deduction that I soon drifted into a dreamless sleep, and woke fully-clothed and chilled just before dawn.

After a shower and what passed for breakfast in my new single regime, I left my excuses for lateness on the answering machine at work and went to wait in the sunlight for the library to open. The old man in the reference section was surprised that anyone should want to consult a map of such an obscure place quite so urgently, but he was helpful anyway, and within minutes I knew that my guess had been right.

On the map I'd ordered was a group of five islands; the coordinates from my notebook met on the island that was next to the westernmost. More exactly, they met on a small symbol that I still knew how to read—a cabin, used from time to time by climbers and hikers with a yen for remote places and by others who had fetched up in the wilds for one reason for another. Me, for example, as a schoolboy a quarter of a century ago. It looked as if I had been invited to a reunion by my old classmate Lewis, about whose adult self I knew precisely nothing, unless you count a morbid taste in postcards and the puzzling conviction that I had somehow saved his life.

A little more than six weeks later I was back on the island. The time between my small revelation about Lewis and the flight north had passed almost happily. I'd applied for leave—they told me I was long overdue for a break, and seemed relieved that I was taking one—and spent most of my spare time preparing for the trip: booking tickets, chartering a small plane (the westernmost island has an air strip, then you have to take the ferry which runs every other day), buying strong boots and waterproofs and, though the pomposity of the gesture made me feel faintly embarrassed, a compass. The rest of the time I'd spent trying to fathom why Lewis had invited me to celebrate the solstice in the scene of our unremarkable teenage adventures.

Lewis and I had been sent to the island by our school and parents for five weeks during the summer vacation before our two senior years. The idea was that we, and the twenty or so other adolescent misfits, no-hopers or macho freaks who made up the so-called "expedition" would be straightened out or toughened up by a few weeks of wilderness training and constipation-inducing canned food.

Most of us, apart from the handful of gung-ho boys, went reluctantly, but it had turned out to be not nearly so bad as we'd all been threatened. Our adult team leaders had seemed more interested in playing card games for low stakes and drinking their way through endless cases of booze than in coaching us for survival, so between the bouts of rock-climbing and forced hikes there was plenty of time to lie around in the sun or under the stars and tell filthy stories, or to talk the interminable speculative gibberish that comes so readily to the lips of owlish sixteen-year-olds.

Lewis hadn't been much of a friend before the trip, and to be scrupulously honest he hadn't been much more of a friend either during it or in the last months at school. I remember being slightly wary of Lewis, and alarmed when told we had to share a tent together. Unlike most of us, he tended to keep more or less silent for hours at a time, and there was a nasty air of potential violence about him, which would become actual when he joined in otherwise casual ball games with frightening savagery. He was strongly built, too, and not very fond of soap and water. But you tend to stink less in the open air, and I began to notice that he was flatteringly patient when I chattered to him about anything that skimmed across the surface of my half-educated mind, from the names and myths of the constellations that we could see every night (with a clarity that even the most brutish of us found amazing), to the contents of the four gloomy philosophy paperbacks I'd brought along to add dignity to the adventure.

After we'd returned to school, Lewis and I remained on amiable terms, though we weren't exactly Achilles and Patroclus. (I was studying classics then; semi-scholarly allusions came easily to me. I was the one who had rechristened the island "Zembla", after coming across the name in an eighteenth-century poem, and was gratified at how well it caught on even among the most defiantly illiterate explorers. At least one of them thought it must be obscene, and therefore funny.) We may have met up once or twice after leaving school—me for university and studies that I've mostly forgotten, Lewis for a well-paid job with his father. As far as I could recall, we'd not had anything to do with each other since we were twenty or twenty-one.

Even so, and despite the cryptic nature of Lewis's three cards, it didn't strike me as altogether surprising that he should have wanted to get back in touch. We were both halfway between our youth and our senility. Plenty of people like to track down their old friends and enemies to see, ruefully or gloatingly or, who knows, perhaps even with a sense of relief, how all those other stories turned out. What did baffle me was the reference to having saved his life. If anything, it was I who had Lewis to thank for preserving my skin—a few months after we came back to the city from Zembla, he'd waded in and chased off a gang from the tougher school in our neighbourhood, who'd kicked and punched me to the ground. On the whole, however, I didn't think nearly so much about his motives as I might; it was so refreshing to have a sense of novelty, and of minor practical tasks to see right.

It was only after the ferry dropped me off at the one concrete dock on the western shoreline of Zembla that I began to have serious misgivings. Maybe Lewis was playing an unfathomable prank; maybe he didn't see me as his saviour at all, but bore a smouldering grudge. (Was that what "You're responsible for it" meant?)

Why had I been stupid enough to come back to a place where there were fewer than thirty inhabitants in a space of what must have been the best part of sixty square miles? It didn't help that a fine rain had begun to fall, and that, though there were many more hours of daylight at this latitude, the sky was inhospitably dark.

I was briefly tempted to pitch my new tent, curl up in my untried sleeping bag and wait out the two days till the next ferry. Instead, I told myself I was being a dithering coward and set off on the twelve mile hike to the old cabin, and the friend I'd barely thought about in two decades.

The rain had stopped by the time I reached the place, though I wished it hadn't: I wasn't at all fit then, and the uphill route had left me giddy with heat and thirst. Which at least solved the etiquette problem of how you greet an old pal who's summoned you to a meeting in the back of beyond after half a lifetime of silence.

"You need a drink?" Lewis asked.

"Please. Water."

He went ahead of me into the cabin, which looked in pretty good shape, probably better than it had been the last time we'd stayed here: hikers must be better housetrained than the selfish bunch of city brats we had been. Lewis poured me an enamel cup full of water, and gave me another cup full of stronger drink to chase it. I sank the first cup in one pull, asked for another, then a third, before sipping at the harsh, clear spirit. It tasted unpleasant and medical, as if laced with formaldehyde. I was still short of breath, and played my panting up a bit so that Lewis would have to speak first. Eventually:

"I wasn't sure you'd come." He looked at me with what seemed like disapproval. "You've filled out a bit. You used to be skinny."

This needled me. "Thanks. Nice to see you again, too."

He saw my annoyance, frowned, and made a dismissive gesture, waving his own mug of alcohol as though throwing it and my triviality out of the window.

"Do you want to twitter like an old lady or do you want to know why you're here?"

I shrugged my backpack off, sat down at the table and started to unlace my boots. Lewis stood and watched me. He had "filled out", too: never slender, he now looked like a full-grown bear, and not much of that body mass would be flab. He'd cropped his hair close to the scalp and was unshaven; it made him look tougher than ever, but also faintly pathetic, like a man who had to seem hard as armour plate if he were to survive. He was also wearing olive-green combat dress, without any obvious insignia.

I don't often suffer from nostalgia, but the sight of him brought back something I'd forgotten about his adolescent self—a sense of his being more isolated, more cut off from the rest of the herd than any gregarious animal should ever be. My annoyance dissolved, and I raised my cup to him.

"Sorry, Lewis. Auld lang syne?"

He nodded, and refilled our mugs from an outsize bottle.

"You first."

Meaning: tell me your story, and then I'll tell you mine. My story didn't take long. After school, college and the great loss of direction, after college the easy deadbeat jobs, the girlfriend or two, the slightly better job, the marriage, the slightly better better job, the house and cats, the non-arrival of children, the long slide into overwork, the silences and rages, the break-up and the numbness. A comfortable life; a life without fire. Lewis only interrupted once, to mumble something about the way I used to talk at sixteen, when my head was full of thrillingly pessimistic tracts. This needled me again, but I guessed that he wasn't deliberately being hostile. Disillusioned, perhaps.

Then came his story. It wasn't beyond all possibility, or even likelihood, but again and again I wondered: did this really happen? Is he fantasising? A compulsive liar? I chased mugs of water with sips of the formaldehyde-smelling spirit as he talked, not knowing whether I wanted to get drunk enough to relax or to keep my guard up in case he turned violent. Lewis told a tale of many jobs, many countries, and a fair amount of nastiness. After the collapse of his father's business, he'd gone abroad, managed to enlist in a foreign army that wasn't too fussy about passports, seen active service as a true soldier and as a mercenary. Left an invalid for a couple of years after his final war, he'd begun to support himself as a salesman, or maybe hustler would be more accurate, working his way around three continents, picking up the rudiments of several languages and staying only just shy of the law at times. It didn't sound raffish and romantic. It sounded squalid and hopeless.

At some point in his hustlings, Lewis had started to read again—specifically, to read some of the books he remembered me talking about when we were sixteen, and then to follow up the darker hints in those readings, and then to go on from those familiar gems of nihilism to less orthodox kinds of speculation. Some of the latter stuff I couldn't really follow, and I thought instead about some remarks he'd made before he digressed towards the major arcana.

From the way he spoke—and the idea held such ready pathos that I could feel tears begin to prick at my eyes—it was clear that the weeks we'd spent on Zembla as adolescents had meant far more to him than they had to me or any of the other boys. At least, he'd managed to persuade himself that this was the case. In his private mythology, this short, banal trip away from the city had offered him a glimpse of another life; and in his version of things, I, with my affected, half-baked teenage ramblings, had pointed him along the road to enlightenment.

Was that, then, what he'd meant by saving his life? Lewis was surprised at the question when I finally nerved myself to ask it. Of course not, he said: he meant the time when I had hauled him out of the mud-pool in which he had almost drowned, when we'd been far from all other help on a long-range hike. Surely it was as vivid to me as it was to him? It was not. In fact, I told Lewis, I couldn't remember any such event; and since my life, unlike his, had been undramatic to the point of torpor, I was sure that if it had happened it would have become one of my routines, trotted out whenever I wanted to impress a girl or a drinking partner with the nonchalant courage of my youth.

Lewis looked worried. Worse, he looked angry. "No, no, no, you're wrong."

He poured me another large drink, another for himself. We sat in silence for a long while, and I could see his jaw moving slightly as he held an unvoiced argument with himself. At a guess, he'd passed many evenings like this before, drinking and brooding on the patterns of his experience, on resentments and on what he took for higher wisdom. I was almost sober again, and alarmed. He looked at me for a while, then he pointed to the rough steps which went up to a sleeping platform.

"There's a mattress up there. You can lay your sleeping bag out."

I wasn't in the mood to sleep now, but the prospect of arguing with this troubled ex-mercenary who had once been a friend, of sorts, seemed less appealing than feigned rest, so I climbed the ladder, unrolled my sleeping bag and closed my eyes. And I must have slept, because when the shot woke me it was already light.

Lewis's body was lying supine next to the table. The upper half of his head had been blown away by the rifle which had fallen away from his mouth. I vomited at the sight, bringing up nothing but formaldehyde-spirit and bile, and ran from the cabin with sick and tears and mucus streaming from my face. It took nearly an hour for me to work up the courage to go back inside.

I draped an old blanket over what was left of Lewis' head so that I wouldn't have to look at it, and was detached enough to notice that the rifle with which he'd killed himself was a semi-antique, with a wooden stock and a big, clumsy bolt action. I also noticed that there was a cardboard folder propped up against the empty bottle on the table.

Inside was a rudimentary last will and testament in his distinctive slovenly writing, dated yesterday—solstice day—and a few other papers and souvenirs. Lewis had left me everything: the contents of his bank account (not a vast sum), the keys and deeds to a house over on the mainland and possibly—if I understood rightly the meaning of the intimate snapshot that was clipped to the deeds—some other parts of his life, too. There was no suicide note, no letters for his family, no apology or apologia.

He had left just one statement of his motives: another postcard, this one depicting, not a military spectacle, but an ancient Chinese philosopher. On the back he'd written a final message, the third line of his farewell triad: "And now it's yours."

Shelley Jackson

Sperm

Nobody can remember when the sperm became large enough to see, but we agree on this: once that point was reached, nothing could stop them from growing larger. Every generation topped the last: they went from guppy to goldfish, and before long they could frighten a Schnauzer, and not much later even Great Danes stepped elegantly aside. And while it seems like at buffalo-heft they've stopped growing, it's possible they're just gathering their resources for another leap. We are afraid that the sperm will grow big as rhinoceroses and hunt us down, but we are much more afraid that they will again grow tiny, that we will have to go back to the screens and meshes we remember from our grandmothers' doors. What if they grow so small filters will not stop them? How will we protect ourselves?

The sperm cabaret is coming to town, and Virginia and I are going to see them. Have you heard of them? The trained sperm are squeezed into specially-made costumes, and they dance and flop about, she says, very comically! Can you picture a sperm in a little hat held on with suction cups, an ingenious device explained in the programme? And a very large tie, and cravat? They even utter some sort of sound, which I cannot imagine would be very musical, but Virginia says that although guttural the cry of the spermatozoa is weirdly haunting, and the au courant are scrambling to acquire recordings.

The sperm conservation society is lobbying to reserve a portion of the sperm's natural habitat as a protected zone, off limits to sportswomen and the food industry. Unfortunately, parasite rights are not yet guaranteed under federal law, lament agitators. Opponents including logging concerns point out there is no shortage of sperm. Not yet, the lobbyists reply.

Surely we have all gone for a stroll in a wild territory which seemed sperm-free, and rounded a curve to see the sleek black ovoid crouched menacingly athwart the path. Though ordinarily timid, sperm have a bullish persistence when their tiny minds are fixed on one object. In some cases the old wives' trick will work: rap them sharply on the "nose" with whatever comes to hand. The sting will startle and confuse them, and they may simply amble away; if they do, count yourself lucky, and clear out. If not, prepare for a battle.

When you see a sperm whose coat looks "sueded" or has a greenish tint, it is an old boar and probably cunning. Play your cards well. If you make a kill, though, you are in for a treat. The meat of these dotards is gamy, and must be marinated for twenty-four hours at least before it is tender enough to chew (weight it with a stone or it will rise to the surface of your marinade—sperm do float!— and your hours of waiting will be for naught) but some gourmets consider their flavor more sophisticated than the popular meat of pup sperm, something like a fine aged cheese.

With a little ingenuity, their incredible propulsive power can be harnessed for your own enjoyment! No, this is not only a sport for professionals. Just make sure you have enough helpers on hand. Lure the sperm into a large net bag (used bags can be acquired cheap from many sporting goods stores). Cinch the bag tight around the sperm's tail. Secure your boat to the bag with a few sturdy ropes and launch it. Whee! Carry a stick: a poke at the right moment will help steer the beast. But not to worry: the sperm's own self-protective instincts will keep you clear of most obstacles.

The cloud-image of a sperm stretched out across the sky over Lisbon and again in Nubia has been taken for a sign by cultists who await the day they will be "exalted" into the creatures they worship, and allowed to join their packs. Adherents are falling to their stomachs in public places and undulating in imitation of the movements of their totem. Ironically, several spermists have fallen prey to members of the species who do not seem to recognize their claim to the title.

At times, for reasons we don't fully understand, the normally evasive spermatozoon will form a permanent bond with one woman. When the sperm is young, the woman may be inclined to subtly encourage this fidelity, perhaps without knowing she is doing so. As the sperm grows older and some awareness penetrates its tiny brain of the gulf that separates it from the beloved, the relationship turns treacherous. The sperm will stalk her with increasing cunning. In the movie theater where she sought refuge, she will spot the ominous dome across the aisle, dully reflecting the changing light. In the ladies' room she will see a glistening tail on the floor of the next stall. Outside the window of the restaurant where she is holding hands with her date something will rise and fall in the dark, blotting out the city lights below. Sperm can bounce several stories, and their elasticity also enables them to squeeze through improbably small spaces. The clever antics of a pup are not so cute when the sperm is fully grown. Indeed, the mature sperm are all the deadlier for their devotion, and more than one woman has been crushed to death by a creature she once jounced on her lap.

Seize a young sperm by the base of the tail. Be careful: they are extremely muscular and will attempt to free themselves. It takes a strong stomach not to be unnerved if the creature should twine its slippery tail around your wrist, but persevere; one solid whack on the edge of a table should stun the animal. Then you must core it to remove the brain. An apple corer will do if the sperm is small; for larger sperm a professional's tool is essential. Aim well; it is possible to miss the brain altogether, since it is very small. Jam the blade into the back of the sperm, near the tail. It is best to drive the corer deep into the sperm with one blow, penetrating the thick blubber, which otherwise will wobble and suck at the blade, spoiling your aim. Once the firmer meat is reached, it is a simple matter to drive the blade deeper, turning it the while. When the blade breaks through the opposite side, push the solid handle through, ejecting the pith. Examine the cylinder for the pale blue of the brain. All remnants of brain matter must be removed or the recipe will be ruined; the brain will regenerate and the cooked sperm will begin to twitch. If the sperm has been chopped or pureed this effect will be all the more disturbing. If swallowed induce vomiting.

My favorite recipe is this: lay the sperm directly on the burner. As the skin crackles and splits, releasing the liquors, turn the sperm. When it is entirely relaxed, remove and cool. Peel off the bitter skin with a fork, and discard. Under it you will find a layer of translucent fat. Cut this off, press it through clean muslin and reduce it to a gruel over a low flame. Run the skinned sperm under a broiler to brown, garnish with orange slices, and top with the reduced liquors.

Sperm-brain swallowing is considered dangerous by the medical establishment, but devotees disagree. What is known is that the sperm brain does not die all at once but fuses, temporarily, with the stomach lining, and marshals an unknown number of the host's cells to its service for as long as six hours, after which time the brain is digested and the host cells revert to their usual condition. Doctors claim the "high" users report is largely imaginary, but stories are consistent of a spreading "spermishness", a sense of haste and unstoppable purpose. The concomitant disregard for personal injury, property or propriety can lead swallowers to extravagant ventures, some criminal or self-destructive, some visionary. Great works of art have been inspired by sperm-brain swallowing; so have hideous crimes, including the infamous "Ballet of Decapitations."

Sperm are ancient creatures, single-minded as coelacanths. They are drawn to the sun, the moon, to dots including periods, stop signs and stars. They worship at nail-heads, door-knobs and tennis balls. More than one life has been saved by a penny tossed in the air.

We take our traditions directly from the Final One, transmitted through our founding member, who was taken by the One in the early days of our order, while we were still building the compound. If the Sperm choose at rare intervals to take one of us, we all sing praise-songs to the lucky one. We lodge our Sperm in stalls we have painted with polka dots, and curry them with soft brushes and chamois cloths. We show them the spigot so that they may approve it, then tamp the sharp end into their side with a small mallet, and hook on the bucket. The milk is thick and sweet. Fresh, it is an aphrodisiac. It is also good for the digestion and rubbed on the face, it clears the complexion. Reduced and dried in cakes it makes a nutritious trail bar and a good soap. We are working on a motor that will run on sperm milk. We do make good money from our products, but we channel it all back into the sacred community, to buy softer bedding for our sperm, to hire musicians to play the songs they love.

Once numerous, their herds raised a line of dust across the Great Plains, racing the locomotive. This opening sequence has become a cliché of film westerns: dust first, then a line of bobbing backs stretching across the screen. The nearby whistle of the train; some of the sperm cross the tracks, some turn, some scatter. Hoof-beats, drowned out by the shriek of the train whistle. Beside the tracks as wheels rattle by, a sperm slumps in the dirt, transfixed by an arrow. Its oily coat is covered with dust, dung and straw. It looks like a breaded drumstick.

I catch them in big bird snares—huge nets I string up across their trails—and sell them to a guy down in LA who gets them on TV, you know, the shows where they got to fight the sperm wrestlers in the ring. Everyone knows the shows are rigged anyway, they dope the sperm, so I don't know why they bother to get the dangerous ones, I guess they want them big, of course sometimes they guess wrong on the dosage or they get a real sly one or something and he lays her out just like that. Because they're not real wrestlers, they're just models, gals who couldn't make it on the runway or old ones on the way down. You know who's the real wrestler? Me!

It is hard to believe that the great marble fountains of Brussels, which depict young spermatozoa disporting themselves in the spray, were once considered masterpieces. Few any longer take the time to decipher the complex symbolism that informs these mammoth atrocities. One wonders how a pest as common as pigeons could ever have been elevated, even in metaphor, to the status of gods. From time to time citizen's groups petition for the demolition of the eyesore, but there is always some sentimentalist or self-appointed keeper of tradition who rallies the public around the monument, which does at least provide the children of Brussels a welcome place to play in hot weather.

You awake in the early morning. The sperm are running. Alleys echo with rhythmic beats as they jounce down the street. Car alarms whinny. Pedestrians and cops alike take cover. Electric sperm-prods are not deterrent enough when the pack runs together. It is an awe-inspiring sight, the bobbing wave cresting in the street, the graphite-silver gleam of countless matched backs. Daredevils race down the street ahead of them, press themselves overtaken into doorways, fall and are crushed.

The midwestern strain of the spermatozoa, who ravage wheat fields in bouncing armies, is lighter in color and has unusual markings which help to conceal it in tall grass, much like those of the African savanna. While all coastal sperm and most of those in moist climates drop their tiny young in water, these sperm have devised other means of providing their offspring the moist environment they need. In early summer, the adults congregate head to head in small circles of five to eight and begin to blow wetly through their snouts. They puff and bubble until they work up a sizable mound of viscous foam, then position themselves and insert the infant sperm deep within the trembling dome. The outside of the dome soon hardens to a glassy sheen under the sun and prevents further drying. The dim shadows of the young can be seen to pike and writhe from time to time, but the hug of the thick foam holds them safely in suspension. They grow all summer long undisturbed—their only real enemy, aside from the occasional vigilant farmer with a pickax, is a long-billed bird, similar in appearance to shore birds who catch their food in the deep mud, but unrelated, which drills through the dome and spears the baby sperm. However, since the bird rarely catches more than one sperm at a time through the small hole it has gone to such pains to open, it poses little threat to the sperm population as a whole. By fall the spermatozoa are large and restless, and their dark skins are clearly visible through the dome. Here we see nature's genius: the shells which withstood sun and wind so imperviously melts in minutes under the first warm rain. The sperm are released into the wet grass. They lie there, quivering with surprise, bathed by the moisture their young bodies still require. Then they take their first timorous bounce.

R. A. Kapler

King

This happened a few years ago, during a cold wet November that hit the Greater Northeast like a bad case of the flu. I was sitting in PJ's watching the Eagles hand another one to Dallas when in limps Kevin, this young guy from Kelso Street who worked for me once in a while. I'm a wedding photographer, and back then Kevin used to lug my equipment in exchange for a few bucks and the occasional camera lesson. I didn't actually need an assistant, and I hardly ever used his pictures, but Kevin made me look like I was connected and carried extra muscle, and working for me I think made Kevin feel like he had some kind of career path.

Kevin had just come from his main job selling pretzels to the red light traffic on Roosevelt Boulevard. He still had on his pretzelman apron, which he wore to—I don't know—make people think he had a hand in baking the pretzels. Kevin was either drunk or morose most of the time, but he was a homeboy, and I was in the habit of watching over him in an older brother kind of way. And if you want to know the truth, I got him the pretzelman job through my cousin Gerald, who was like second lieutenant to Jili Carbone, the pretzel don, or whatever they call him. The whole thing was arranged on the QT. Frankly, I hate doing anything for anybody.

That Sunday Kevin was looking especially morose, leaning against the bar, soaked to the bone in his goofy apron. Happy is not a prerequisite for male bonding with me, don't get me wrong, but I like happy, I'm comfortable with happy, at least once in a while, at least in theory. But all I could think to do to lighten things was to pop him on the arm and make like I was glad to see him. "Yo, Kevin! You just missed it. Barnett snags one on the Birds' 20, jukes like four tacklers, and goes 30 yards before he trips and DROPS THE LOAF. Drops it, man! Can you beat that?" But Kevin, he didn't even look at the screen. He just said "Yeah" and called Louis over for a draft.

"Okay," I said, "what's up?"

Kevin mumbled something about standing in the rain watching these dorks drive by in their nice cars with their nice girlfriends.

"Is that all? So why don't you just go find yourself a girlfriend?"

"I-I don't know."

I knew. Basically, Kevin is not built for romance. He has this immense grizzly bear body and this big hammy face under little crop of spiky black hair.

Now if that isn't enough for the ladies, he's also got a leg that's about three inches shorter than his other leg.

Kevin had a couple of operations, and all of his shoes, even his Chuck Taylors, are fitted with a thick rubber sole. But his knee still crooks in, which makes him limp, not a lot, mind you, but enough that you notice. That bum leg has always been the source of Kevin's moroseness or morosity or whatever you call it, but on that day I decided it was high time he got over this flaw of nature.

"Because you got the bad wheel? So what?"

Kevin flipped me the bird. "So screw you, Staz."

At that point I knew there was no other course but to bullshit, which I do with great ease as a result of all my years in the wedding photography business.

"Listen, Kevin. My Uncle Jack was totally bald all his life, not even an eyebrow. And he always had a woman hanging on him like a bracelet. Know why?"

"Why."

"Because he rolled with it. He acted like he had won the lottery. He joined this bald men's club and they took like trips to Vegas, and Telly Savalas would show up and do about 20 minutes on how great it was to be bald, how all the women beg to rub their bodies against bald heads. And they even had this contest to find the baldest guy in the club and Uncle Jack won hands down, and they gave him a trophy, which he kept on his windowsill, and after that he scored more than Herschel Walker and Dan Marino combined."

"So what's that got to do with me?"

"Well, you get a lemon, you make lemonade, right? When you get a bad wheel you roll with it. You say to a doll: 'This is a gift from God. This makes it easier for me to find someone who cares about what's inside a person.' So you fish for a little pity. Hey, if it gets you laid, so what."

As expected, Kevin flipped me another bird. But I knew that I had hit a tiny nerve.

The next weekend I had a wedding to shoot out in Bryn Mawr, a job I had snagged on a referral from another shooter who was already booked up and whose regular fallback was in Atlantic City. I asked Kevin if he wanted to assist. He said he'd have to think it over, like he was maybe expecting a call from Michael Jordan.

I said, "Sure fine, take all the time you need. But I suggest that while you're mulling it over you have your suit dry cleaned and be at my shop on Saturday at 1 p.m. sharp. We're going to be working for Main Line people and Main Line people expect promptness and a nice appearance."

Saturday afternoon, I was packing up the trunk when Kevin swung by in his Dodge Dart looking like a bouncer at a funeral parlor, but halfway decent, at least for Kevin.

St. Matthew's Catholic Church is one of your larger religious facilities and very deluxe, by which I mean doughed up beyond all reason. Basically, it's a matchbox cathedral. The nave is lined with granite columns, each about as thick as a redwood tree. The floor and altar are polished pink marble, so that from the pews you can see a reflection of the bronze crucifix suspended above. Four chandeliers, not quite as large as helicopters, hang from the ceiling. That Saturday, the soft light from those chandeliers made the stiffs in the pews look like they had spent a week in Miami Beach.

I set up a remote-controlled Pentax on a tripod near the foot of the aisle so that I could shoot the party as they marched outside without relying on Kevin, who was better company than he was technical support. Close to game time, I slipped back to the altar platform. Kevin was on his knees, reloading the Nikon.

"Jesus, can you beat this?" he whispered, looking around. "I've never seen anything like it."

"Jesus might tie it," I said. "But He couldn't beat it."

The wedding party began to take their places. The maid of honor and best man looked like products of the Greek system. Flanking them were three groomsmen in charcoal tuxes and three bridesmaids in gold satin, all very healthy specimens, arranged smallest to tallest. Old Father Reardon faced the crowd, and under those lights his pearl chasuble gleamed and his cheeks looked like they had just been waxed.

The groom was a plastic surgeon named Brian, who glided to the altar in tails and a cravat, waving to the crowd as if he had been on his way to the links and just stopped in to wish everyone well. At the altar, he leaned over and cracked wise to the best man as though it were someone else's wedding.

Brian then treated Father Reardon to a hearty handshake. The old priest smiled and nodded to the organist, and a moment later those familiar chords echoed through the church, and all eyes turned to the rear. I had met the bride, Theresa, in my shop, and I had snapped a few frames of her mother pinning on the veil, so I had already seen the stress lines around her eyes that weddings produce. But few brides in my experience compared with her now, this vision in antique silk floating up the aisle. Kevin looked at me and all he could do was nod. She was the real deal.

Father Reardon had nixed all flash during the actual ceremony, and treated us to a dirty look to drive his point home, but I wanted to be ready when the big kiss occurred because I didn't like to stage that if I could help it. I handed a detached flash to Kevin and told him to stand by for my signal.

The wedding commenced, and with my telephoto I watched the bridesmaids weeping in bridesmaid joy, all except the smallest maid, who kept turning around to check out the peanut gallery. She was about an inch shy of five feet, and for her size, she had a nice rack. Her hair was dark and sleek and she had a smile that could be used as evidence of criminal intent. She seemed to grow bored of the peanut gallery, and I caught her giving Kevin and me the once-over. Following my policy, I didn't pay her any mind, but I saw that Kevin was giving her the eye right back.

When the kiss finally came, I started shooting but quickly realized that Kevin still had his goggles glued to the little bridesmaid and the flash pointed at the floor. Thank God that Brian and Theresa liked to suck face because I practically had to kick Kevin in the balls to get him to hold up the flash. We got the shot after four or five wasted frames, but as we moved toward the rear of the church for the rice throw, I shook my head at him like he was the king of all losers.

Now the trick to wedding photography is the word "special" because if you ask women what kind of wedding they want, nine out of 10 will tell you they want it to be "special." Therefore, your job is to arrange a wedding party in the same old poses you've used a hundred times while occasionally tossing in the word "special."

That particular Saturday I took several standard group shots outside the church and then I said, "I was thinking of something special." I set up this gag shot in which the groom stands in the middle with the bride on one side and the bridesmaids on the other, and they grab his arms in a tug of war as if the bride is stealing this prize stud from all the really good women in the world and they can't bear to let him go.

Everybody thought it was a great idea, but as we were setting up someone said "Where's Mary Beth?"—the name of the little bridesmaid. At that point I realized that Kevin also was missing in action. Slightly panicked, I threw out a groomsmen dragnet, and a few minutes later Kevin and Mary Beth were found in the parking lot, sitting on the bumper of a van. When they finally strolled around the corner of the church, it struck me that something was a little off.

"Hey, buddy, have you met Mary Beth?" Kevin said, guiding her elbow with a couple of kielbasa fingers.

I held out a hand. I said I was glad to meet her.

"Staz. What's that short for?"

"Stassel," I said. "It's Latvian."

"That's really different. Kevin tells me you do excellent work. He says you're really quite an artist."

I laughed. "Kevin makes it easy to do good work."

Mary Beth laughed, too, and suddenly I saw those fierce brown eyes. "Good answer. So how long have you two been in business?"

"A-about a year," I said.

"It must be hard being partners with your best friend."

"Nah," I said. "We both know who's boss."

She laughed again. "Well, see you over there."

Mary Beth and the bridesmaids went to find their rides to the reception. I intended to have a word with Kevin about shirking his duty and lying, but I let it slide because it was starting to drizzle and we were already due at Malachi's on City Line.

"Hey, hey, Staz, how about this Mary Beth?" he said as I wheeled the car into traffic behind the wedding convoy.

"Rein it in, Romeo," I said. "These people are business and you're here to assist. So assist."

"Okay," he said, "But you only have yourself to blame."

"How's that?"

"I did what you told me to do. You know," and here he slapped his bad leg: "The gift from God."

We rode the rest of the way in silence, but suddenly it occurred to me that when Kevin and Mary Beth had rounded the corner of the church, he had almost lost his limp.

Malachi's was not the usual smoked glass and plaster catering joint I was used to working. It was kind of low-key Victorian, much swirling patterned wallpaper and eggshell linen, with a nearly all-male wait staff, which is like some throwback to the last century. They had a real stage on which a 14-piece orchestra sat. As I watched people taking their places at the tables, it occurred to me that if you collected all the baubles in that room and sold them for half price you might put a nice dent in the federal deficit.

Kevin's job was to shoot the guests, starting with the wedding party table and working all the tables down the line, while I followed the bride and groom around as they greeted the well-wishers, most of whom they would see maybe twice more in their lives. Kevin usually did a half-assed job of the guest shoot because so few of those pictures ever made the final cut. But on this evening he was full of energy, joshing with the old ladies and even moving glasses and centerpieces to get rid of loose ends in the frame. The limp was still there, but with him edging around all those tables, it was barely noticeable. He spent a lot of time taking snapshots of guests visiting the head table, and twice I glanced over to find him talking to Mary Beth, who looked to be about half his size and maybe 125 pounds lighter.

Then I lost sight of them altogether, and for the rest of the evening I was so busy with the newlyweds that I didn't have a chance to hunt them down. The later it got, the more I worried, and as the band struck up for the last time, I crossed the dance floor to a row of windows facing the parking lot. I was fumbling around in the half-darkness for the part in these heavy drapes when I felt a tap on my shoulder. I turned around and there was Kevin and Mary Beth, slow dancing.

"Hey, buddy," Kevin said. "How's it going?"

She was so small he had to stoop way down over her, and as they moved around in a little circle, she was smiling at her friends. I just nodded at them and threaded my way across the dance floor to pack up the equipment. Have this night, I thought, because tomorrow the coach turns back into a pumpkin.

The following Thursday, Kevin stopped by the shop. He was sporting this very cush wool coat that I had never seen before, and his hair was spiked and shiny like it was under the influence of a quarter-pound of Dep. With a big stupid smile plastered across his big face, he pulled me to the front window and pointed to a car parked at the curb, a snow white Mustang 5.0, and from inside the shop I could hear the bass line of some rap song blaring from the car's tape player. Turns out that Kevin had a real firecracker on his hands in this Mary Beth, who he said was a sophomore at Villanova and "way fun," a word that I had never heard in Kevin's vocabulary before.

With a little questioning, I learned that Kevin had drained his bank account to buy these threads and rent, yes rent, the car for $32.50 a day, and had spent something like two hundred to tie the feed bag on Mary Beth at LaLoof and ply her with five-dollar beers at Jambalaya, and he was ready to spend another century for a room at one of those cush hotels on Rittenhouse Square, as soon as the moment was right.

"…And that's where you come in, Staz."

"I paid you and I ain't got another dime for this Mary Beth."

"It ain't the scratch," he said. "I'm flush."

"And how long is that gonna last?"

"Long enough…if I'm lucky."

"So what is it? I'm busy here."

"Her parents. They invited me to dinner this Saturday. Mary Beth is having her friend Stacy over and she wants me to bring you."

"Why me? I'm kind of old for a college girl."

"It's not like a date. You're just coming along as my partner. At least they think you're my partner."

"Whoa, Nellie," I said. "That charade must end. Look: I'm not exactly shooting spreads for *National Geographic*, but I am in business, and I want to stay in business. I don't mix with the clientele, or anyone who even knows the clientele, until I have a check in my pocket. Furthermore, I didn't hire you to throw money away on some Main Line girl with a silver spoon up her ass."

Kevin laid a hand on me the size of a fielder's glove. "Don't talk about her like that, Staz. Please don't."

I yanked back my arm and peered into his eyes. "What's the matter with you, anyhow? Are you on something?"

"Staz, it's…I'm in love with her, man."

"Oh no, oh come on, Kevin. Please. You know that this thing is going nowhere."

"I know that and I don't care. It's always hard for someone like me, Staz. But when I walk into a room with Mary Beth I can feel the eyes. And I know that people are thinking, hey, this guy must have something going, something the world can't see. And at that moment, I'm royalty, man, I'm…."

Kevin's voice trailed off and then he cleared his throat and limped over to the door. I called after him. "So where do they live, anyway?"

We drove through a light rain into Center City and crossed the Schuylkill River. A half a dozen roses sat on the back seat. Kevin had slathered on so much cologne I had to keep opening the window to air out the car. Finally, about 20 minutes down West Chester Pike, we passed a sign that said "Newtown Square." It dawned on me that in all the years I had lived in Philly, a small lifetime, I had never once set foot in Newtown Square. It might as well have been France. According to Kevin's directions, the Kinnards lived on Derbyshire Road in the Deer Run development. We knew we had the right address because the sign on the iron gate at the end of the drive said "The Kinnards." That's one thing you can't take away from your better neighborhoods: good signage.

We rang the buzzer and a youngish couple came outside and introduced themselves as Chuck and Gail Kinnard.

"We better be on our best behavior," Chuck said, "with all this paparrazi lurking about."

Chuck laughed and held out his hand to shake, and when Kevin did the same, Chuck filled his palm with a cold bottle of beer. Then he turned and played the same trick on me.

"He's a joker, this one," Gail said.

Chuck pointed to his wedding ring. "I guess the joke's on you, hon," he said and laughed again. Chuck was a small, muscular guy, with hair like the business end of a broom. Gail was paper thin, and fair, and sported one of those bobbed cuts favored by a certain type of woman.

Kevin and I carried our beers into the foyer and Gail took our coats. "Oh look—flowers. How romantic." She called to Mary Beth and pointed us down the hall.

"Gotta run," Chuck said. "I'm assisting the chef."

Kevin looked surprised. "You got a chef?"

"Yes" Chuck said, mugging at Gail, "and she's quite a dish."

I just pulled Kevin's sleeve and started walking.

In a large room at the end of the hall, we found Mary Beth and Stacy on a sofa, both dressed in big sweaters over leggings, both sitting with their legs folded beneath them. They were watching a Snoop Doggy Dogg video on a television set so large it made the one in PJ's look like a box of corn flakes. The set cast the only light, but I could see at the other end of the room a row of floor-to-ceiling glass doors, which seemed to open onto some kind of patio and pool area. Mary Beth and Stacy were both drinking beer, and from the smell, they had been at it for a while.

Kevin mumbled something dumb and thrust the flowers into Mary Beth's face. She took them and giggled with her hand to her mouth while eyeing Stacy, who just smiled. "Thanks, Kev," she said. "You're a sweetheart." Like most bridesmaids, she looked better in street clothes.

Mary Beth excused herself to put the flowers in water. I said hello to Stacy and gave her a hand to shake. As she reached over, she held her head at an angle so that her straight blond hair hung down over an eye, baring one side of her neck. She was a squinter and had that milk-fed chunkiness women get when they're enjoying life a little too much.

Stacy shook hands with Kevin. "I've heard you two have been really painting the town, Kevin."

"That's the rumor," Kevin said, his eyes trained on the door so as not to miss a moment of Mary Beth.

She finally came back and we all sat down and made chit-chat for about half an hour. Stacy did most of the talking, something about how she and Mary Beth met on a ski trip and got drunk and how Mary Beth fell off the lift and broke her ankle. Then we all laughed, no one louder than Kevin, and Gail called us in to dinner. "Yeah, yeah," Mary Beth said, almost annoyed, and led us back down the hallway to the dining room.

The dinner was pretty artistic to look at, if that's more important to you than how it goes down. Gail served salmon that had been rolled with some kind of seaweed and cheese and baked in this sticky almond stuff and cut into slices. For a vegetable we had three spears of asparagus. Mary Beth and Stacy picked at their plates and but managed to wash down what little they ate with several glasses of white wine. Counting the beer bottles in the rec room, I figured they were into a six-pack each.

Chuck spoke a little about his office furniture business and then asked a bunch of questions about wedding photography. He wanted to know what to "be on the lookout for" so that he wouldn't get fleeced when it was Mary Beth's turn to utter the holy vows. He also asked a pretty intelligent question about using a light meter when the subject is backlit. I flipped a little switch inside my head and talked straight for 10 minutes.

"My dad is a real gearhead when it comes to photography," Mary Beth said. "He's got a ton of stuff."

"I plead no contest," Chuck said. There was a lull. "So Kevin, tell me how you two became partners." He took a long, hard look at Kevin and right away I knew he was out of his jokey mood.

Kevin's eyes left Mary Beth and fixed on his plate and his big face turned bright pink. "Not much to tell," he said. "We kinda threw in together."

"Where did you meet?"

"You know, the neighborhood."

It was unbearable. "I took on Kevin as an apprentice," I said. "It worked out so well we became partners."

"Kevin and Staz have their own photography studio in Northeast Philly," Mary Beth offered.

"You don't say," Chuck said. "I go in for the natural stuff myself. You know, Ansel Adams, the Yellowstone series. And Robert Frank, his American period in the '50s. Whose work do you admire, Kevin? I mean, besides your mentor's."

"Lot's of them," Kevin said. "I like anyone, as long as they've got the eye." He winked at Mary Beth.

Mary Beth smiled. Gail smiled. Chuck smiled. "Uh-huh. Anyone in particular?"

"No. I'm kinda into music videos, right now. At least, that's what I want to get into."

"Uh-huh. Interesting." Chuck sat back in his chair and laced his hands behind his head. "You know, Kev, I've been sitting here racking my brains trying to figure out where I've seen you before. The Northeast, did you say? I have several stores in the Greater Northeast, so I'm always cruising around that area. No offense, but you look like this guy who sells pretzels on Roosevelt Boulevard."

Kevin blinked a few times, and then Chuck looked at his daughter like he was trying to work out a problem in his mind. I used my knife and fork to cut a spear of asparagus into about 20 pieces.

Finally, Chuck excused himself and hoofed it upstairs. The girls and I carried fresh beers back to the rec room. Kevin stayed to help Gail clear the dishes. In the hall, Stacy peeled off to use the bathroom, leaving Mary Beth and me alone in front of the TV.

"It's a shame," she said.

"What is?"

"I wanted to turn you guys on to something, but it didn't come through."

"What was that?"

She looked toward the door and whispered. "A little toot."

"Oh."

"My regular guy has been in Aruba and this other guy, this new guy, is like studying for the bar right now. So he's not that reliable."

I looked at her.

"I mean, the situation is desperate," she said. "By the way, you don't know where I could get some, do you?"

I took a sip of my beer. "Get what?" I said.

"Coke, if it's available."

"How much do you want to spend?"

"I could go a couple hundred, I guess."

"A couple hundred. Sorry. I don't have access to that."

"What do you have access to? Pot?"

"I don't have access to any drugs."

"Oh," she said. "But then why did you ask me how much I wanted to spend?"

"I don't know," I said. "I guess I was just curious."

Kevin came in, and a moment later, Stacy. "So what's on the agenda?" Kevin said. "You guys up for some clubbing?"

Mary Beth and Stacy looked at each other. "To tell you the truth, I'm feeling a little wasted," Mary Beth said. "Can I give you a rain check?"

Kevin laughed. "Come on; the night is young."

"I have to get up and do some stuff for school tomorrow. I'm really not into going out right now."

The rain was coming down harder now. Kevin and I made a dash for the car. Inside, the smell of wet wool hung in the air. Kevin started the engine and slipped a tape into the deck. "Nice people, don't you think? I mean, they acted like they knew us for years."

"That's true," I said. "They acted like they knew us."

Kevin shifted gears, and we drove around the circular driveway. The front door opened and Mary Beth ran out into the rain and waved us down. "Look, I just wanted to thank you for coming out and especially for the flowers," she said to Kevin. "You really are a sweet person."

"Hey, my pleasure," Kevin said. "I'll call ya."

"Okay," Mary Beth said. "Seeya, Staz."

"Good-bye," I said.

We turned onto West Chester Pike toward the city. "So, what was the two of you talking about when I walked in?" Kevin said.

"Mary Beth wanted to know if I had any dope," I said. "I told her no. I'm wondering why she thought I was selling dope."

"I don't know. She asked me the same thing the other night. Hey, feel like heading over to PJ's?"

"Sure...but why would she ask me if I had any dope? Where would she get that idea?"

Kevin turned up the wipers a notch. "I told her to ask you."

"You told her that I knew where to get dope?"

"Well, she said..."

"Are you out of your mind? I'm a businessman, Kevin! You think I'm playing some kind of game?"

"I said you might know."

Kevin turned to look at me. "Drive," I said.

As we crossed into Philly, the flooding started getting worse. It was hard to avoid potholes. Finally we hit one so deep that we bottomed out and blew a tire. Kevin told me to wait in the car while he changed it so both of us wouldn't get wet.

He opened the trunk and came around my side. I saw him out there, this big dark hulk, and I felt the car rise as the jack expanded. His shoulders and head moved across the windshield, and I caught a glimpse of his face as he struggled with the lug nuts.

I rolled down the window. "Need some help?"

"Nah," he said. "I'm okay."

He worked at it for a few more minutes. And then he stood and seemed to throw something and I heard *whump* and then I heard it again. I rolled down the window and stuck my head out into the rain, and there was Kevin, slowly whipping the fender with the lug wrench, leaving dark welts as he worked his way around the hood.

He reached the front of the car, raised the wrench one last time, and flung it into the street. He placed his hands on the hood and looked at me through the windshield, his breath coming in short gusts. In the headlights of a passing truck his face sagged like creased wet dough. I closed my eyes, and all I could hear was the rain beating on the roof, making the sound of applause.

Gregory Maguire

The Hurricane Lamp

Maria Clothilde Swinbourne—née du Plessix, and the eminent du Plessix of Anjou, for those to whom the distinctions matter—survived the hurricane of 1847. If you could call it a hurricane. If you could call it surviving. If you could call her Maria Clothilde Swinbourne, which her good neighbors in New Devon, Massachusetts, rarely did, for they rarely called at all. And after the hurricane you could call her missing.

The house was largely intact, at least in a structural sense. The Federalist symmetries of window shape and flanking chimney stacks still expressed their latter-day Puritanical rectitude over the gouged beaches and altered dunescapes of Devon Bay. From the wharf, looking up, the Swinbourne home seemed like a fortress on a headland, a permanent feature of the benighted coastline. The merchants, the sailors, the gossiping goodwives of New Devon below had a hard time saying what had changed in the profile of the distinguished homestead. When they climbed the rutted road—they decided that the Christian requirement of comforting the bereaved gave license to their prying—they saw more particular damage that made them forget their questions about was different with the silhouette of the building.

Silver salvers lay dented across the lawn, like the shiny footprints of a sea demon. The crimson damask drapes fell with *orientalisme* through the broken sashes of tall windows. A weird accident of flung seaweed etched the outline of a wave on the pewter-gray front door. The wreckage inside was, perversely, more absolute. An apron of salty sand flooded outward from the wainscoting in every room, as if the rooms had been exuding beach from the base of their flocked-paper walls. The mirrors were crusted with dried salt. The Chippendale highboy, its legs swollen with damp, leaned at a perilous slant. The brass rods up the severely pitched Georgian staircase bled green stains of oxidation into the Turkish runner. The bedroom—the women made the men go first, then shoved them aside once *that* propriety had been observed—the bedroom was awash in ten thousand red petals of a plant too voluptuous ever to have rooted in the stony soil of New England. Though the furniture looked as if it had been left to age for decades, the petals neither browned nor curled nor lost their heady aroma.

When a decent interval had passed, the solicitors for the estate of the missing Maria Clothilde Swinbourne and the newly drowned Captain Caleb Excalibur Swinbourne, of the poor frigate *Jewel of the Bosphorus*, foundered off Cape Rosier in the State of Maine that very same night in the very same storm—well, the solicitors had to open the windows and launch the petals onto the wind by the blanketful. They scattered like airborn drops of blood, arabesquing seaward, eastward, a spume of rose sequins, a plumery of perfumed Valentines. A dozen hearty New England spinster poets of that town gave up the Congregationalist impulse and turned to penning lyrical odes at the sight. And this, be it known, was more than a year after the hurricane.

Maria Clothilde Swinbourne—*née* du Plessix, which grew to mean an increasing amount to her following the effective defection of her husband to his mistress the open sea—was born of grand and Catholic parents three decades before the hurricane. Lace could not drop from their windows more elegantly than prayers from the mouth of their privately engaged priest. It proved convenient to have a personal confessor with which to keep their spiritual accounts more or less up to date, because they met their deaths in a local *contretemps* that scholars and pundits saw as a last, little, domestic-scale aftershock of the Revolutionary fervor. The child Maria Clothilde, though dispossessed of her family's estate, was mercifully left to live, and she was spared the sight of her parents hanged by their own hose (several pairs twined together to provide both elasticity and durability). She was taken in by a cloistered order of religious women, the Little Sisters of the Wedding Feast of Cana, who managed kindly to obliterate in Maria Clothilde any shred of happy memory she held of her parents by explaining, with Gallic passion, how her parents deserved what they had received.

When Maria Clothilde had admitted for three years in a row that she could not locate in her soul a vocation to the novitiate of the order, she was sent to a hospital in Nantes to do good works until God had managed to change her mind for her. There, the young American man named Caleb Excalibur Swinbourne, recovering from a mysterious ailment of the parts unmentionable, was taking milk tea and bread on the terrace one morning when she was sweeping. It was summer and the air was warm. Because of a particularly holy quality to the day that called many of the nursing nuns into chapel to pray, Caleb Excalibur Swinbourne had managed to shuck off his striped silk dressing gown and to stretch out his unclad legs. Maria Clothilde imagined that the breeze she was stirring with her broom was the wind that played so disrespectfully with the gauzy cloth of his muslin shirt. Though this was a strictly religious environment, it must be remembered that this was also France, and Maria Clothilde was no stranger to the peculiarities of the male form. When she noticed he was looking at her with a low-lidded appreciation, she was not astounded to see the form that his interest took. Excalibur, she quickly guessed, had been a nickname applied by his romantic schoolboy friends.

Caleb and Maria Clothilde could exchange little more than their names. For one thing their hearts were beating too quickly, their nostrils dilating, their blood hammering in their temples. The sun steamed on the flagstones, the wind pushed the hem of the nighshirt higher. Caleb was at the height of boyish beauty, broad of clavicle but soft of cheek. His calves were turned and browned like the most succulent of French loaves. As the French say, he fit his skin very well indeed. For her part, Maria Clothilde knew that the effort of sweeping had rushed a *Chinoise* laquer red into her cheeks, and her hair fell about her face in a billow of wheat-colored tassels. His French was execrable. She forgave it. Her English was charmingly useless. They spoke with the tips of their fingers. They converted each other with their eyelashes. They translated the breeze on the terrace, the breeze through her spilling hair and against his lifting nightshirt, with a catalog of sighs.

"You are exquisite," he said. "I must have you. "

A fortnight later they were married. He took her to Paris and showed her the shrines of her religion. In the puzzle pieces of broken color spilling through the south windows of Notre Dame, they kissed with penitential fervor. They were taken for lusty Florentines by the clergy in attendance, and forgiven on the spot. Besides, she was a glass of fashion, a figurehead on a ship with *Japonoise* elegance, and he looked as if he might have modelled for the naked stone torsos in the Tuileries representing the spirits of *Fraternité, Egalité* and most especially *Liberté.* Those lucky clergy who had retained their heads in the revolutionary fervor of the previous decades were inclined to be lenient.

The happy couple sailed for Boston Harbor in the summer of '37. It was a long crossing that year. An aberration of heat in the Caribbean laid the doldrums all across the northern Atlantic. For more days than they expected, they foundered in listless air. The ship's crew repaired lines and invented shanties and eyed the comely young American and his ravishing bride with an interest more prurient than ocean voyages usually allowed the time to develop. But Caleb and Maria Clothilde had eyes for none but each other. The doldrums around them might have been the natural result of their youthful excitement, as if the world could not sufficiently power their passions and the ocean currents at the same time. The sails in the yardarm gave up their tympanic fluttering, allowing the crew access to the most private hesitations of breath, buckled moans of surprise, the whisper of bedlinen as it slipped against skin and bunched onto the floorboards. More eyes than those of husband and wife clenched shut to hide the tears within. The sea wept against the bow, and swept away.

In time the wind returned; the ancient skies released the New World to their view; Boston bristled with adolescent importance on the edge of its pretty harbor. Caleb Excalibur Swinbourne carried Maria Clothilde off the ship into a phaeton. A week of feting in the finest parlors on Beacon Hill, a week of peering over the screen of a painted silk fan at the assembled Brahmins, and Maria Clothilde was happy to repair to the home that Caleb had inherited from his parents, the white clabbarded manse on the best site overlooking New Devon.

She was eager to settle in. She ran from room to room, a child allowed to play for the first time in her life. She would decorate the formal old place as a child would adorn a dollhouse. Anything that suited her fancy was all right with Caleb. He drove her before him from room to room, pinching her soft *derrière*, plowing her neck with the adze of his tongue, coming behind to sink his sun-bronzed wrists deep into her *décolletage*, wrecking her careful *habiliments* into enticing *deshabille*. (He was finding he enjoyed her languge, too.) She was nearly naked by the time they reached the stairs to the Widow's Walk that crowned the house.

But when he told her what it was—what it meant—that architects fashioned the high porch to provide a perch from which lonely wives could look for the ships of their sea captain husbands—she would not mount the stairs. He fell against her, unable to control himself, though he had had a waking dream of taking her under the skies, in the daylight, perhaps standing upright, so all of proper New Devon could see and be sick with envy at her—at him, too, for he was a man proud of his bearing. At the foot of the stairs, in the squares of sunlight on wide-beamed oak planking, he drove into her again. The smell of the sea was in his ejaculation; the roar of the tides echoed in her private harbor.

They flourished for five years, childless but happy. Caleb invested his birthright in the whale fleets of New Bedford and Nantucket, and when money no longer served to entice him, he longed for the more robust life of the open sea. Maria Clothilde was loathe to let him go, as she had begun to see the hypocricy of life in American villages for what it was. She cast about for ways to amuse herself. Amusement, it seemed, was not a central concern of New Englanders.

She attended the Mission for Seamen on the Thursday evenings it was deemed proper to do so, and brought with her what she could remember of French pastry. (Whatever else they had given up, the nuns had not eschewed the best of their national cuisine.)Maria Clothilde at 25 could excite the most grizzled and sun-gnarled of ancient seamen with her flans and meringues and her coquettish glances. Her ministrations were considered by the good citizens of New Devon to be less charitable than seductive. Each Thursday evening they made sure that Maria Clothilde was bundled off home safely with a stout matron for a chaperone. The longer that Caleb Excalibur Swinbourne was away on his excursions, the more necessary it seemed to apply a kindly pressure on the exotic Frenchwoman, so to keep lofty the local standards of decency.

Not that the citizens of New Devon would have been opposed to accepting an invitation to tea or to sew quilts for the wretched poor of some pagan wasteland or other. Thanks to the local copper-tressed Annies and Bridgets who could be had to come in and sweep and clean and serve for the Swinbourne household, rumor had it that the manse was a veritable museum of Caleb Swinbourne's travels. The craze for porcelain from the East was at its height, and Caleb Swinbourne—ever a lover of beauty—collected from his ports of call the most exquisite renditions of native artisanry. When his own flagship, the *Jewel of the Bosphorus*, arrived in port, it took a fleet of carriages to transport netsuke from Japan, silks from China, alabaster caskets from Abyssinia, mahogany from the Philippines, brass from India, ivory from the coast of East Africa, carpets from Turkistan, lapis lazuli from Samarkand, pearls from Malay, abalone from the Dutch East Indies, hookahs from Morocco, oil lamps from Arabia, miniature paintings from Persia, marble karyatids from Athens, wrought-iron grillwork from Córdoba. With the treasures of the world with which to play, Maria

Clothilde fashioned a theatre of the splendid, a palace of unsurpassed exoticism. None in New Devon saw it except the maids hired to clean and polish.

She was not happy, a jewel among jewels.

Caleb was increasingly distant. His life had become a race to procure the rarest *objets d'art*. When he spent a week or two at home, he kissed her with spent interest. He was hardening, in all that sun; his body was still strong as an oak. When he stood from the copper tub, dripping, the great strength of his legs and the full globes of his buttocks and the articulated panels of his stomach muscles and the twin pillows of his breast—she could still weep for the shock of his beauty. But he seemed less able to weep for hers. The more she chained herself with the bangles and beads of the exotic world, the more eager he seemed to return to his journeys. The more naked she showed herself, the less he seemed to notice her. She began to cry, soundlessly at night when he was at home and more vigorously, angrily, when he was away. Even the cold comfort of the nuns who had raised her would be better than this neglect.

The day came that Maria descended to the village to select the best of the seasonal fruits for a delicious provincial *tartelette* with which to wish her distracted husband well on his next trip. She returned to a silent house. When he didn't answer her call, she dropped the basket of berries and pears and tore through the lavish rooms. His valise was gone. A note said *The Norway Basin, dearest.* He had left without even saying goodbye.

She dismissed the housemaids for the evening. She tore through the house like a whirlwind, like a maelstrom, like a maenad, like a harpy. She smashed Irish lead crystal goblets against Venetian mirrors. She threw a Dutch clock upon the strings of the Spanish pianoforte. With a Javanese kris she pitted an ikon of the Holy Family from the Ukraine. She shredded kimonos from Korea, boas from the Argentines, fur muffs from Hudson's Bay. From the parlor mantelpiece she grabbed a granite paperweight, carved exquisitely to be a model of the *Jewel of the Bosphorus*—and bashed a pair of Georgian candlesticks with it. She reached for anything else to bash—bashing helped—and found some Prussian beer steins and an Arabian gravy boat. The beer steins made satisfying shards of porcelain with which she might slit her wrists. The gravy boat was soft to the touch and would receive the impression of the paperweight like pastry dough...

But the gravy boat must have been sitting near the chimney flu; it was warm to the touch. She nearly dropped it, but instead clutched it nearer to her, between her breasts, and she began to weep, remembering the warmth of Caleb's touch, those ten summers back, when she had been a maiden imprisoned in a Catholic hospital.

The wind beyond the windows picked up, a summer storm, its raw colors of purple and charcoal building up in the underside of thunderheads off the Atlantic. Passion spent, she cradled the gravy boat—it was shaped like a slipper— and ran her fingers along the raised metalwork of its ornamentation.

Her head fell back. Outside the window, green leaves rose in a sudden updraft; laundry that the maids had left in the quiet sunshine now tore loose and rolled like ships' sails into the heavens. The vessel dropped from her grasp and a lid with a handle like a rosebud tumbled off. From the oval of the vessel's mouth issued a pungent, coffee-colored incense, a redolent steam of sandalwood, attar of roses, and sunny meadows of timothy and thyme. Maria Clothilde, who had imagined the visitations upon saints by a theatrical deity to be only a lively metaphor, came near to swooning. But the smelling salts were in a Magyar stoppered bottle several rooms away, and she couldn't move.

The inside storm roiled, fingering the edge of her summer frock like feathery breakers upon the strand. It rolled upon her, it fell upon her; her very lashes beaded up; her tongue caught the wetness of the succulent geyser. In the world beyond the room, a pine tree pitched over with the shriek of a toppling mast; the sky had gone black and gold, and the distant ocean sounded as if it were pounding in the parlor below. "Merciful heavens," said Maria Clothilde, "as if my husband's desertion is not enough!" She added, "*Zut alors*," in case the presence emanating from the oil lamp—as now she identified it—happened to be civilized.

Consolidating, weaving itself out of tendrils of smoke, the vapor became manifest. It was a Woman. It was a Djinna, or so Maria Clothilde guessed from the engravings she'd seen in clandestine books from the mysterious East. She had a ring in her nose and a jewel set in her forehead, and except for a couple of bangles around her ankles, she repined in the air just above Maria Clothilde's reclining body as naked as a Nubian slave.

"Who are you?" said Maria Clothilde.

"I am the Djinna of the Lamp," said the beautiful wraith.

"Why do you come to me?"

"Because you called me to come. "

"I certainly did not," said Maria Clothilde.

"You rubbed and you rubbed and I came," said the Djinna.

"You are hovering a tad too close, if you don't mind," said Maria Clothilde. "I am not as timid as one of these Yankee hatchet-faced harridans, but even so. I can't catch my breath. The barometer is falling. Look at the storm, come up out of nowhere. Pull back, if you please. "

"I am here to do your bidding," said the Djinna.

"I have no bidding," said Maria Clothilde, "I have nothing," and she began to sob.

"I am here to do your bidding," said the Djinna patiently.

"What can I ask for?" said Maria Clothilde. "I have no needs. I am the wealthiest woman on the Atlantic seaboard. But my husband cares not for me, and if you can tell me why, you would be doing a great deal!"

"Your husband turns to the boys of the high seas," said the Djinna. "I can tell you more if you care to know. "

"I can not imagine what you mean," said Maria Clothilde.

"When he was drunk on rum one evening in the Bosphorus," said the Djinna, "he called on me—by accident, as you have done—and, believing me to be a phantom of his loneliness and his inebriation, he requested of me an act of carnal pleasure. "

"And did you give it? Since you will do my bidding, I bid you tell me the truth," said Maria Clothilde.

281

"Myself, I did not," said the Djinna, "being of inclinations otherwise. He cursed me in his slurring way, and said he would have a cabin boy if he could have no other. Being bound to provide him with what I could, I conjured up for him a well-muscled young man dressed only in a blue turban and henna-etched hands and thighs, bound with tassels of velvet cord, arranged for your husband's pleasure on a bed of silk cushions. Thinking he imagined it in a delirium of demon drink, he fell to his supposed fantastic passion with the appetite he shows in possessing any beautiful thing. "

"You must not be telling the truth," cried Maria Clothilde. The winds under the eaves of the respectable house began to howl.

"He might have used me to better advantage," observed the Djinna drily. "When he awoke the next morning, his vision of masculine Arabian ecstacy was gone, and he assumed it to be an instructive dream. With the headache born of too much rum, he had forgotten my agency in the matter, and he shipped to you the humble lamp in which I make my home. He has followed his appetite ever since, in ports of call around the world. More strapping young sea cods than you could credit have learned to buck the rolling main in his Captain's berth. "

"I would that he drown in a flood of his own juice!" cried Maria Clothilde, eyes rolling back in her head.

"What else would you have me do?" murmured the Djinna, into the space between Maria Clothilde's trembling skin and her bewitched, rustling clothing.

"Give me what he could not," said Maria Clothilde, all but out of herself.

The Djinna obliged. She became incubus and succubus, unfurling a storm front of electrical firework along the coastline of Maria Clothilde's limbs. The Djinna lapped against the toes, which were suddenly bare of laced-up shoes and hose; the Djinna pummeled with lacy intention along the promontories of Maria Clothilde's milky calves and shins. She wreathed her knees with an aching, aromatic fog, and rolled in at the same time from several directions: Along the brow, cloaking Maria Clothilde's sight, filling her ears with the sound of surf, and beneath her, from shoulder blades down along the *Odalisque* arch of her spine. The Djinna made mouth simultaneously upon all Maria Clothilde's vulnerabilities; the Djinna churned creamy tidal pools in the hidden furnace of Maria Clothilde's sex, in the secret pocket beneath the tongue, in the places of the body that have no names. The Djinna took in and gave out in sighs as long as the unbroken land from the Bay of Fundy to Cape Horn. "Take me!" breathed Maria Clothilde, and the Djinna, who had been waiting since fundaments were laid for such an assignment, took her.

It was weeks before the good people of New Devon finally were able to pinpoint the change in the look of the august old Swinbourne manse on the bluff above the town. It wasn't just that the exotica was scattered all over the grounds; that the bedroom was filled with unidentifiable blossoms that would not decay; that the mystery of Maria Clothilde's disappearance occuring on the same night that her husband should have been swept overboard by a freak breaker almost made one believe in the power of the Evil One.

The Hurricane of 1847, it seemed, had torn against the coast of the mid-Atlantic states, the New England States, and the Canadian maritime provinces, wreaking record-setting tides and unparalleled havoc. It had also removed the Widow's Walk from the old Swinbourne house. Every lathe-turned bannister, every post, every rail. Nothing remained at the very top of the house but a battered, empty, tarnished old gravy boat with bas-relief carvings worked into its bowed sides.

James Mathews

Devil's Rain

Lance's pillow felt smooth and cold against his ear, like a train rail. Then the pillow began to quiver and he smelled tar and realized, almost reluctantly, that it was a train rail. He forced his eyes open and saw a single, lemon-colored lamp of a freight engine, floating in the desert night, getting closer. When he tried to move and couldn't, he decided that he must be bound, perhaps gagged as well, left for dead by the gang of Korean hooligans who had robbed him; but then he remembered that he was just very drunk and, with this information, coaxed himself onto his hands and knees, awkwardly rising, his palms grimed with the black sweat of the wooden ties. The train's light spiraled down on him and he leapt sideways, his tennis shoe snagging the rail. As he pitched forward down an embankment, he watched his fists scrape across what seemed a vast field of gravel shards, and all he could think was: *God, that must be painful.*

The train horn blared, and a great wind rushed into Lance's face. He lay still for a moment, then rolled over, safe and numb. He watched several boxcars teeter past him, finally trailing off into the stubbed silhouette of the Franklin mountains. El Paso, he thought. Thank Christ. If tonight had been six months ago, he would still be at Osan Air Base in South Korea, where only a military pilot, under orders, would ever land on purpose. The Air Force, God bless them, had kicked Lance out because of his drinking problem. In the two years since his return to his hometown, Lance had managed to claw his way back into the driver's seat of his life only to careen back off the cliff each time. Letting people down had become something of a profession for Lance. He worked hard at it. He deserved himself. About the only thing he did not deserve was his wife, Jean, who continued to put up with him. "As long as you stay faithful, I can deal with the rest," she had said. Sure, she could. Who couldn't?

Lance pushed himself to his feet again, somehow, and made his way back over warm tracks and down the embankment. He spotted a comfortable glow off in the desert brush and staggered in that direction. He fell twice over prickly bushes, collecting more injuries, although he was no closer to feeling any pain.

He finally stumbled into a clearing, drawn by the glow, which turned out to be a heap of melted tires, crackling in an orange blush. The fire had once been the nucleus of the party. He remembered getting there and slamming some of the jungle juice his buddy Mike had concocted and kept iced and private in the trunk of his Monte Carlo. There was also a keg, which now sat abandoned on the other side of the fire. Lance stopped short of the fire and stood there, his cut, bleeding hands wedged into the pockets of his jeans, weaving as if on the deck of a ship. He was too close to the embers and he was sweating, but he couldn't bring himself to back away.

A few shadows moved around him, like conspirators, but nothing interesting enough to make him want to focus. Then one of the shadows—a plump one—waved to him, and evolved into a pale woman in a cowboy hat and jeans. She strode up and stopped beside him, so close that the brim of her hat nearly touched his nose. She was grinning as if she expected him to be happy to see her.

"Hey, stranger," she said. "I thought you were coming right back. That must've been a helluva whizz."

Lance tugged on his memory and managed to recall her vaguely. She was the friend of one of Mike's friends. She had been drinking only Diet Pepsi because she claimed to be on medication, even though she was giddy enough to pass for drunk. The two had partied for a while, and though he sensed her interest in him, Lance forced himself not to be interested back. All this took place before things got blurry, and now he wondered if he had chucked his reservations and they had screwed or were going to screw, but he couldn't remember. Then he thought about Jean and decided that no matter how angry and drunk he was, he would never cheat on his wife. That was the line. Cross that one and Jean would be as far from forgiveness as he was from sobriety. He could see himself coming close, like any man, but never going through with it.

"So did you get lost or what?" the woman said, and punched his arm lightly, like an old chum.

His tongue felt so dry, Lance wasn't sure he could say anything that would make sense. He finally managed to utter, "Mike?"

The woman tipped the hat back on her head as if astonished. "Mindy," she said. "Boy, you really are blitzed."

"Mike is my friend," Lance said. "Did he leave?"

The woman named Mindy shrugged. "There were lots of guys here. I'll bet more than half were named Mike. What's all that black stuff on your face? Don't tell me you tried to hitch a ride on that train."

Lance turned and stumbled away from her, irritated and sure that she was making fun of him. There was a body wrapped like a scarf around the keg barrel. Lance snatched a cup off the ground and began pumping the keg, which bobbed doggedly in the ice water, refusing to cooperate. His mouth tasted like he had been eating rubber tubing.

"You sure that's what you need, airman?" Mindy said. She had followed him around the fire and that's when he became worried again about what he had told her and what had happened during the blackout.

Her mouth strayed open somewhat and he could see her fillings winking in the emberlight. "Did we..." He started, then hesitated, unable to think of an easy way to word his question. He finally said, with a sudden confidence, "Do I love you?"

She gave a little laugh. "Not really. You need a lift somewhere?"

He pressed the tap and cottony foam snorted into his cup. He looked hopelessly around at the scattered desert. To his left, a web of city lights swarmed up the base of the Franklins where the freight had gone. Something howled in the darkness. It sounded drugged and human.

Lance turned back to Mindy and said, "Home."

"*Di di ma*!" Mindy said. "That's Vietnamese for 'hop along.'" She about-faced on her bootheels and strode off into the dark.

Lance followed her to an adjoining clearing where at least thirty cars had been parked earlier but where there were now just a handful. She climbed into a white, utility van with two ladders strapped to the top. There was something written on the side of the van that he couldn't make out. Something about gutters.

"Where to?" she asked him when he hauled himself into the passenger seat. She had taken off her hat and he saw that her hair was blond, cropped short and boyish.

"Ysleta," Lance said. "Homewardbound Trailer Parks."

"God, they really call it that?"

"It wasn't my idea."

She goosed the engine and pulled out, the desert sand rasping the underside of the van. Lance pitched raggedly from side to side as they bounced along the uneven dirt road. A scaly tumbleweed rolled into their path and the van promptly ran over it, chewing it up. The dashboard was cluttered with wads of fast food wrappers and 7-Eleven coffee cups. The seats smelled like gas and snuff.

Lance tried to get a grip on how wasted he was. The fear of almost being killed had begun to wear off, leaving an earnest drunk in its wake. He wondered if he could face Jean in this condition. Oh sure, she'd welcome him. Like a bad case of the crabs, she'd welcome him.

"Ysleta, you say?" Mindy said.

"Right. All the way up Alameda til it quits."

She pulled right out onto Route 10, and Lance sighed gratefully as the ride smoothed out. He put his hands, like things to keep hidden, between his thighs, and turned the wedding band on his finger. The ring cut into his wounds and stung him through the drunk so he stopped.

"You don't have to go home, you know," Mindy said. "If you just need a place to crash for the night—"

"No," Lance said. "I have to go home."

"What I mean is, if your wife is going to go rabid on you, then maybe you should wait until you're sober to face her." She acknowledged his blank expression with another short laugh and said, "I take it you don't remember telling me about your wife?"

"What did I tell you?"

Mindy took in a long breath. "That she wishes you stayed in the Air Force, that she hates all your old friends and thinks you spend too much time pretending you're back in high school, and that if you went out tonight, she'd go back to her parents in Sweetwater, blah, blah, blah."

"Jesus," Lance said.

"Personally, I think a person should never let go of the past. Even though I'm twenty-two—and don't say anything because I know I look older—I still like to act like a little kid sometimes. Don't get me wrong, I'm all for marriage, but it has to be open or what's the point, you know what I mean?"

"Do you have anything to drink?"

She gestured vaguely toward the glovebox.

Lance fumbled for the button and the glovebox popped open suddenly, spilling stained napkins, a road map, and a couple of paperbacks onto his feet. The flat, pint bottle of whiskey with a strange brand name lay underneath the mess. He pulled it out and took a meaningful swig. It tasted cheap and very eager to please.

Mindy whistled. "Boy, you sure can drink," she said.

"Thank you."

"What school did you go to?"

"You mean I didn't tell you that already?"

She laughed again. "When you weren't talking about your wife, you were trying to get me into the bushes with you. Mister, you had about ten hands tonight and they were all looking to score."

Lance groaned and sucked again at the bottle. He could feel the whiskey's heat working through him, numbing the areas in his body that were trying to sober up. The approaching street lights blurred again. The dark buildings and storefronts began to resemble faces of people he'd known and disappointed. People who would like to see him dead.

"Listen, don't worry," she said and patted him on the knee. "You were a little sloppy, but you were nice. Not like some guys I know. The rough stuff is interesting sometimes, but it gets old. You probably saw a lot of that over in Korea, eh? I hear they treat their women like bugs. Besides, what happens in the desert stays in the desert. Your wife'll never drag it out of me."

"I'm not worried about that—" Lance sat up, blinking. "Shit, that was Alameda."

"What?"

"You just passed Alameda."

"Did I?" She looked into the rearview mirror and shook her head. "I swear, if I keep talking like this, we'll end up in Chihuahua."

"Don't you think you should turn around."

"I'll just take Dyer. A little out of the way, but I don't mind. It'll give you a chance to sleep off some of your buzz."

He laid back, and immediately felt as if he were falling. His chest fluttered and the whiskey settled warmly in his stomach, recharging the beer and jungle juice already there. Before he faded completely, Lance mumbled, "I don't think Dyer hits Alameda..."

"You sleep now, kitten," he heard her say. "We'll get you homeward."

Lance awoke, shirtless and dazed, in a strange bed, the faint sound of Robert Plant crooning "I should've quit you, babe" beside him. The first thing he saw was a gold lion stitched into the center of a dirt-brown flag. It was tacked to the ceiling beside a light fixture that was cluttered with dead insects. He lifted his head, toward the music, and saw a digital clock-radio that read 11:06 a.m. Around this lay an open disk of Skoal, a Bic lighter, and several paperback books stacked a foot high. Actually, they were Fodor travel books. Japan, China, India, Thailand. He remembered the one he'd gotten with his PCS orders after basic training. It had been glossy, packed with picturesque scenes, telling him what a wonderful time he would have at Osan. The book turned out to be as useless as the standard send-off everyone received with such a shit assignment. "Osan's what you make of it," they said. From the moment Lance stepped off the plane, the only thing he wanted to make out of Osan was a drunken blur. He had left Jean behind in El Paso shortly after they were married because the Air Force didn't allow dependents to travel to Korea. Do your time in Osan, and a choice assignment would surely follow. That was the promise they made to Lance and that was the promise he made to Jean. But Lance couldn't manage to do his time.

Gripping the side of the mattress, he sat up. His head took its time following the rest of his body. He rubbed his eyes and they immediately began to burn, so badly that he let out a reedy, child-like cry.

A door opened and he heard a woman's voice say, "Oh don't do that. Don't rub your eyes whatever you do."

"I already did. Christ! What the hell is on my hands?"

"Iodine. Your fingers and palms were really messed up. You must have fallen pretty bad."

Lance groped the air. "Get me some water, for Christ's sake!"

He felt a pair of soft arms encircle him, leading him from the bed into a bathroom. He washed his eyes and sucked greedily at the water, which took on the taste of iodine and old blood. When he finished, he remained slumped over the sink, panting. An orange prescription bottle stood alone beside the faucet. The label read: *Stelazine: Mindy Carlson. Take three times daily. Do not mix with alcohol.* There was also an address on the label which told him he was a good forty-five minute drive from home.

The vagueness of the night before returned, and a sense of being shaken and carried, of being reassured and pampered, seemed familiar, patches in the black. It occurred to him that he should probably be more concerned than he was. He would have been, he was sure, if his mind wasn't so clogged and slow.

He heard Mindy's voice again, asking him if he was alright. Instead of answering her, he clawed open the toilet seat and began to piss. The door shut behind him.

When he emerged, he made his way out of the bedroom and down a narrow hallway. He didn't realize he was shoeless until he stubbed his little toe on the door jamb, which sent him hopping stupidly down the hall.

There, holding one foot, he found himself in a living room furnished with several blood-red pillows that looked like giant kidneys. The walls were covered with more strange multi-colored flags, nothing he recognized except for a yin-yang placard on the back of the front door. In one corner, a black and white t.v. with rabbit ears sat on a folding metal chair.

No matter how hard he tried, he couldn't drum up any alarm so he just settled on being confused. There was a lot of light in the room, a lot of color, and he assumed this made being worried that much harder.

He followed the scent and cackle of frying butter into a kitchenette. There was a folding table beneath a window with three metal chairs that matched the one in the living room. Mindy stood over the stove, mixing a glass of egg yolks, wearing nothing but an over-sized, olive-green T-shirt. Her bare feet and legs were pale and powdery.

She smiled at him and said, "Ohio!"

"Where are my shoes?" Lance said.

"I took them off."

"I figured that out. I'm asking you where they are."

"Don't worry. I didn't bring you here for your shoes."

"My feet are cold."

"You want some slippers?"

"I want my shoes."

Mindy regarded him sternly and he saw that she was much prettier than he had given her credit for. She was overweight, it was true, and her cheeks were round and fleshy, but she had huge, graying eyes that looked stricken enough to be exciting. He couldn't quite place her age although she was definitely more thirty than twenty. "Did you know," she told him, "that when Hawaiian natives walk barefoot, it's called 'holahola,' but when they *run* barefoot, they only call it 'hola.'"

"I'm not Hawaiian."

"I know that. Are you always this crabby in the morning? Sit. I've got just the thing here."

He limped over to the kitchen table, feeling suddenly drained of confidence. He sat facing an open box of Dunkin' Donuts that looked suspiciously inviting. The surface of the table was grainy with sugar or salt.

Mindy padded over to him, plucking something out of a piece of tin foil. "Here, chew on this."

"What is it?"

"Sinsemilla bud. I soaked it in cinnamon oil. Go on."

Lance examined the spindly weed for a moment and then began to gnaw on it. When he asked her to explain why he was there, Mindy went through the story rapidly, without pause. She told him how she had driven all the way to the trailer park, although she had had to ask for directions, and that when she got there, she tried to wake him up but couldn't, so they went clear across town to where they were now. If she'd known which trailer was his, she insisted, she would have braved a knock on the door and made up some story for his wife. But Lance just wasn't giving up that information. "I guess I could have dumped you at the entrance, but who knows what would've happened to you. Don't bother to thank me, I'm just that kind of person."

"What did the place look like?" Lance said. "Describe it to me."

"You don't believe me, do you? You think I just kidnapped you because I've got nothing better to do?"

Lance sensed irritation in her voice, and this made him feel like believing her. "Forget it," he said. He stared down at his wasted knuckles, the barked skin pink with iodine. His fingers looked swollen and foreign, as if they belonged to someone else and he was using them on loan. "By the way, thanks. For the hands."

Mindy poured the mixed eggs into the saucepan. It hissed like steam escaping from a ruptured pipe. "Glad to do it. You were D.O.A. last night, no question."

He looked out the window into an alley to find they were in a ground level apartment. It seemed important, even logical, to form some kind of image of what the exterior looked like. Then he noticed a wallphone half obscured by the curtain and he snatched it up decisively. He dialed the number to the K-Mart where his wife worked. The woman who answered told him Jean had called in sick.

He tried the trailer next and a man with a mouthful of food answered. Lance didn't say anything at first, until he could match a face to the voice. It was Jean's brother, Ed, who had visited them from Sweetwater on two occasions, both of which had ended with Lance lending him money. When Lance asked him what he was doing there, Ed mumbled, "Jean said she needed my truck. I drove it down."

"From Sweetwater?"

"She said it was an emergency. Said she'd pay for the gas."

"Where is she?"

Ed coughed. Lance sensed he was having trouble finding words to explain, but then realized the man was just swallowing whatever he had in his mouth. "I'm not one to judge, Lance," he said finally. "In fact, I've always thought you were a decent guy, even though I can't say I really know you."

"Let me talk to her, Ed."

"You can't right this second. She's real busy."

"Doing what exactly?"

"Putting things in my truck. She said if you call that I should hang up. If you noticed, I haven't hung up. The reason is that I think you're getting the chewed up end of this deal, Lance. She thinks you're messing around, but I told her, 'How would you feel, Jeanie, if you run off and left and it turns out he just got drunk, fell into a lake somewhere, and drowned?' and do you know what she said to that? Do you know?"

"What," Lance said.

"She says, 'There ain't enough rain for a lake in this hellhole.' That's what she said. I don't claim her."

"Do me a favor, Ed."

"Name it, brother."

"Don't let her leave. I'm on my way there now."

Ed's hesitation came back like static. "I don't know about that, cowboy. Ol' Jeanie's not looking to be stopped. She tore up all your pictures and said she was going to get the wedding ring back if she had to gnaw off your finger."

"Can you try? Please? I'll give you a few bucks for the effort."

"I suppose I can tell her my truck won't start. Or that I can't find my keys."

"Whatever it takes. I'm on my way."

He heard the trailer door slap shut in the background and Jean's voice say, "Is that him?" Then a scuffle and Ed shouting, "Christ, don't yank on it, Jeanie, you're gonna—"

The line snapped dead.

Lance sat looking at the phone, confused again. He had never spent the night away from Jean since returning from South Korea. His drinking was supposed to stop once they'd married and bought the trailer. Everything would be tight and happy. But here he was, stoking a hangover in a strange place with a strange woman.

It amazed him how unconcerned he felt. He was sure that once home, facing Jean, he could turn her and make her believe his promises. She was the only thing holding him to earth, the only thing keeping him from getting what he wanted, which were things that were harmful to him anyway.

With this in mind, Lance became enormously aware of exactly where he was, and even though he knew nothing had happened with Mindy, a spidery fear crept through him.

He stood up. "Listen, I hate to run…"

"You can't leave."

"Why the hell not?"

"Because my mom took the van to work. She'll be back for lunch though. I'll run you home then."

He dropped back down into the chair. "Perfect." It came to him then why he lacked real concern. The fear had nothing to do with Jean leaving him. Somehow, he'd already faced that down. The fear came with the idea of returning and finding her still there. He'd never have the strength to lie and beg forgiveness.

"No more than an hour, I promise," Mindy was saying. She winked at him. "It'll give us time to get to know each other." She jiggled a shaker of pepper over the pan. "Tell me about South Korea," she said.

"It's next door to Japan. Have these donuts been here long?" Lance had gotten the sudden idea that something doughy would settle his stomach. But all the donuts were fossilized. One had had a single bite taken out of it.

"You didn't like the idea of coming back to El Paso, did you?" Mindy said.

"I loved the idea."

"I can't imagine why anyone would give up the chance to see Asia."

"It was easy."

"I tried to join the service once. They wouldn't let me in because I was too high strung." She looked over at him and waited for him to say something. When he didn't, she said, "You don't feel like talking, do you?"

"I feel like going home," he said.

"We can talk about you later. Go ahead ask me something, anything. You ask, I'll talk."

Lance ran his hand through his hair, not caring that it hurt to do so. He looked at a set of free weights in the corner, next to a pair of hiking boots. "You live here with your mother I take it," he said.

"Pretty much."

"Does she pump iron in her hiking boots?"

Mindy gestured at him with the greasy spatula. "You know, you've got a great face for a beard. Have you ever thought about growing a beard?"

"I've thought about it," Lance said. "So who else lives here?"

"Just me, my mom, and my husband. When he isn't out chasing the clap in Juarez."

Lance shook his head. "Does he own a gun, this husband of yours?"

"Oh don't worry. Like I told you, we've got an open marriage."

"I'm not worried. Why do you keep telling me not to worry? We haven't done anything."

She shook her head dismissively, and scored the eggs hard with the edge of the spatula. "Ask me something else, go ahead."

"What's with the flags?"

"Decoration," she said. "The one on the ceiling over the bed is my favorite. Brown with the gold lion. You probably saw it when you woke up. Now which country do you think it represents?"

Lance shrugged indifferently.

"Sri Lanka. Beautiful, isn't it? It's one of the most beautiful in the world. Our flag's okay too, don't get me wrong, but it could be better. They've got this ritual over there called the Perahera. Guess what it's for, go ahead."

"You've got me."

"Buddha's tooth. No kidding, they worship his tooth."

"So let me guess," Lance said, "you're going to visit all these places as soon as you get the money. That's why you keep those travel books."

"Totally wrong. First of all, I'll never get the money. Secondly, I hate to travel. I don't even like to go to Mexico and it's right down the street. I like to read about stuff like that so I don't have to travel anywhere. Understand?"

"Sure."

"You don't understand," she said. "Because you're a searcher, I can tell. I've seen everything in my life clearly and know exactly what's going to happen to me. You're lucky. You have no idea what's waiting for you."

"If you say so."

"I know so. What else? Ask me, go on."

He was tired of the game even though the sound of Mindy's voice made him feel better. He attributed this to the bud he had chewed up, the grit of which he could still feel in his teeth. But the first thing he thought to ask interested him, so he said, "What's Stelazine?"

She paused, lifting the pan off the flame. She looked down at what she'd created as if her part was done, and the eggs were now expected to leap out of the pan. Then, with a strange gentleness, she let the eggs slide onto a paper plate. "It's my medication. For a problem I have."

"What problem is that?"

She shook her head, but nodded quickly as if she had decided she shouldn't tell him, then changed her mind. "I'm hyper and it makes me not hyper. It's a side of me that doesn't go well with people. In some parts of India, when villagers work in the fields, they wear masks on the backs of their heads so tigers won't sneak up and attack them from behind. Isn't that wild?"

"Yes," Lance said. "It is."

She set the plate of eggs in front of him. She folded one leg beneath her and sat, stretching the T-shirt over her bare knee. He could tell Mindy was comfortable where she was, although he couldn't imagine her being uncomfortable anywhere. He wondered what she would be like more hyper than she already was and, for some reason, this excited him.

Despite his protests, she insisted he eat. She even gave him the first forkful and, to his surprise, his stomach did not rebel. He began to eat more and the more he ate, the more delicious the eggs tasted. Mindy watched him, her interlocked fingers forming a hammock for her chin. She laughed at his hunger with youthful awe, and Lance found that he had come to know her small laugh and that it was nice to hear.

"The milk is the key," Mindy said. "Don't forget that."

"Never."

While he ate, she talked to him about her father, a G.I. from Ft. Bliss who her mother had picked up at the enlisted club and one-nighted in the middle of the base polo field. Her mother kept tabs on him until he was shipped off to Okinawa and no, that wasn't the reason why she was interested in Asia. In fact, knowing her mother, it was probably a made-up story to get Mindy to quit asking about him.

Lance chewed, listened, and occasionally glanced at his watch. When Mindy finally paused, he said, "Maybe you'll catch up with him one day."

"Who? My father? Don't be an idiot."

Lance stopped chewing. She was frowning at him and this made her look ugly. He was about to apologize but before he could, Mindy leaned across the table and kissed him. When he kissed her back, she pressed herself against him, pinning him down into the chair. She pulled off her T-shirt and speared her tongue deep into his mouth, as if pursuing the flavor of what she had fed him. He felt her yielding skin and breasts against his neck. He wanted nothing more than to do many things with her, for her, to her. But then he opened his eyes and pushed her away.

"I can't," he said. "I'm married."

"I am too."

"I know, but mine isn't open." And as dumb as he knew it would sound, he said, "I love my wife."

Mindy stood up and took a step back. She wasn't as heavy as he'd thought, just generous everywhere. Her breasts were good-sized, white with sharp red nipples. Her blond pubic hair looked silver against her paleness. "It's not because you're married," she said, again with her ugly frown. "It's because you're too used to boring things. You don't know how fragile that is."

"You're right," he said, although he didn't really understand what he was agreeing with. "You're absolutely right."

She padded out of the kitchen and into the back room. Several minutes later, he heard the front door open and close. Lance got up and went into the bedroom, looking for his shoes. He found them under the bed, beside a lavender shoebox. He stared warily at the shoebox while he pulled on his sneakers as if it might attack him.

He listened to the quiet in the apartment, then drew the box toward him, flipping open the top. Inside, he found three or four stacks of letters, bound tightly by rubberbands. He unwound one of the bundles and flipped through them. Most were addressed to Mindy Carlson from a Sgt. Joseph Carlson, with return addresses from places like Okinawa, Japan. Koonson AB, Republic of South Korea. Clark Air Field, Philippines. But none of them had ever been mailed from these far off places. None bore stamps of any kind. They were simply addressed envelopes that had been carefully slit open at one end, somewhat worn as if handled often, their letters removed and returned regularly. The other letters were from Mindy to Sgt. Joseph Carlson. The handwriting on both sets was identical.

Lance felt a chill cut through him, and he shoved the box back under the bed. Something fluttered above him. He turned expecting to see Mindy standing over him, demanding to know what right he had to look so deeply inside her. Inside anyone. But it was only the brown flag above, bowing lightly to a breeze through the open window. The slow rippling movement made the gold lion on the banner appear to be running.

Sri Lanka, Lance remembered. Where they worship Buddha's tooth.

Lance was standing in the living room when Mindy returned. She wore exactly what she had worn the night before, jeans and a western style shirt, the only difference being that the shirt was untucked. She told him that she had managed to borrow her landlord's car, and Lance got the impression that this would cost her something.

When he got a good look at the complex from outside, it made him feel sad and disappointed. The apartments, strewn together like a motor-inn, were constructed of yellowing factory brick that matched the parched courtyard grass. Every screen on every window was torn or missing. A forbidding rock wall encircled the complex. Graffiti slithered over everything, starkly absurd under the heat and brightness of the sun. Lance wanted to feel sorry for the place, but couldn't get past being disappointed.

The two climbed into the landlord's car, an old, simple-minded Buick which drove with a chopping motion like a plane through turbulence. It was just after they'd turned east onto Dyer from Mesa that Lance felt over his finger to turn his wedding band, and realized what had made his fingers look so foreign to him. He turned and faced Mindy, feeling a mixture of stupidity and anger, and said slowly: "I had a ring on my finger. Where is it?"

Mindy rolled her eyes and slapped her forehead with her palm. "Oh shit, I took it off. To clean your cuts."

"Turn around."

"I can bring it to you later if you want. I don't mind."

"Wrong. Turn the fucking car around. Now!"

Mindy cut across two lanes into a Whataburger parking lot, sped recklessly past the drive-thru window, and back out onto the road. She was reacting to Lance's anger with something like aggressive embarrassment.

"Do you think I'd steal from you?" she said.

"I didn't say that. I just want my ring."

"Because if I wanted to steal it, I wouldn't have told you I had it."

"I understand that." But he hadn't understood. His only thought was that he had been conned. And even though he knew he only had a few bucks in his wallet, he resolved to check that as soon as possible.

As if he had spoken his thoughts aloud, Mindy said, "Why don't you check your wallet, if you think I'm a thief."

"I don't need to do that. I don't think you're a thief."

"Maybe you should," Mindy said. "You wouldn't be the first."

The white van with the ladders was parked in front of the courtyard wall. The side was painted with the words, Red Devil: Shingle and Rain Gutter Repair. Beneath this was a cartoon of a little devil holding a pitchfork, giving the thumbs up. The speech bubble beside it read, To Hell with leaky roofs!

Mindy got out of the car, then leaned back in the window. "I don't suppose you want to meet my mother and husband."

Lance answered her by looking at his watch.

After she left him, he sat there sweating, and wondered if Jean could forgive him for losing the ring. He figured she probably could. She had only blown up the day before because she was worried about him. At least, that was the theory. He thought about what she would say when she saw him and how he would answer her. Maybe he wouldn't answer. Maybe he'd just not say a thing, let her think the worst. A scary image intruded, demanding to know what the big hurry to get back was anyway. Jean would be long gone. She was a tough woman, much tougher than Lance. She never made threats lightly. For a second, he had a sense of relief, of being free, without pressure, but immediately felt guilty, immensely dumb.

A Mexican boy in a black t-shirt soared by on a skateboard, its wheels clicking time on the sidewalk cracks. Moments later, a mob of his friends—or enemies—scampered after him.

Lance looked at his watch again, then got out of the car.

A short, moon-faced woman answered when he knocked on Mindy's door. She had just eaten a stale donut from the kitchen table. He could tell by the gummy, white powder in the corners of her mouth. She wore a gray uniform, so tight around her waist that her pants pockets stuck out like ears. Her name— "Paula"—was stitched into the chest pocket. She was an older, heavier version of Mindy, but her fat appeared much more unhealthy.

Mindy's husband, a man as young as Lance, sat on one of the pillows with his back against the wall, staring at the television. He was very tan and had a pug nose. His shirt said, "Gilbert." He wore the same uniform that the woman wore, but his was open to the stomach revealing a hairless, muscular chest. He held a pocket knife in this lap, opening the blade halfway and letting it snap back repeatedly.

"So you're the latest stray, huh?" Paula said to Lance when he stepped inside. "At least you ain't another foreigner. Not a bad-looking fella, is he, Gil?"

"A real cutie," Gil said, without looking at Lance. "Looks like he's still in high school."

"Don't give Gil a second thought," she said to Lance. "He never spent a day in high school in the first damn place so how would he know?"

"Where's Mindy?" Lance asked, although he felt strangely certain he would never see her again.

"Blowing her bladder, I suppose. Have a seat. Make yourself at home."

Gil said, "Hell, feel free to change the channel on the goddamn t.v. while you're at it."

"Oh, shut up," Paula said to Gil, and shuffled off into the kitchen, a ring of keys bouncing on her hip.

Lance didn't sit down. He looked toward the hallway, wishing he could walk into the bedroom, but didn't want to come between Gil and the t.v. He wondered if he could take the man if it came to that, but decided he probably couldn't. He had never been much of a fighter.

"What do you do for a living, brother?" Gil said. "Besides drink and pass out."

"Construction," Lance said, thinking this was a safe answer.

"Construction," Gil said. "Like we ain't got enough of it." He looked up at Lance for the first time, and he let the knife blade spring open and lock. He pointed with the weapon and said to Lance, "You were one sorry sack of lizard shit last night, brother. But if I was you, I'd think twice about gettin' mushy with old Mindy. In fact, I'd pretend I never saw this place. I should know, I've been married to her for six year." He opened his hand and showed five fingers to emphasize this fact.

"Thanks," Lance said.

"Don't you want to know why?"

"Listen, I'm married—"

"Because she's craz-ee," Gil said through a huge grin. He waved the knife point in a circle around his ear. "Her belt don't go through all the loops, you get me?"

Paula came back in, carrying two toasted sandwiches, one in each hand. "Don't listen to another word from this one," she told Lance. "There ain't nothing wrong with Mindy that the right man won't cure. She sure ain't getting it here."

"I'm married," Lance repeated.

The woman handed Gil a sandwich and then sat down onto a pillow, rolling backward and forward, trying to form a comfortable valley. "Channel four, Gil!" she snapped, and licked a sliver of mustard from her thumbnail.

"Say, brother, how about switching the channel for an old man," Gil said. He impaled the sandwich with the knife, holding it in front of his face like a flattened candied apple he'd found on the roadside, then began to nibble on the crust.

Lance turned the channel on the t.v., to a soap opera, which cut to a commercial almost instantly. Both Gil and Paula expressed dismay and looked at Lance as if it was his fault.

"You see that?" Gil said to Paula. "He changed that channel like a goddamn dog. Boy, I kind of like you. We oughta keep you around permanent."

Lance stared back hard. He really needed to say something then. Not saying anything was bound to make things worse, but he didn't want to get Paula involved. Besides, he sensed the guy would calm down as soon as the show came back on.

"Awww," Gil said. "Did I hurt your feelings? Paul, you think I hurt his feelings?"

Paula looked up at Lance as if she had only just noticed him and found his presence insulting. "Fuck him," she said disgustedly.

Gil grinned at Lance. "That's right, fuck you."

Lance looked from one to the other. Their eyes were exactly the same, narrow and scary. He felt sorry that Mindy belonged to them.

Mindy came out of the hallway. She appeared harried, her eyes bloodshot, as though she had been scrubbing them with soap. "Where the hell is it?" she said to the room.

"What's the matter, hon?" Gil said. "Did dreamboat here lose his virginity?"

Mindy strode across the room and fell to one knee beside her husband. She clasped the top of his greasy hair, jerking his head backward against the wall. "I know you got it, Gil," she yelled in his face. "Give it up or I swear I won't be responsible!"

Lance couldn't believe it. He had taken a step forward, not really sure what he would do. Gil sat with the food idle in his open mouth, his hand clutching the knife-sandwich at his side.

Mindy gave his head another violent tug and Gil winced. "Christ," he said, digging into his pocket. "Take it. What the hell do I care about some fairy ring?"

When Mindy released him, Gil turned immediately to Paula. The droopy bulge of his eyes was more evident in shock. Lance realized that Gil might be mildly retarded. Gil said, "Did you see that, Paul? You see what she just done?"

Paula laughed at him with a seal-like bark, her mouth packed with bread. She glanced from her daughter to Lance to her son-in-law. "I sure as hell did," she shouted merrily. "God bless you two! You're a hatful! Are they a hatful or what?"

Mindy waited until they passed the Whataburger on Dyer, where she had turned around earlier, before she handed Lance his ring back. "I wouldn't put it on just yet."

Lance said, "Why not?"

"Because the worst cut is over that knuckle. You're sure to open it up again."

He inspected the knuckle of his ring finger. It was beginning to scab, bordered by traces of the iodine. He pressed the ring into his jeans pocket with his thumb. "I appreciate what you did for my hands," he told her.

"You said that already."

"Look, I'm sorry if it sounded like I was accusing you—"

"Don't talk," Mindy said. "Don't say anything."

They passed the University of Texas on the left, where Lance had taken a class, met Jean and quit. Its gray dormitories and buildings looked like a prison and always did. To Lance's surprise, Mindy veered right off Dyer onto Alameda. He had his arm out the window and the sun felt hot against his skin. The wind breathing on his face was dry and tasteless.

"Do you want to know about Korea?" Lance said to her.

Mindy remained silent, unhearing, so Lance began to tell her about a country he knew little about. It was a rare day that he ventured off Osan Air Base, but he recounted the time he had once taken leave to Sindok, on the Yellow Sea. He told Mindy what he remembered from the trip and even added things, like the great stone levees which were actually in Del Rio, on the Rio Grande, not in Korea. He had never been to Seoul either but his roommate had, so he told Mindy what he remembered from his roommate's description. There was Seoul's South Gate which he described as majestic and simple, something that had taken his breath

297

away. He told her about the famous Buddhist shrine in Hajodae (although he did not pronounce it correctly), and was amazed when the words, the picture of it, came clearly to him. He said, "Graceful. That's all I can say. It was like a place you go in a wild dream. When you stare at the shrine, it stares back like you're appreciated. It makes you feel like the world couldn't breathe without you."

Still looking straight ahead, Mindy asked him quietly to tell her about the people, and though the Koreans Lance came in contact with held only contempt for Americans, he told her that they were a kind people, a forward people who had seen the ugliness and sickness of war and never talked of it, never complained. Nearly everything he said was made up, but this didn't seem to matter to Mindy, so it didn't matter to him. For all he knew, what he said was exactly how it was.

When he finished, tiny stars of rain began to speckle the windshield, gleaming in the sunlight. Mindy turned on the wipers and smeared them across the dry glass. "Devil's rain," she said.

"What?"

"That's what it's called when it rains with the sun shining. It never rains hard though. Just sprinkles. I guess the devil figures that's all it takes."

"Where?" Lance said. "Where do they say that?"

But Mindy didn't answer him. They were only a couple of miles now from the trailer park, from knowing whether Jean was gone from his life. Up ahead, a train crossing gate had closed on the road, its warning lights pulsing aggressively. Mindy eased the Buick behind a line of cars. Lance could see the slow engine churning around a bend in the tracks, and he thought briefly about his close encounter the night before.

The rain stopped.

He sighed and cursed under his breath, a little louder than he should have. He didn't know why, at this point, he would suddenly feel anxious to get home to what could be an empty trailer. "Looks like a long one," Lance said, even though he could not really tell if this was true.

Mindy jerked the wheel hard and gunned the engine, swerving around the last car and into the left hand lane.

"What are you doing?" Lance said to her, although he knew exactly what she was doing. "Mindy, it's too close."

But she stepped deeper into the pedal and swung the Buick sharply around the lead car, a Ford Bronco. The Bronco sounded its horn and so did the train as Mindy straightened out, aiming the Buick's front end toward the narrow gap between the gates.

Lance gripped the dashboard. "Don't do it!" he yelled.

"Don't be afraid," Mindy said.

"Mindy, stop! Jesus!"

She jammed on the brakes with both feet. The Buick skidded just past the arm of the gate and a mere foot or two from the tracks. The train horn blared again as the engine roared past them, nearly on top of them.

Lance's heart beat frantically, punching up at his throat. He watched boxcars career past, their couplers clanking, the horn still blaring, although fading now.

"We could've made that easy," Mindy said, barely audible over the roar.

Lance didn't say anything. He didn't want to look at her.

"I guess you're stuck with me," she said. "Unless this train derails and kills us."

Lance watched the boxcars, rolling out from around the bend, following one another without objection. And there he envisioned with obscene clarity Ed returning things from his truck back to the trailer while Lance stepped out and away from the Buick. Behind Ed, Jean would be standing in the trailer doorway, a damp Kleenex balled tight in her fist. Proudly braced in the doorframe, having changed her mind against her better judgment, her wet eyes would zero in on the strange woman in the car. Ed would offer Lance a predictable shrug and half-grin.

Then Jean would look down to confront Lance as he approached her cautiously across their small yard. Her look would ask him where he had been and who is that woman and what had he done?

Then, in a suddenly frightened and bitter voice, she would speak, demanding, *Do you love her? Do you?*

Jeff Minerd

The Humpty Dumpty Game

To Roland, it was no surprise that Laura should get into the biggest trouble yet, that her principal should call him at work, while Ellen was at a travel agents' convention in Miami. He believed that life eventually punished you for all your wrongdoings (this was one of the purposes of children) and that someone-up-there had been watching and waiting for a good time. As he said, "Yes, I'll be there. Four o'clock," and hung up the phone, he didn't know what, exactly, he would be punished for, but said to himself *here we go.*

Principal Mary Brady was a sixty-ish woman who had tried to dye her whispy hair back to its original red, and the result was something that looked like smoked-salmon-flavored cotton candy. In her low heels, she was taller than Roland, and he imagined a sparkle of condescension in her eyes when she asked him to sit down in her office.

Laura dropped into one of the chairs with a huff; the chair creaked as if surprised at how much she weighed, continued to creak as Laura jiggled her legs. Her thighs, stuffed into black jeans two sizes too small for her even though he and Ellen had told her so, spread and contracted like bellows.

Roland stood at the edge of Mrs. Brady's desk, brushed the flaps of his overcoat back, and put his hands in his pockets. Looked down at her. "Make it quick. I have a lot to do at home."

Mrs. Brady bit her lower lip, let it slide back into place. "All right, Mr. Newell. I'd like Laura to see the school counselor."

Roland smiled and shook his head. The same smile and shake he used on Ellen to convince her she was overreacting. It was not a charming smile; he knew better than to try to charm women. His hairline had receded so much that what used to be his bangs was a thin island of hair above his forehead. His nose, perpetually shiny, still pink from the cold and saddled by the heavy frames of his glasses, was the kind they called "distinctive."

"One word," he said, "No." His thighs pressed against the edge of the desk. "Detention I'll give you. But saying Laura needs counseling just because of a schoolyard tiff…"

"It was more than a 'tiff,' Mr. Newell. I saw the bruises on Sandra MacIntyre. And this isn't the first 'tiff' Laurals started with her."

Roland remained outwardly calm by allowing his hidden hands to fidget. His right hand checked to make sure all his keys were on the ring, and in the back of his mind a voice ticked off *Taurus key, Ellen's Accord key, club key, front door key, office key….* He looked over his shoulder at Laura. She wasn't listening.

She'd snuck a piece of gum into her mouth and was trying to chew it on the sly. Why, Roland wondered, did his daughter seem to inherit all of his worst parts and none of his best? He rocked on his heels, then took a step sideways, as if absently, in thought, but that step blocked Mrs. Brady's view of Laura, and Roland felt freer, in a better position to argue.

"What about this other girl, Sandra? Does she get detention, too?"

"Every indication I have is that Laura is the problem. She starts the taunting and the pushing."

"And what 'indications' would those be?"

"Reports from teachers, classmates."

"And you're taking their word over Laura's?"

"Laura refuses to say anything."

"Well, we'll see about that. Laura? Come on, we're going." When he spoke to her in that tone, Laura stopped the leg jiggling. She swallowed her gum. Stood up. To Mrs. Brady he said, "A father-daughter chat is all that's needed to straighten this out."

"Laura will still serve two more days of detention. That is not up to you."

"It is up to me, but I'll allow it."

Laura walked ahead of him in her clenched way, something she'd started doing after reading a magazine article on isometrics: every muscle tightened trying to make her body firm, head down to watch the rolls of her stomach, as if any moment they might disappear. As Roland closed the door behind him, he said, "What a load of bull." Loud enough for Mrs. Brady to hear.

When Roland was in seventh grade, he tormented a boy named Franklin. The other children left Franklin alone, but not out of compassion, or even pity. They simply didn't like to talk to him, touch him, look at him.

Franklin was misshapen. He had a large lopsided head and sickly yellow hair that somehow didn't sit right on it, that always looked like a wig askew. When he had to wear his shorts in gym class, everyone could see how his legs dwindled to pink sticks at the calves, and how his body was held up with metal braces that clamped to his feet and knees and waist. He swayed when he walked.

While the other children went outside for recess and lunch period, Franklin ate alone in a classroom and waited there, reading a book, for the bell to ring. Roland used to slip into the building, creep down the halls until he found Franklin, then stand in the doorway and watch him. The brown bag containing the remains of Franklin's lunch would be crumpled in the wastebasket, filling the room with the smell of egg salad, or liverwurst and onions, always some strong smell that offended Roland, infuriated him.

"What's the matter Franklin?" he'd say. "Don't have any friends?" He'd tell Franklin how ugly he was. How he made everybody sick. He'd tell him he was going to beat him up right there, and he'd make a fist and hold it close to Franklin's face. Franklin would keep looking down at his book and pretend not to notice, but his eyes stopped moving over the words, and he never flipped a page. Sometimes, if Roland was ingeniously malicious, he could get Franklin to put his head down on the desk and cover his face with his arms.

At the supermarket, Laura left him in the pasta aisle trying to decide if he should buy a package of spaghetti and a jar of sauce or take the even easier way out with a box of instant macaroni and cheese. She reappeared with a pint of fat-free mint chocolate chip ice cream. Held it up for his approval.

"No," he said. "Those things are a crock."

"I thought it would be nice to have some dessert."

"Get some fruit then."

"You're right. Fat people shouldn't eat ice cream."

"Don't try that. That won't work again."

The smile she gave him, before she caught herself and spun around, walked away without her clenched steps, told him held made a slip. His "again" referred to their disagreement over the sweater. A white angora sweater she had pined for at the mall when he and Ellen took her shopping for school clothes. Her nose almost touched the glass of the window display where the sweater hung from the stick-thin body of a headless mannequin. He and Ellen told her the sweater was too expensive, needed too much care. They compromised by getting her the black jeans, which they thought were a little too…grown up.

"You're right," Laura had said. "Fat people shouldn't wear white."

They didn't answer, but Ellen gave him that *did we make a mistake?* look, and the bags of clothes and school supplies felt heavier in their arms. Next weekend he and Ellen drove to the same mall, bought the sweater. It was hidden under their bed in its cardboard box, wrapped with Christmas paper. And now Laura knew it.

He chose the instant macaroni and cheese.

Laura made him scoop her portion of macaroni out of the pot before he added the butter and gritty orange flavoring. She stirred the bare noodles into her microwaved frozen green beans, and seasoned the mixture with a little salt and pepper. It looked like slop, and he knew she was doing it to make him feel guilty. Her fork ticked against the plate, came up with one bean and one noodle which she chewed much longer than necessary.

"Microwaved stuff gets cold really fast, doesn't it, Dad?"

Roland set his fork down. "Go get your yearbook."

"Why?"

"I want you to show me what this Sandra MacIntyre looks like."

Keeping her eyes on her plate, she forked a larger bite. "I lost it," she mumbled through her food.

"When?"

"I don't know."

"Why didn't you tell us?"

"I didn't know it would be some major deal."

He pushed his chair back, tossed his balled napkin on the table. "I'll just see if I can't find it."

"Dad, don't…"

"You stay there."

In her room, a rag-tag zoo of stuffed animals lounged on her unmade bed, seeming to nap or read from scattered magazines. She had decorated her walls with pictures cut from those magazines, mostly male actors or "musicians" with unshaven jaws and the smoulder of sex in their eyes. He didn't want to think about that. She'd converted her bookshelf into a rack for her tapes and compact disks. It was her desk drawers she didn't want him to see, crammed with empty candy wrappers, half-empty bags of mini Snickers and Butterfinger bars. A package of Oreo cookies. But in the bottom of one were the children's books he used to read to her. Kneeling on her floor, he flipped through *The Great Big Book of Nursery Rhymes*. The cover was smudged with handprints, the pages soft and ragged-cornered.

When she was very little, they used to play the Humpty Dumpty game. She'd sit on top of their high backed couch and they'd say "Humpty Dumpty sat on a wall." And when they said "Humpty Dumpty had a great fall," she would topple forward giggling into the cushions with him there to scoop her up.

Her feet marched up the stairs. He replaced the book, re-covered it with candy wrappers, and slid the drawer closed. The door swung open, banged against the wall. She faced him, hands on her hips. "Dad, you can't paw through my stuff."

"Where's the yearbook, then?"

"I told you." But she glanced at the closet.

He found it on the closet shelf, on top of a stack of other yearbooks going back to the first grade. He sat on the edge of her bed and opened it. She made a grab for it but he blocked her with his arm, pointed a finger at her with a warning look that made her step backwards and drop her hands.

When he turned to the class picture, he spotted Sandra immediately because Laura had defaced her with red pen, drawing wavy lines that were supposed to be stink wafting off her and flies that hovered around her head. A giant knife jutted from her neck, dripping blood. The other children had dressed up for the class picture, but Sandra, sitting cross-legged on the end of the first row, wore a small t-shirt that allowed her belly to bulge exposed above the waist of her jeans. She was the fattest girl in the class, and not even faking a smile through the strings of her hair.

Roland set the book flat on his knees. His right hand slipped into his pocket. T*aurus key, club key, office key…*Laura took the opportunity to snatch the book away; she tore the page out, crumpled it, threw it on the floor.

"You…bastard!" Her chin wrinkled with the effort of keeping her lower lip pressed against the upper, and to Roland she looked like some kind of monster: face bloated, red, twitching with unspeakable thoughts.

He stood up, hands still in his pockets. "I'm going for a walk," he said, his voice a low monotone that sounded strange to him. "When I come back I want the dishes done and you in this room. No stereo. No television. You're grounded. Understand?" He frowned at her from the doorway—she said nothing—then yanked the door closed.

The windbreaker he chose wasn't warm enough. Five minutes of tramping through his development and Roland was shivering. It was the first week of November and Halloween decorations were still out. A paper cut-out of a witch riding a broom clung to the door of one house. A sheet that someone had hung for a ghost twisted by its rope from the limb of a tree. A jack-o-lantern, broken open by the kicks of neighborhood boys, grinned up at him from the street with its rot-mottled face.

One day after school, as everyone herded through the courtyard to the bus loop, Roland fell in step behind Franklin and imitated the way he walked. He whistled a tune, the theme from the Laurel and Hardy show, and made it stay in time to Franklin's swaying shoulders and head. Franklin didn't turn around, didn't say anything, but he moved faster toward the buses, the effort exaggerating his waddling walk.

Roland caught the eyes of several of his classmates, looking for approval, hoping they might join in with jeers of their own. The girls turned away from him as always, but one or two of the boys smiled, recognizing the old game. None of them joined in, but their smiles incited him.

Franklin's heavy black shoes clunked on the pavement. The joints of his leg braces creaked. He had to climb aboard the bus by gripping both railings with his books tucked under an arm, then pulling himself up to the lowest step, sliding his hands higher on the railings, pulling up to the next step. Roland followed him, muttering, "Franklin is so slow. Franklin holds us all up."

The bus was almost full. Franklin made for the nearest empty seat, but Roland kicked out a foot and tripped him in the aisle. Franklin went down face first, his books scattering under the seats. His cheeks and neck—his whole body—turned livid red, and a vein beating in his temple made his head look like a throbbing heart.

"Jesus!" somebody said behind Roland. It was Mark Kramer, standing with Bobby Torelli in the aisle. They were the two strongest, most athletic, most popular boys in class, and they stared at Roland with awe in their eyes.

"You are one mean son-of-a-bitch. Jesus."

Roland grinned back at them.

Franklin gathered his books, pulled himself up, and found a seat. He turned his face to the window. Mark and Bobby shook their heads, pushed past Roland and took their usual seats at the back of the bus. Roland followed them, not daring to sit next to them, but close, a few seats up. He also turned his face to the window, because his grin wouldn't quit; it spread until he thought his face would burst, and he knew he looked ridiculous.

Ellen called that night from her hotel room in Miami. They had talked for only a few minutes when she said, "You sound funny."

"No, everything's fine."

She wanted to speak to Laura. Roland called her down from her bedroom. As he passed the phone to her, his eyes and the shake of his head said, *I didn't tell her. Don't you either.*

Laura answered her mother's questions with moody monosyllables. Handed the phone back.

"You two are fighting," Ellen said.

"Not really."

"I guess I'll find out about it when I come home."

Roland and Laura went to bed without saying good night. In the morning, she spooned her cereal and he munched his toast without talking.

"Don't take the late bus," he called as she headed out the door with her book bag slung over one shoulder. "I'll pick you up after detention."

The door banged shut.

At three o'clock, when he knew Laura's school day had ended and her detention was starting, he was unable to do any more work. He leaned back in his chair, chewing the end of his pen, and watched the second hand of the small, brass and wood clock on his desk. He rocked the chair, making its old joints creak. The sound made him uneasy. He dropped his pen, pushed away from the desk and grabbed his coat off the rack by the door.

Twenty minutes before the end of detention, he was waiting outside the detention room, watching through the window in the door. Mrs. Brady sat at the front desk, flipping through a stack of papers as if she'd lost a particular one. Laura hunched in a first row desk, thighs pumping, her back to the door. Three boys—all wearing heavy unlaced boots, baggy jeans, baseball caps turned backwards—slouched in the back of the room. They had been spaced far apart, but they snickered silently and signalled back and forth with their hands. Roland wondered what was so funny, and then he noticed: they had taped a sign to the back of Laurals chair. In big bold letters it said THE KILLER WHALE. One of the boys laughed out loud. Mrs. Brady's head shot up and she snapped at him to be quiet, then went back to her papers. Laura looked behind her and discovered the sign. She pulled it off the chair and read it. Her face flushed purple, but she straightened up, turned her back on the boys, crumpled the paper and dropped it on the floor where they could see it.

Good for her, Roland thought.

Mrs. Brady's head shot up again. "Pick that up."

Laura hesitated, but stood to obey. The boys put their heads down on their desks and peeked over their arms, shoulders shaking.

Roland opened the door, paused for a moment, hands in pockets, then began sidling between the desks toward the front of the room. Everyone looked up at him. Laura, who had been bending over for the paper, straightened up without it. Mrs. Brady glanced at the wall clock.

"Mr. Newell, detention isn't over for another fifteen minutes."

"Well, Mrs. Brady, for Laura it's over now." He gave the boys a look that said, *you better hope I never run across any of you in a dark alley*, then bent and picked up the crumpled paper. He tried to take Laura's hand, but she shook him off. Before they left, he tossed the paper on Mrs. Brady's desk. "Maybe this is the one you're looking for."

One afternoon Roland came home from school and his mother stood waiting for him in the doorway, her arms folded across her blue apron, a metal serving spoon in one hand.

She said a teacher from the school had called. She asked if what the teacher told her was true, and when he looked up at her dumbly she knew that it was. She shook the spoon in his face. "How could you? A poor crippled boy? Are you a monster?"

The spoon stung his shoulders and the sides of his legs, cracked against his head. He didn't run away, just dropped his books, backed into a corner, and covered his face. He was glad to get hit; glad of the chance to scream and cry. He cried for his shame and for everything Franklin suffered. He cried because he hated not only himself but his classmates, and because the whole world, right down to his own heart, seemed full of meanness.

That night, lying awake in bed, Roland closed his eyes and imagined what it was like to be Franklin. He sat at Franklin's desk and pretended to be writing something important while everybody filed out for recess; he ate one of Franklin's brown bag lunches; he watched himself attack, saw his contorted face, heard his words, and he opened his eyes to get rid of it. Chewed on his blanket to stifle the noise in his throat.

On the bus next morning, he didn't look at Franklin. Sat as far away from him as possible. During the ride, everyone compared grades on the last math test. Lucy Dervis and Wendy French giggled over their C's. Mark Kramer and Bobby Torelli bragged about their D's. Roland had received a B, but called out, "I got a D, too."

The girls gave him un-encouraging smiles. Mark Kramer said, "Who cares?"

At school, as they pulled off their coats, stowed their lunches in the vestibule and piled into homeroom, nobody was especially glad to see him. Nobody ran up to him bubbling with news, or with the idea of some new mischief brightening their faces. Nobody asked him if he'd seen that show on TV last night, or how he'd worked out the answers to the hard homework problems.

And there was Franklin: sitting at his desk, lifting the top of it and sticking his head in, pretending to rummage around inside, hiding the fact that he was alone. Roland sauntered by and said, "Hey, ugly, when are you ever going to comb your hair?"

When Franklin didn't answer him, he slammed the desk closed on Franklin's fingers.

Roland knocked on Laura's door, loud enough for her to hear him over the thump of her stereo. When she didn't respond, he went in. She lay on the bed, holding a stuffed giraffe on her belly, stroking it, her head propped up on a pillow. She tried not to look at him, but couldn't help glancing at the flat, Christmas-wrapped box in his hands. He clicked off her stereo and sat on the edge of her bed.

"You know what you've been doing to Sandra MacIntyre is wrong, don't you?" She set the giraffe aside, crossed her arms. Nodded.

"Well then…" But he knew better than to ask her why she did it. Better than to threaten her with more punishment or to make her promise to stop. Better than to say any of the things that, as the father, he was supposed to say.

"Then here." He handed her the box.

She tore through the paper, ripped off the lid, and held the white angora sweater against herself with an "Oh my god." Moving faster than he'd known she could, she swung herself off the bed and in front of the mirror. She pulled the sweater over her head, smoothed the fabric over her body, touching it as she would her own skin. She smiled at herself in the mirror and posed.

"How do I look?"

He considered the question, studying her reflection. All of his features were there in her face. His eyes, his distinctive nose, his blunt chin. He noticed especially how her neck didn't hold her head straight up, but carried it hunched low, protectively, as if she perpetually expected someone to slap her. When mirrors took him by surprise, he saw the same posture. He held out his arms to her and said, "You look like my daughter." She came to him and let him put his arms around her, allowed him a long squeeze. A gentle squeeze, because, to tell the truth, she looked as round, as white, and as fragile as an egg.

Pedro Ponce

Stories of the Unexplained

Bicycles

A woman without a man is like a fish without a bicycle.
—Gloria Steinem

The scientist looks at his watch, does one last calculation, and blots his brow with a wrinkled handkerchief. The final test has been successful. He stares at the wall of tanks in his laboratory, feverishly watches as the gears of submerged ten-speeds turn, making small currents in the water. The bicycles trace slow circles along the sandy floors, guided by fish that have arranged themselves in symmetrical patterns around spokes, pedals, handlebars, a symbiosis spanning millions of years of evolution, revealed at last through the scientist's experiments.

He reaches for his notebook to record tonight's results, the crucial link in all his endeavors. But as he begins to scribble, he is filled with self-doubt. Has it all been worth it? he asks himself. The years of research? The pestering of private donors, eager to turn his discovery into a profitable venture? The hundreds of late nights spent alone, watching the bubbling tanks? All so that the next time someone claims that a woman needs a man like a fish needs a bicycle, he can finally respond, "Exactly."

It could all be taken away so easily, he thinks. Another good analogy could send him back to the lab for the rest of his life. A woman needs a man like a cow needs a curling iron. Like an octopus needs a toaster oven. Like a frog needs a cordless phone. He imagines these and dozens of other possibilities.

The scientist puts down his pencil, reaches into a cabinet overhead, and withdraws a dull brown bottle of liquor. He pours himself a drink, using a beaker for a glass. The rest of the night is a stop-action movie in which he watches the contents of the bottle disappear in steady increments.

In the morning, he will forget his discovery.

Secret Satan

It is a simple misspelling that sets you apart, a reversal of letters that marks you as untouchable. For, while the rest of your office has been assigned Secret Santas to usher in the holiday, a bureaucratic error has paired you with a Secret Satan.

308

All week, you watch colleagues unwrap presents delivered anonymously to their desks: fancy chocolates, tree ornaments, booklets of inspirational verse. You get rat droppings, a mutilated pig, a pop-up edition of the *Kama-Sutra*.

Your office equipment begins to act in strange and disturbing ways. No matter what number you dial, your phone will only connect you with the sex-chat line. You are convinced that you need an exorcist, but it is too late: Whoever you call is always someone with a breathy voice who tries to solicit your credit card number.

Your desk diary mocks you. After filling in the "To Do" box with a carefully considered list of tasks for the week, you return from lunch to find that the list has vanished and been replaced by the words "Nothing Important." The slots for the weekend, usually blank, have been helpfully filled out for you: "Watch TV. Jerk off. Go to sleep."

One day, your Secret Satan leaves a videotape at your workstation. It is a movie of what life would be like had you not been born. There is much singing, dancing, drinking, and love-making. At the end, when the boy gets the girl and everyone lives happily ever after, you find yourself rooting for the hero and heroine, holding back tears at their celebrity wedding, in spite of yourself.

The next morning, bleary-eyed at the coffee machine, a co-worker places a consoling hand on your shoulder. "It's not so bad," she says. "At least you don't have to worry about what to give in return."

This is true. Secret gift-giving usually goes both ways, but what could your personal demon, with all its supernatural powers, possibly need? You have thought about trying to turn it around with compassionate offerings of bread dipped in hot chocolate, stuffed animals, cassette tapes of the Mormon Tabernacle Choir. But you are afraid of provoking it to even cruder forms of generosity.

On Friday, the office holds its Christmas party. The Secret Santas reveal their identities to one another and present their final gifts. The last round of presents is a pricey assortment of jewelry, crystal statuettes, fountain pens, and gift certificates. As the party proceeds, the pile of brightly wrapped boxes next to the food shrinks until all that remains is a slim rectangular parcel covered in black tissue paper. There is no card attached, but you know who it's for. You unravel the dark sheets and find a silver platter, monogrammed with your initials.

You wonder if your personal demon will choose to appear. But as you feel the room stare and ripple with gossip, you realize that it has already shown itself, in the everyday accidents that plague you, in the doubt that clouds your thoughts like a rich food, in the confounded face that stares back at you from the platter's silver surface.

Afterlife of the Party

He arrives late and is always overdressed. Picture his arrival decades earlier: He would be the one knocking the lamp shades from people's heads and crushing them under his shiny black shoes. Now that lamp shades are no longer fashionable gauges of fun, he contents himself with picking through your CD collection, mocking your musical taste between puffs from a clove cigarette.

He's the afterlife of the party and his effect is instantaneous. The drink in your hand turns to turpentine as it slides down your throat. The smoke you inhale coats your mouth with the taste of ashes. The extroverts look at their watches and marvel at how late it is. Perhaps they have stayed too long. The introverts, crushed by a sudden and overwhelming self-consciousness, scatter for the door like beached sea turtles.

Discretion wears thin and people begin to speak their minds. There are confessions of love on the couch, confessions of infidelity in the kitchen, confessions of boredom on the lawn chairs in the backyard. By the dying embers of the barbecue, a man stops himself in the middle of discussing a newspaper editorial he read this morning to ask the woman he is speaking to when he can stop this charade and fuck her. Behind them, the host, a young, baseball-hatted bear of a man in jeans and a sweatshirt, realizes that he will one day die. Engrossed all at once by his mortality, he sets down the tap of a spent beer keg, goes upstairs to his room, and begins recording his thoughts in the margins of last month's *Sports Illustrated*.

Meanwhile, the afterlife of the party probes the secret pockets of the house hoping to catch people in the act of love. He stumbles on the gropings of couples in the basement, in closets and bathrooms, underneath the front porch steps. He robs the women of their desire and the men of their potency. The amorous grow cold to each other, dress in silence, and leave the party separately.

There are many witnesses, but their accounts are hazy. Several report waking up from a blackout and finding themselves sitting next to a tall figure in a dark trench coat. According to these reports, he is unresponsive to small talk and offers of food or drink. After several moments of awkward silence, the figure simply vanishes from view, reappearing minutes later in another part of the house.

He is feared by the gregarious and well-adjusted. But he is a hero of the socially inept, who believe that if the conversation falls flat, if the drugs make you paranoid, if you fail to charm attractive strangers, if you leave with nothing but a long, cold walk to look forward to, you can always blame it on the afterlife of the party.

Stories of the Unexplained

Up late again, I'm in the kitchen, watching *Stories of the Unexplained*. It's the last show of the night. After this, there will be the national anthem and then the usual test pattern that signals the end of the broadcasting day and bathes my darkened apartment in the glow of a dirty fish tank. For now, the host, a sober-looking man in a dark blue suit, sits behind his space-age news desk and encourages me to join him next time for more real-life encounters with the paranormal.

As the credits roll, I notice your postcard lying on the table in front of me. I have only read it twice today. My fingers brush the edges of the pictured city skyline. It is a city I have never visited and I know that I never will.

310

An American flag billows on the screen and the national anthem comes on. As the music reaches its operatic climax, I hear something outside my window. I shut off my TV to listen.

There is singing in the alley below. From where I stand, two floors above the street, I see a man in a tattered overcoat shuffle into view. He props one hand against a garbage can and leans heavily against a worn chain-link fence. He faces the back of my apartment and sings. It's not a song I recognize. The notes dip and soar, the lyrics elude comprehension. His voice grows stronger, louder, and as it does, he steps away from the fence and stands unsupported.

From the right, two men approach. They stand to the side, watch the singer, and share a bottle cloaked in a paper bag. The singer becomes more animated, swaying in improvised choreography to his song. As he moves, I begin to understand his words. The singer is in love. Somewhere in this sleeping city, someone waits for him and he impatiently counts the hours until morning.

Or, the singer is in search of love, hopes to find it soon, gladly shoulders the burden of solitude to wait for what is meant to be.

Or it is nothing. There is no story here. There is only a man, nearly legless from drinking, singing nonsense into an empty alley.

His audience has left, taking their bottle with them. I watch the man until he stops singing. He stands silent and perfectly still, frozen in the middle of his crude dance, arms spread out like wings. Under the orange street lights, he could be a statue in a park for lovers, lips pursed for a first kiss that never comes.

Lou Robinson

Havoc Wreaked by the Bean of Doubt

Horses prefer classical music. It lifts them and lets them hang suspended, their four legs able for once to dangle and rest. Immune to sentimentality, they hear country western music as noise. I learned this from a woman sitting next to me at the clinic. Barbara is a psychic for horses. She got her vision after a head injury sustained during an interstate collision with a six-horse trailer. Can you use the word "during" for something that has no duration in memory? "Sustained" for something against your will and instantaneous? She said it was safe for me to ride. My horse was well aware of my own accident and would carry me carefully.

I had failed the short term memory test: repeat these words in two minutes: "flag mailbox table." I just could not carry the table. For weeks I woke in the night, rehearsing them. Three other words overlaid them, in the now familiar way that consonants and numbers were doubling out of control. "Food shelter clothing." I once read that if you cannot provide yourself with all three you can be committed; this triangle of need the test. I would wake from dreaming I lay covered by a flag, huddled inside a mailbox, the table too large or legless or floating just out of reach in murky rising water.

When your brain is bruised, you lose the rhythm of thinking. There can be no movement from darkness to realization, from confession to absolution, no moral spiritual framework, no rise, fall, climax. Your head heats with frustration for the because-of-that-then-this narrative. When the word isn't there or the wrong one willfully intrudes, you long for the painstaking <if> something <then> something of electronic logic.

Before I was hit by the car, I had been writing a mystery with a friend. We invented a witness whose testimony has holes. For inspiration, I had been reading a journal on post-traumatic stress. Here was a reason for a wreck in a black sort of way, as a pun can be an excuse for two different words being too similar. So many words reveal themselves to be evil twins. WHY must amalgam be so similar to anagram? Who is responsible for this laziness?

The word "intersection" took on an apocryphal charge. Here your life will fork. Here you may meet your afterlife. All sorts of unconscious movements based on trust became conscious Sophie's choices. Every foray out of sleep leads into peril, and sinking into sleep the same—floods, apartments without locks, firing squads.

In one my sister was "snatched," a phrase we all know to mean taken by aliens. We had ignored the warning sign: certain articles of clothing disappearing from her drawers.

After the snatching dream I would suddenly think of a sweater or shirt I hadn't seen for awhile and have to find it. The phrase "haven't seen for awhile" reverberated, laden with malice. The living room filled inward from the periphery with articles of clothing, books, notebooks. They had to sit within sight until they became familiar again. If you have belongings, you can travel out from them, safely identified elsewhere. If you are lucky enough to have a place to store them, and if you can remember it. Otherwise you have to wear them. I began wearing more for fortification, clothing and shelter. The demanding material world. I would have thought a blow to the head would loosen its hold.

Once I could read again, I had no interest in fiction. Facts for me, and only the kind summarized in little boxes. *The Horse Owner's Veterinarian Care Book.* If I forgot a disease, minutes after learning of it, I could look right up at the little box of symptoms. *The Consumer Report.* I found its charts especially soothing. Cars can be understood. "SUZUKI—BAD, I wrote."

"Stoicism is only possible with an intact mind. Your negative personality traits become exaggerated when you are hit on the head," the doctor at the clinic is saying, confirming my worst fear. She tells me about a hot-tempered guy who was hit by a car and now rolls around in a wheelchair brandishing a frying pan. "Luckily he was too disabled to hurt anyone," she says. Another woman was hit in the stop-eating part of her brain. She is up to 500 pounds, eats anything, toilet paper, can't be left alone, ever. The other unharmed parts of her brain watch on in horror. Seeing my wet face, the doctor says, "You're sympathetic. Now you're probably finding everything unbearably sad." I was picturing my father, my heart breaking over how his fingers got too fat to play the banjo.

People would tell me to rest, as if I could just lie back and float in a wordless dream while some cells died quietly and others gently licked their wounds. I insisted that I was working at home. What I did was make phone calls and lists. Hot and frantic, I called car dealers and insurance people I thought were withholding information from me. I fixed on a half-remembered image in a cult film with the word worm in the title that would be perfect for the jacket of a book. I called film groups. The production company had folded. The distribution company didn't know who had the rights. I called them daily, I knew they were lying. I rented the video and discovered that the image I remembered didn't exist. I photographed different frames on pause and pasted them together to get what I remembered: A full-frame shot of a woman wearing a phallus.

At night I would go to sleep almost cozily on the practice of visualizing again again the impact. I was recapturing lost bits. "Sunnglassses," I wrote on the pad by the bed. I pictured the approach of the car that seemed to be flying, all the various things I might have done but didn't have time to do, things a stunt driver, or my father, might have done. I went over all the sentences I had in the interim between sight and sound. I remembered more and more sentences, horrifying in their banality, considering they might have been my last, but still, I was comforted by how many there were in such a short time. Sentences such as: "I might live. But I might never be able to ride my horse again. I won't even have a car to visit him." I was able to picture him clearly at the time, off in the corner where he goes for privacy. I knew he was in some way alert to my predicament because his head was high and anxious as it is when Arabian ghosts are passing, in the guise of plastic bags. "I might go crazy if they strap me to that stretcher. The thing to do is go unplugged." Here is the sentence I wanted to study. But first, I would say, put them in order. Context is crucial. I tried hard to adhere to the linear time I had once so disdained.

One eye had gotten glued shut with something warm. Blood, I guessed, idly, after the car stopped sliding. I remembered the same lazy feeling once on a trip when my friend Willy cut his finger shaving, then had a fit of epilepsy. How I strolled to the car to get the first aid kit. Debated long minutes whether to wear my cowboy hat back. We were in Oregon. I thought about first straightening the surprisingly jumbled mess in the back seat, emptying the ashtray. The sight of blood had triggered a spontaneous kind of natural magic: If I slow my own, his will cease to flow.

After recognizing the warmth as blood, I tried this trick sitting in the car, silent now except for sporadic showers of tinkling glass. Then I heard two women in the back seat moaning. I couldn't move my head. There began a wide falling space of doubt about my possible responsibility. I heard someone say the word negligence. Either that or negligible. I couldn't be sure. I performed a long and bitter conjecture upon the unfairness of language. By now men swarmed the car, arms were everywhere, voices telling us NOT TO LOSE CONSCIOUSNESS, as we waited for a big machine to come from miles away, maybe the West Coast, to cut off the ceiling of the car so they could lift us out. Every now and then I would ask the young sweating face in front of me, whose hands appeared to be holding on my head, "What is that shape out there? Is it the back of a stop sign? Why is it facing the other road? How are you supposed to read it from here?"

Only hours earlier when we stopped for lunch, we had joked about the uncomfortable size of my back seat. As they had peeled themselves out in the parking lot I'd said "I hope you aren't crippled." I have an uncanny talent for blurting out the as yet unknown calamity. I say it glibly, as if it's so incongruous as to be funny. Before we had stopped in Portland those years ago, Willy had been saying how he hated when people joked about Louisiana. I had answered, "Just don't go all epileptic." Then we got to our friends' house; he shaved; he cut himself; he fell on the floor with his first fit ever.

I wondered why I wasn't moving to help the women in the back seat. Finally I noticed those two arms, shaking from being so long outstretched, holding my head immobile. I don't remember the face. Instead I looked at my own as if from outside. A pale bewildered face with a phallic crystal of glass, a four-inch stalagmite, sticking out of my forehead. I very much wanted it to remain in place. Blood, brains, voices, screams might pour out from under it. It turned out to be only the size of a molar.

After 22 stitches, after a rain of words in the hospital—severe contusion, ragged, deep, scar—still for many days I didn't realize I'd hit my head. I thought flying glass had landed and dug in. I didn't realize my brain had collided with my skull and my skull with the car, and it with the other car. After a week I called the hospital to find out if it was normal for there to be no feeling at all in half my scalp. The nurse who answered said, "Did you hit it?" "I don't know, I don't think so." I said. "You must KNOW if you HIT your HEAD." I could not truthfully say that's what happened because, though I was fully conscious (fully conscious, I repeated this over and over to the nurse after I hung up on her) I did not remember hitting my head. I wasn't going to say something happened that I didn't know happened, first hand, for sure. This is how people get in trouble. They would just have to find some other explanation. You have to be stubborn about your experience, you can't just go letting others fill in the blanks.

Do your cells preserve sentient details yet prevent registration of the feelings at such times so that the unbearable in its instant can be borne? Are feelings felt but filed somewhere accessible only through hypnosis, coded dreams, isolation tanks, psychics with inadequate vocabularies, dangerous hit-or-miss kinds of therapy? Are they recorded at all or is it only what you deduce, what you are told that forms a memory of the event? A manufactured meaning? Or is it simply that meaning travels under 40 mph? Shouldn't there be a simple way to time it?

I remembered Ted Bundy saying, "If this incident occurred and if I was involved in it." Of course he could have merely been lying. I remembered reading that a trial psychiatrist pronounced someone sane, but said he would have changed his diagnosis had he known how given the defendant was to lying.

Say something bad happens once and you lose the feelings that attach to it. The next time, you realize you can will yourself to go unplugged. Haven't you now entered the realm of choice and consequence? And what if the sentence "go unplugged" came to me before the collision, not after. Maybe in that split second when I saw the flying car, I practiced an old form of survival instead of a wild swerve to safety. Maybe the coma descended before the blow? Negligible, negligent seconds?

Does everyone have a void within? An inevitable, necessary abdication from the common blows of life? Does such a void call forth rage to fill it? Or a sweeping plains rain of sadness, or an insatiable hunger for inedible materials? Or speeding cars? Are the most basic urges negative, driven by an absence of memory, a thousand small losses? How ignoble. How actionable.

In the second grade I spelled every word right in the spelling contest, winning on the last word, ignoble. The prize was a book about a wild brown horse that rolls in a riverbed of mica and appears at night in reflected moonlight as a silver stallion.

I put everything I had gleaned from many phone calls into two folders, one called Woorm and one called The Wreak.

Later I found I had written down dreams and added them to the folders. Those to do with obligation or blame went into Woorm. Those to do with going unplugged went into The Wreak.

In Woorm I found a dream in which my old roommate overheard me mocking her to another woman. She accosted me, pinning me against the wall by my injured shoulder. I apologized, I groveled. She released me but I followed her around her oppressive doily-covered rooms, offering her adjectives for myself such as "irresponsible, selfish, insincere." "Don't forget vain," she said.

Also in Woorm was one about my trial. I'm being sued by the woman in the back seat. I have to fill out a form that asks "what was your first dream after the wreck, and what was your last?" I'm puzzled, but dutifully place post-its in the folder by any dream that seems to apply. The trial takes place at the YMCA. I'm handed a tank suit and told to swim. At the edge four men in suits confer with the woman. I swim side stroke in circles trying to hear. One comes over and says, "We were hoping you would swim in straight lines." "Oh but I usually swim laps," I say earnestly. "I was just trying to stay within earshot."

In Wreak I had put the one about the parking garage. Willy had come back and we were walking across a broad field of grass. I wanted the past back, the pull. I was looking for one sign to show me I could ruin myself that way again—but all his gestures are ambiguous. Now it is dark and I say good-bye, setting off for the parking structure on the hill where I left my gold 72 Olds Cutlass. It is the blackest most impenetrable parking structure and I know I am going to die inside it. I call out to him, he can't yet have gotten far, but he doesn't come. Then it is later. I am not there, but a younger, dark-haired woman is finishing the story. She is a light-weight—disingenuous, coy. Apparently, Willy didn't come to help but he did call the police. They found me in the morning in a field with pigs. The mother pig had taken me in and nursed me with her babies. No one could reach me. I never spoke again. This new narrator is telling the story as if it is her own. She says, "I'm slowly beginning to feel that I might one day want to go driving again." I despise her.

I am again besieged, just as I was at the age of three when I wouldn't speak to strangers but only hissed like a cat, because my cat had so advised. What was a dream? What was not? Was the shadow on the wall a man or a tree? Did I reach across a vast expanse of swelling bed to my mother, who was rapidly shrinking to a dot, didn't that really happen? Sometimes the bed was a circus tent that covered acres, or a huge sheet on a line and we were crickets bounced further and further apart with each gust of wind. Moments of sensual immediacy flicker in a dark field of not quite involuntary distance.

Everywhere still, adult people are doubling, disconnecting, sending out simulacrums to deal with strangers or the authorities. Look how many people are hearing voices. Look at the stupid things their voices tell them. Men, their voices mostly say 'go ahead and kill her.' Women's say 'cut yourself, you won't feel it.' Many say they multiplied at the first point of invasion. Under siege, the body divides.

But many more benign blanks can be traced to a harsh word or a small embarrassment, an earache, an enema, a brother's pinhole camera.

I'm looking at a steep staircase down to a basement room with a pool table. Someone is sucking a wintergreen mint. Julie London sings from a record player. Ice hits thick-sided glasses. The chunk of balls colliding brings a lowering, sinking fear and longing. They are too solid, too dense, too perfectly hard and too heavy. Two of them. Silver, in a velvet case. Two is the number and they go up inside his mother, whenever his father says "Lets go upstairs," usually when he comes home from lunch. He doesn't know how he knows this. This is not a memory, or at least not mine, but I'm the one who has it now.

I see a person on the street, a man with a ponytail walking a Dalmatian pup, and I see for him it is gilt, specifically frames. Because of a gilt-framed painting of roses. That he gave his mother when he worked for the gallery, before so many died. His generation, his adopted family of the disinherited, will not outlive their parents. Golden varnish his particular undoing.

For another woman it is summer, something is always burning, hamburgers on a grill in a more southern town with longer twilights. It is supposed to evoke a celebratory halo. But the hollow smell of lighter fluid stabs her with guilt and loss, and at the same time, a need for it, to breathe it in. The penetrating smell of rift.

Maybe lungs strung too tight are strummed by anxious breath and release a chord. Someone driving around listening to the classical station, receptive, can be impressed with it just as violin music makes patterns in trays of neutral, sleeping sand. Because the driver has no attachment to these particular sharp moments, free of their contexts. Or maybe the drivers' own still void acts as a magnet to orphan feelings.

317

Giving feelings a home, the work of fiction. This is as far as I got with the theory, because something was missing. The worm, of course.

I don't know why everything buried has to have a worm in it. It can't just be a little forgetfulness, it has to be a pattern of disassociation, caused by something bad and long ago, overt or covert.

Why can't a ragged hole just grow a scab, why must it take the infantile shape of loss and longing, things joined and separated with a sucking sound? Why do you have to dredge it up to give witness?

What does it want? The wounded flesh. A thumb? A nipple? Someone to say it's not your fault. To say it's all your fault. To say this could have been prevented. To say this will never happen again.

I lay on the stretcher and thought about my father's pale sore penis, curved as if to hide. Days earlier I had been back home to help my parents after my father's prostate operation. I don't remember ever seeing the thing before. Now here it was, damaged and shamed. He told me about how the doctor got on his knees in the bathroom and told him to try to pee so he could insert the catheter. I said, "I've never been in the hospital. I've never even been in a car wreck."

In The Woorm I found this dream: My father is dying. He falls heavily, like a great noble draft horse. No one could hope to soften his fall. He is trying to speak but can only whinny.

As far back as I can remember, I have roamed around among my father's entrails. Every intestinal cramp. Peered through the windows of diverticulitis. Encouraged the one lung left from the war. The one kidney. I shared with the other four-year-olds in my kindergarten class, I am told, this story: "My father can swallow a potato on a string and cough it back up. It goes into a long soft tube like a worm that is starting to wear out and get holes."

The bean is a hard smooth nugget of smegma that accumulates in a little curved pocket of the male horse's urethra. I learned about the bean from *The Horse Owner's Veterinarian Care Book*, during my frenzied convalescence. You have to pull the penis out of the horse's sheath. If he resists, try giving him beer in a bucket. Otherwise you may have to sedate him with a shot, but anesthetic is dangerous to horses. (Of course, falling down drunk can break his legs.) Once you have his penis, face his hind legs, stick your finger into the little opening, and find the bean. You have to get it out. Otherwise one day he won't be able to urinate and then he'll get cancer.

In between calling film studios and car lots, I cleaned my horse's sheath. Passersby saw a woman wearing a large bandage on her head struggling with the penis of a horse. The bean itself is smooth and pale, exactly like an evil navy bean, and very satisfying to hold, exposed to the sun.

That night I dreamed I was a turbaned Joan Crawford on tour in India. To prove I was something special, I demanded a wild elephant to ride. He arrived, grinning with pride and complicity. After an astonishing tour of the countryside, no mishaps, he shrank to the size of a miniature pony and ran around on the table top. I fed him crystallized violets, which he scooped into his mouth with his trunk, making a perfect semi-circle. To the left, his groom took up blue chalk and wrote on a blackboard: REMEMBER. HE IS A WILD ANIMAL. YOU ARE NOT INSIDE HIM.

Elizabeth Roca

Final Curtain

Nathan looks at his watch. Five minutes to eight. It's time for him to ring the bell that summons everyone to their posts, but he lingers in the dressing room doorway to watch Jenny finish her makeup. She stands in front of the mirror in her long black gown, studying herself. A bit of white pancake makeup has smudged her collar, and she wipes it off with the tip of a black-nailed finger. Her face and hands are colored chalk-white, with the long veins traced in black. She leans in closer and smears charcoal-colored greasepaint in the hollow of her cheek. No need, Nathan thinks. Already the hollows of her face appear dangerously collapsed, her cheekbones glaring sharply above them. A special technique she developed over the years makes her lips look shrivelled, her teeth unusually prominent. Her throat, normally so smooth and firm, has been made wattled with latex and spirit gum. Nathan has always loved the contrast between his graceful, pretty wife and this professionally terrifying hag. His own makeup, which he glimpses over her shoulder in the mirror, is equally effective. Where Jenny's face looks leaner, his appears broader, moon-pale and heavily jowled. Jenny has a knack for seeing the what-could-be in a person's features: he looks like a villainous innkeeper.

He tries to catch her eye in the mirror, but she refuses to look at him. He'd like to touch her shoulder, but instead he says, "Jenny, I'm sorry."

"I know," she says, blending the paint into her skin with a wedge-shaped sponge.

He hopes she'll say something more, but she doesn't.

"You look perfect, as usual."

Her eyes are red-rimmed. She was late coming downstairs this afternoon, and when she finally appeared he could tell she'd been crying. Now it looks like part of her makeup.

She smiles into the mirror. Her teeth stand out yellowly against her white face. "Honey, don't worry. I'm fine, really. Business as usual, right?"

"That's right," he says. "I'll be moving along, then. Call me if you need anything."

"I will."

He shuts the door carefully behind him to trap the illumination inside, and hustles down the dark hallway. They both know that this night isn't like any other. It's the last night. The closing night of Hatchet's House of Horror, an attraction in downtown Orlando for over twenty years. Twenty-three rooms of terror, at twelve dollars a person. It did very well until the last year.

The house was Jenny's idea, soon after they were married.

"You've given me this great name, we might as well use it," she said, and Nathan was agreeable. They spent one whole weekend lying on the living room floor while Jenny covered page after page from a yellow legal pad with her precise handwriting. Lists of the materials needed for each costume: witch, mummy, butcher. Lists of different themes for each room of the house: morgue, vampire, slaughterhouse, *Psycho*. Possible income balanced against expenses: rent, entrance fee, hourly wages for their employees. The finances were Nathan's responsibility.

He reaches the room with the display from *Psycho*, reaches behind the staircase that Norman's mother comes barreling down, night after night, and pushes the button that sounds the chime to warn everyone into position. They'll all be in place already, waiting to jump out at passing groups of teenagers, young dating couples, scaring them out of their wits. Hatchet's House of Horror employs fifteen workers, mostly college students, all hired by Jenny. That was why she wept this afternoon, he thinks. He waited a long time without telling anyone, hoping to regain the business, and now they'll all have to scramble for work. That would worry Jenny more than anything. They're so young and disorganized, most of them, that she feels personally responsible for them.

Nathan moves to his position by the front door, and Vince slips past him. "I'm a little late," he says, fiddling with a skull-shaped cufflink. On either side of his suit jacket, sticking out from his ribcage, is an extra set of arms that twitch and jerk with the movement of his real arms. He's wearing a top hat and tails, tall and thin and elegant, with gray and white face makeup, hollows around his eyes like the Phantom of the Opera's, and fake blood trickling from the corners of his mouth. Except for the arms he looks like Mr. Rochester, Nathan thinks, or, better, Heathcliff after Cathy dies: morbidly handsome. When he works outside he's an effective draw for teenage girls. Vince has been with Hatchet's for eight years, longer than any other employee. He likes working nights, it saves his days for looking for acting jobs.

Nathan touches one of Vince's real arms. "Vince, I'm sorry. I should have told all of you what was happening sooner. Given you more time to find another place."

Vince looks at him from hollow eyes. "That's all right. I think it's hard for everyone to believe we're actually closing down."

"You've been here longer than anyone. If you need some money while you're finding something else—"

"No," Vince cuts in. "Thanks, that's great of you, but I'm OK. I've had some good news, actually—a TV commercial."

Nathan laughs with relief. "A change from fake blood and fangs, I guess."

"I wouldn't be too sure; it's for razor blades," Vince says, and glides down the hallway.

Nathan positions himself outside. Reggie is already in position, wrapped in a bloody butcher's apron, juggling knives. A good-sized crowd has formed, attracted by the "Last Night!" signs. At the head of the line is a group of teenagers, three girls and two boys. Nathan feels the little inward loosening that means he's falling into character, someone he thinks of as Mr. Hatchet. He takes their tickets, lets out an ominous, hissing chuckle, and lifts the velvet rope for them to enter. One of the boys laughs nervously. They shuffle into the darkness, around the first corner, where Rosemary is waiting as Regan from *The Exorcist*. Someone shrieks piercingly, indicating that they've seen her.

He's been apologizing, apologizing, to Jenny and everyone, and what he should but doesn't say is: "I'm sorry, but I don't want to do this anymore. What seemed like an amusingly offbeat profession for a thirty-year-old man seems like a somewhat creepy activity for someone past fifty. I don't want to feel this way, but I do." He pictures, for a moment, Jenny's firm neck disguised with drooping latex, Vince's clear eyes looking out from artificial hollows. Surely they should stop while it's all still a game?

At ten-thirty he calls Reggie's name and points to his watch. Reggie and Vince take turns working outside, and it's time to switch. Reggie nods and ducks inside.

A moment later he's back. "I don't see Vince," he says.

"What?" Nathan says. "Where is he?"

"I don't know, he's just not there."

Vince's position is the dead baby room. Nathan leaves Reggie at the front door and ducks inside. He swings through the narrow, dark halls, passing glowing skulls, body bags, fake corpses.

A crack of yellow light is showing under the door of the employee dressing room, despite the strict rules against any kind of illumination after eight o'clock. Nathan pushes open the door. He sees Vince, and with him Jenny. Jenny is holding Vince right hand in her own, fingertips to wrist, in what could be a regretful farewell or a tender greeting. They turn to him as if expecting him, and Jenny begins to talk quietly.

"It's not your fault, Nathan. Please, honey. We weren't going to say anything unless it became unavoidable."

They look at him, Jenny and Vince, from behind their ghastly faces. Good disguises, perfect to hide behind. But as Jenny steps forward, tears running down her cheeks, he again catches sight in the mirror of his own face, deadened with white paint, its shadows deepened with gray. His mouth twitches. The paint is cracking.

Helen Schulman

I Heart Dan Jansen

Allison had her first miscarriage on her first trip to Disney World and, if she hadn't been so sad and crampy, there might even have been a bitterly ironic laugh or two in it, losing a baby in babyland. As it was, she wasn't laughing but weaving, between the bed and the bathroom, and the bathroom and the toiletries kit in her suitcase. She'd started in with the Advil a couple of hours before, and when she officially swallowed the equivalent of an O.D., she threw caution to the wind and broke into the minibar. Grey (boyfriend) had walked off with the little key. She quickly split the seal on half a dozen of those tiny airplane-sized bottles of liquor, aiming for a coma.

After all those weeks of being good—no caffeine, no alcohol, vitamins until she could taste them in the back of her throat, smell them in her urine—now she longed for the old days when she always had a spare joint in her pocket, for a couple of lines of coke. Cigarettes, which she'd given up years before, Quaaludes. Crystal, THC, even. High School. Anything that would get her lit enough to forget the wringing of her insides, the pressure and quease that made her feel like she permanently had to go to the bathroom; and the now unrefutable fact that that tiny mess of cells, that little clot of future, had swirled around in a whirlpool of hotel plumbing and was now shooting out to sea.

It had been a week of touch and go. Three different doctors performing three different sonographies. Grey actually accompanied her to two of them pacing like a husband in the waiting room.

"I don't get it," he'd asked aghast, "it's like a giant dildo?"

How could she explain the anatomy of the procedure? It had been like a giant dildo, covered in a condom even, slicked back with a light green lubricant that she wondered vaguely if, in the dark down there, would glow. The two female doctors had just hauled off and stuck it in, the male had asked Allison to insert the wand herself. Then all eyes turned away from her to the computer screen, searching the graphic of her uterus for a fetus, as if her interior were now a hot new CD-Rom.

For awhile, her reknowed physicians suspected that the pregnancy could be ectopic, in the fallopian tubes, which would have been no picnic for Allison, although her closest girlfriend Lenora had assured her that the surgery could be done with a laser through Allison's belly-button, leaving no scar. Lenora's brother was an OB-GYN, and with credentials like that, Allison trusted Lenora's opinion over that of all her pricey specialists. But even Lenora hadn't known how much Allison wanted this baby. How she sneaked around the drugstore day after day, browsing through the soaps, shampoos and hair conditioners, before gaining the nerve to dash forward to the register to purchase a home pregnancy test. At the end of a week of testing and retesting, the teenage girl, with the big hair and the loud voice who worked the cash register, had said (waving the box discreetly in the air): "I hope you find one that tells you what you want." By the eighth day of her missed period, the test finally came up positive. It had a fine, light blue line, like a tiny vein, etched delicately across the white square of the plastic wand, and Allison's heart had soared.

But a couple of weeks later even Lenora was talking ruptured tubes and spiraling infections, and Allison finally got scared. Hence the second and third opinions, the pricey ultra-sounds. By the end of it all, Allison felt as if she'd done the football team. But the third doctor, the male doctor (Allison was sorry to concede) had maneuvered that probe right and left and up and down, under a large paper-towel that draped over her knees, just like a kid with a joystick. As if that stupid sheet prevented Allison from knowing what was going on down there! And this guy actually found the fetus, wizened and unviable, that "blighted ovum" as he had called it attached to a septum in her uterine wall. Or something like that. None of it made sense, after awhile, there were so many variations on the final call. The point was that Allison finally knew that the pregnancy was doomed.

The doctors had urged her to take the trip to Florida anyway, she wasn't far enough along to require medical assistance, why disrupt her life? Feeling sorry for her, Grey had even offered her an out, Disney-wise—"You don't have to come," he'd said, Friday evening as they were practically out the door, leaving for the airport. And then with newfound nobility, "I don't have to go. If you want I'll call up Jacobson and tell him I can't do the story."

But what was the point? To stay home and miss a free trip even if it was only to Orlando? A king-sized berth with a remote control nailed to the small faux-wood night table? Little soap? How could Allison say no? Grey needed this assignment, *they* needed the money, and Allison couldn't bear the thought of staying home alone. The truth was, that until very early that same morning (four or five o'clock) when her pelvic area had begun to fizz with heat—there was no other way to describe it—when the first few blood clots began to plop out like spit bubbles, dark shiny dollops attached to gossamer red veils, membranes (just the thought of the word made her choke) that swirled in the water of the toilet like some fairie animation, she had wasted her time daring to hope. Even on the plane out from New York, Allison spent the whole two and a half hours dreaming about her baby's damp, fragrant scalp, about waltzing into one of her many gynecologists' offices for a post-natal checkup, her infant's downy pink head peeking out of the snugglie, proving them all wrong.

Grey was a features writer. That is, he was a novelist, an aspiring novelist, who made his living writing features for various magazines that he abhorred. At LaGuardia Airport they had made the rounds of several newsstands, purveying that month's publications. There was a science to his attack. He'd scan the rows and stacks, then swoop in quickly, using his back as a shield from an imaginary newsstand audience (Grey was a little paranoid) and hunch over the current copy. He would open the glossy cover, take a step back away from that first sickening hit of the perfume ads, and grumble over whatever he found in the table of contents, even when the article was his own. He'd had a glorified Q & A in *GQ* this month about some spoiled talentless young buck who was segueing from a lucrative music career into typical film stardom.

"Butt-licking asshole," cursed Grey, when he happened upon his own by-line.

He ended up buying copies of *The Times, The Washington Post, The Journal,* and *The National Enquirer.* Allison, an erstwhile actress, now an English and Drama teacher, brought along her 10th graders' essays on *Black Boy* to review. They'd sat out the flight side-by-side in silence, Grey drowning in all that paper, Allison reading over his shoulder.

They arrived in Orlando at one o'clock in the morning, found their room at the Caribbean Beach resort by two-thirty-five. The pink and cream-colored structures were clustered in islands, Allison and Grey's hotel was in the Antigua complex. And while their particular glorified motel room overlooked the handicapped parking lot, the front of the building faced a fake beach with fake waves and real imported sand, which is why Grey picked it, when the park publicist had called, outlining their options.

"I thought you'd lie in the sun," Grey said, kindly. "Read a goddamn book that isn't on the tenth grade list for a change—you know Jackie Collins, or maybe something by a dead white guy."

How was he to know that for the four days they were destined to be in Orlando nothing was predicted but rain?

Their room was up a flight of stairs and half a mile down a verandah. Grey carried all the bags, because it was late, he was feeling whole-souled, and after all Allison was still officially pregnant. The room was undistinguished except for the Mickey Mouse shampoo and soap; the drapes and spreads, the carpet, were all yellow and green, not unlike the avocado and gold of Allison's youth. Everything that could possibly have mouse ears, here, would have ears. Molded butter came with the morning toast. The water tower that they had used for a landmark when they drove in circles around the entire sainted Caribbean—St. Martin, St. Barthelmy, St. John—before a near head-on collision with the sign at the entrance to Antigua, had sported giant black ones. There were two little girls with mouse-eared headbands, sound asleep, slung over their parents' shoulders, in the parking lot when they pulled in. What kind of people kept kids out so late? The mother was fat and the father was bald. Did either of them deserve to be parents? Grey and Allison collapsed on the bed without even bothering to undress or take a shower or place an arrival call in to the loyal Lenora, who'd promised that she'd wait up.

Poor guy, Grey had about two hours sleep before Allison's cramps woke them both.

But that was long ago, ancient history, something that seasoned Allison, made her stronger, something that happened to her in her youth. Now it was three-thirty in the afternoon, almost twelve hours later. She lay in bed, ironically, in the fetal position, the empty liquor bottles littering the floor, the TV on, not watching General Hospital in full defiance of Lenora's prescriptive advice. Grey had left hours before, he'd had a job to do, but he'd called in every thirty to sixty minutes. "How's my girl?" he'd said the last time. Grey. Grey said, "How's my girl?" During one of the two previous calls he'd unfortunately asked: "How's my baby?"

She was thirty-four years old. Thirty-four. Which was probably not ancient, but certainly not young. She'd been living with Grey for five years, they had no intention of getting married. Marriage was the end of the movie. When the viewers tuned back in, the couple was either fat and neutered and living for their children, or in the wacky process of getting a wackier divorce. It was a swift segue from engagement ring to sweat pants and *neither* of them wanted that, Allison told herself. The only issue had been kids. Grey wasn't exactly predisposed, but then again he had nothing against the little fuckers either. He just wished they had more money. Well, who doesn't thought Allison, who had just been given a raise and a promotion to twenty-five thousand dollars after eight years of teaching at Miss Parkers. Eight years. And now she was to be the chairman of her department, which in and of itself was a scary thought. Poor people have children all the time, she'd said to Grey. And he'd shot back, "Yeah, the news is full of them." Still, he'd relented about two months before. Perhaps it was the peer pressure; everyone they knew was having kids—Grey's favorite editor was having three, her husband had spent the better part of a year shooting her in the butt with fertility drugs. And the friends who already had a little decorative offspring dressed them up in Elvis tee-shirts and baby high-tops and tiny leather jackets; and they schlepped them to all the restaurants, openings and art shows, that they themselves, pre-parenthood, had grown bored of.

Children were the latest accoutrement in their circle, and the fashion element must have been what had swayed Grey finally, because Allison knew her nagging usually fell upon deaf ears; for years she'd wanted a dog, wanted one so badly she'd ended up writing a letter to Jimmy Carter, asking him to conduct a little domestic mediation; he'd been so good in the Middle East. But Jimmy Carter politely refused—in a standard form letter—to come to her rescue, so she'd learn to leave things with Grey up to fate. And as fate would have it, it was in the middle of a particularly good round of sex without a rubber—"riding bare-back" as he'd called it—when out of nowhere Grey had grinned up at her and said: "Here goes nothing." It still amazed Allison, after all those years of Health Ed, and the lectures of her doctor father, that this was actually how it was done. It would have made more sense to her if she'd gotten pregnant from being bitten by some wild, exotic bug, or by the moon's shifting into some shimmery new planetary alliance and casting a potent silvery shadow across her belly button. She wondered abstractly how long it had taken cavemen to make the sex-kid connection, a connection she doubted she'd have ever had the insight to make on her own.

Lying in bed, Allison started to think that maybe she and Grey should adopt whatever baby was found this week abandoned in a dumpster. On *General Hospital*—which she was determinedly not-watching, screw Lenora—two underage gorgeous kids were boffing their brains out. They rolled around in bed, they rolled right to the floor. Without even bumping heads. That's how much in love they were. Watch, they'll get a baby, she thought. If only she were sixteen again, and in the backseat of a car somewhere—back then it had worked like a charm, before she was twenty-two she'd had had two abortions. Was this miscarriage her punishment? She'd had a reckless, fertile youth; she was paying for it now.

Allison punched in the remote control. *Headline Sports.* The Winter Olympics. She heard Grey slide his card-key into the door. She rearranged the bedclothes around herself to make her seem more pitiful.

"How's my baby-girl?" Grey said.

He was gorgeous. Far better looking than Allison. Long, curlyish blond hair, caught back in a ponytail. Tall, big shoulders, faded jeans that hung just so from his hips. No butt, no gut, just the faintest hint of love handles. He was five years older than she was, but he still looked like a kid; except for the lines that set his mouth, the skin that was so handsomely weathered. Grey was a study in unstudied casualness, although more than once in the years that they'd been together she'd caught him in front of the mirror, artfully untucking a shirt, poking a larger hole in a stylishly holey sweater.

At the sight of him, Allison started to cry. What would a guy like that want with a girl like her? Her brown hair was flat against her head; it had a middle part. She was sweaty and her nose was running. She was wearing Grey's yesterday's discarded shirt and a big bulky maxipad fastened to her underwear, which were unfortunately pale green and waist-high and had come in a box of twenty.

Allison had never been as pretty as he was, although when not standing next to Grey in comparison, she'd always been considered pretty enough. Why he drained her of her beauty. Oh she was smarter, although he was plenty smart, she was smarter, hadn't she just been voted chairman of her department! And what *she did had value*—that's what her mother said—no puff pieces for Allison, no sir, she was nobly molding bratty minds.

But did she really want to officially commit to a career in education? What had happened to the theater and her acting? Wasn't that a thing she might want someday to try to revive? Yes, no, maybe. What had once seemed like a temporary solution to a particularly virulent form of stage-fright (she'd kept vomiting in the wings) was now turning into her life. Which was one of the reasons she'd wanted a kid in the first place; so she could explore this existential crises leisurely, and in private; so she could legitimately opt out. That way when her relationship inevitably ended—its ending was inevitable, even Lenora copped to that; Grey was too immature, too sexy, currently hovering too close to the brink of success, to being forty, and just beginning to get invited to terrific parties, to be around for the long haul—she would have managed to have wrung something out of it.

Allison sunk down lower in the bed.

In an instant Grey was by her side, feeling sorry for her. A few of those little glass liquor bottles rolled off the spread on to the wall-to-wall carpeting, with a series of varying thuds like weighted chimes. Grey picked one of them up. "A little Karen Anne Quinlan-action?" he asked her. "Hunh?"

Allison curled up against him, let him pet her greasy head.

"How was your day?" she said.

"Terrific," said Grey, reaching over her to press the clicker and turn up the volume. "You?"

It was the ill-fated skater, Dan Jansen's, third event.

"I love this guy," Grey said.

"You do?" said Allison. The skater was tall and good-looking in a middle-American kind of way; his curly brown hair was cut into bangs, a shallow fringe. But his thighs, his thighs! They were mammoth. They made Lenora's look like Cindy Crawford's.

"This is his second-to-last chance at a medal. He's the world's greatest, everyone knows it, but when it comes to the Olympics, poor bastard, he can't ever win a race. Performance anxiety or something, I think he had a sister who died once."

"She died once?" Allison said. She was a little annoyed with the direction their conversation was now taking.

Grey's eyes were glued to the set. The starter gun went off. Bang! Jansen immediately took the lead. One lap, two laps, three, the announcer announced his best time ever. But in the fourth lap, Jansen slipped—it was inevitable—he touched the ice with his hand and lost momentum.

"I love this guy," Grey said.

How cold that ice must have felt, Allison thought. How it must have burned him.

The race ended without Jansen even placing.

Grey shook his head in amazement. "I wonder why he bothers," Grey said. "What a waste of time."

The next day, Allison was feeling slightly better. Except for wearing pads for the first time since she was eleven—they felt like a diaper—with a couple of hits of Tylenol and two Seven and Seven's for breakfast, she was feeling fine. They decided to venture out into the parks. The subject of Grey's piece was "Organized Adventures," after riding the rides here he was scheduled to bungee jump in Joshua Tree Park, white water raft on some western rapids with a guide, perhaps even go to school to learn how to hang-glide. What fun. At least there were frequent flier points to be had, this was his rationale, at least they would have a little vacation. But when they got to the park's entrance at around 11:00 in the morning, there were no complimentary tickets waiting for them. So Grey set off to investigate, while Allison watched one group of retarded and terminally ill kids after another enter the mouse-eared gates. It was the kind of scene she'd imagined seeing in another six months, belly out to there, turning tearfully towards Grey and saying: "Honey, should we really be having a child when it could be subject to so much pain?" How she wished she could have the privilege of being so beatific and so sensitive. Now if she made a remark like that, he'd probably just agree with her. By the time Grey got back with the tickets, she'd bought herself three balloons and bummed a menthol cigarette. At this point, what did she have to lose?

Grey shook his head when he saw her puffing away, but he didn't say anything. Instead they walked into the park and immediately got on line. It was a grey day, threatening to rain, cool for Florida anyway, and kind of blustery. Grey put his arm around Allison's shoulder as they waited on line for Space Mountain. There was a sign that said: Not for very small children or expectant mothers; hadn't Allison recently been in both of these two exalted categories? Grey's arm was a

328

heavy arm, a solid arm, and usually she liked to feel its weight, but now she felt like it was driving her into the ground. She shrugged it off.

"What's wrong with you?" Grey said.

"What do you mean, what's wrong with me," said Allison. "What's wrong with you?"

Grey shook his handsome head, some loose greying strands of his golden hair curling out of his ponytail and glimmering around his face. He tucked an errant lock behind an ear.

"Hormones," said Grey. He said it wisely.

"Fuck you," said Allison. "Fuck you, you patronizing, aging narcissist."

Grey laughed out loud.

"How dare you laugh at me," said Allison, a little spit spraying out. She pressed the back of her hand to her mouth to force it back inside again.

"Look it," said Grey. "It's not such a big deal. We'll try again, okay. We'll try again or we'll wait. I mean maybe this was a blessing in disguise, the wrong time and all that—you know I never thought we were exactly ready."

He said this calmly, rationally, with maturity—for him—and grace.

"I hate you," shrieked Allison, "I hate your stupid guts."

A little girl next to them on line moved closer to her mother. Her father turned to Grey, thudded his finger into his chest and said: "If you and your wife are having some sort of problem why don't you take it out of the park. There are kids here for Christ's sake."

"Hey man," said Grey, "I suggest you get your fucking finger out of my fucking sternum." He was growing inside his shoulders, squaring off for a fight.

"I'm not his wife," said Allison. "I wouldn't marry that loser if you paid me." And then she was running blindly, blindly, tears and snot flowing, hot and bubbly across her face. But Grey didn't even call after her. Perhaps he was too busy getting the shit kicked out of him.

One could only hope, thought Allison.

So although it was pointless, she ran for awhile, through the crowd, around the peanut vendors, twisting and turning as if she were being followed, but of course Allison wasn't being followed, and so this behavior eventually seemed too theatrical even for her; she felt like a jerk. A fresh burst of blood seeped out wetly between her legs. The pad was creeping up. It was disgusting. And she was weak and light-headed, she needed a bathroom and iron supplements. She needed to sit down.

Ahead was a park attendant. He could show her the way to a ladies room. Allison circumvented a clown, a duck, a hot dog stand and thousands of babies in baby carriages, slung low in snugglies, riding high in backpacks like mini-kings and queens towering on their thrones. Every other woman she passed seemed to have a jutting belly. They waddled about with an air of superiority, as if somehow getting knocked up had changed them from a bunch of ordinary sluts into something goddamned holy. As if everybody didn't fuck… "I fuck too!" Allison wanted to scream out into the air.

For a moment Allison was so angry, angry at the world, angry at all these women whose bodies didn't fail them, that she wanted to kick one expectant mom right in the belly—a bleached-blonde with six months of black roots in a jumpsuit of pink terry—but the ugliness of this thought and her own misplaced animosity frightened her so, she decided to hate herself instead.

"I hate myself," thought Allison, and her eyes swum again with tears. She patted the park attendant on the back.

"The ladies room," she said. "Please."

The man took one look and fast pointed her in the other direction. "Two lefts and a right," he said, then disappeared, seemingly anxious to get away from her.

By the time Allison had done her business, flushed and exited the stall, her head was feeling light and her neck was feeling sweaty. She soaped up her hands and rinsed them in cool water. When that didn't do the trick she ran her wrists under the cold tap cocked up to a full blasty force. She was standing at an endless row of sinks. She looked up at her face in an endless row of mirrors. Her face was white, very white, except for the areas where it was pink. Her face was pink in the whites of her eyes, pink around her nose from all that crying and that blowing. It was pink where it should have been white, and vice versa, her cheeks had all the bloom of a chicken bone.

I'd better lie down, Allison thought. She'd lost a lot of blood. She probably should have stayed in bed and not done all that running. She probably should never have gone on this stupid trip. Her mother was right, Grey was a good-for-nothing, and at this very moment she could have been lying in her own bed in New York City, being waited upon hand and foot by the loyal Lenora.

The ladies room had an antechamber. It was just as brightly and fluorescently lit as the room with the toilets and the sinks, only there was a waist-high broad shelf protruding from one grafittied wall and there were thankfully no mirrors. Perhaps it was a makeup shelf? It looked like a perfect place to lie down on. And it wasn't too funky, in fact, the shelf looked kind of clean—too bad one couldn't say the same for the rest of the lavatory. It smelled bathroomy, of urine and mold and disinfectant. Allison tested the shelf with her weight, then hoisted herself up and spread out. Finally, her feet were off the ground. And in the nick of time, for once she was horizontal she realized how near she had been to passing out. A sea of dots swum in front of her. She closed her eyes. She placed her forearm over them to keep the harsh yellowish light from seeping in. All her muscles seemed to let go at once, her legs turned out from her hips, her belly went soft, her palms rolled up to face the sky. Allison relaxed for the first time in what felt like forever. She went so liquid, she almost fell asleep.

What was the big deal? Perhaps Grey was right. It wasn't as if she were living in a war zone, or out in the street, or lying on some hospital gurney dying from radiation poisoning. Certainly they could try again—that is if they hadn't just broken up. The doctors said after a couple of months of course they could try again. It wasn't like this was such a freak occurrence, a lot of people have miscarriages, several miscarriages, they told her, and they still have beautiful children. Don't any of them have ugly ones? Allison had wanted to know, because it was always that this-one had three misses but now a beautiful baby boy, and so-and-so had a stillbirth, but now she's the mother of

330

the two most beautiful twins you ever saw. There must be someone somewhere who had a miscarriage or two and then gave birth to an anencephalic monster. Let's face it, there are people life just *didn't work out for*; and in her heart Allison always suspected she was one of them.

Grey didn't get it. We could try again, he said, and of course they could, hadn't she spent the last ten minutes making a case for just the very same thing inside her head? But *this* baby was lost, lost for good, and no matter how many others were born, nothing could every replace her—which was terrible.

But lying down, torturing herself, that was okay; it was kind of a relief hanging out this way. Still, how long could a grown woman lie on a clean shelf in a dirty public lavatory? There was something pathetic about it. She turned her gaze to the wall. "Ronnie loves Nelson, 4-ever." "For a good time, call…" The standard fare. What did she expect, Keith Haring? This was Disney World after all. She took a pen out of the inner pocket of her jean jacket. " I heart Dan Jansen," Allison wrote. And she thought, I heart him, I really heart him.

The grey door swung open. Someone passed through the room with the stalls, someone carrying something that squalls, and then that someone was heading towards her, because the squalls were getting louder and the someone was getting closer.

Allison could smell her.

Tabu.

Shit, thought Allison. She swung her legs over the side and sat up on her shelf.

A girl walked in, a young girl, not more than sixteen or maybe seventeen. She was wearing braces and her blonde hair was over processed in a curly perm. She wore white tennis shoes, acid washed jeans and a school team jacket with white leather sleeves and in her arms was that little squaller. Over her shoulder she carried a diaper bag. Blue, so it was a boy.

"Excuse me," said the kid to Allison. "Buster here's got to get changed."

Buster, thought Allison, she named a baby Buster?

Her shelf, her very own private shelf, her sanctuary, was a built-in changing table.

How appropos. She slid down off her perch.

Buster was screaming at the top of his lungs. His head was so swollen purple, it looked like it might shoot off.

"Shut up, you stupid baby," the girl cooed in a baby-talking voice. "You disgusting little bastard, you shit all over yourself."

Allison blinked. She shook her head. The words didn't match up with the music.

"Isn't he a pig?" the girl said to Allison. She was wiping up his bottom.

Allison nodded, yes, the baby did look like a pig, a big fat pink pig wallowing in his own refuse. Still, he'd stopped crying now, there was some snot crusting on his upper lip, but his color was going down and his head didn't seem quite as big, now that it wasn't purple.

Allison leaned up against the wall. Perhaps she'd stood up too fast. Perhaps the sight of this baby was making her dizzy.

"My parents," said the girl. "They're driving me crazy. Buster's too young and too stupid to even know that he's at The Mouse in the first place." She folded up his diaper, placed a new one between his legs and fastened it.

"Hey," she said to Allison, "Are you hurting?"

Yes, nodded Allison, I am, I am.

The girl smiled knowingly, shoved the freshly diapered Buster back on Allison's shelf. He faced the wall now.

"Well I could sure use a hit myself," she said. She was reaching into her inside jacket pocket. Then she hesitated, she gave Allison a fishy eye.

She said, "You're cool, right?"

Cool. Sure she was cool.

"I'm cool," said Allison, sagging within her weight. I might faint, she thought, but I'll do it coolly.

The girl turned on a wicked smile. She brought out a little pipe. She brought out a tiny vial. Buster was kicking at the wall with his socked feet and moaning. She unscrewed the tiny vial and tapped out a little rock, a crystal, dusty at its edges.

Cool, Allison thought.

The girl reached into the side pocket of her jacket and brought out a plastic lighter. Buster was crying again, but she ignored him.

Shut up, Allison thought. Shut up, you ugly fucking baby.

You pig.

The girl brought the pipe to her lips and fired up the bowl. She inhaled deep.

"Wow," she said, and a light rapidly burned out behind her eyes. And then it was as if all at once she were catapulted away, receding inside herself far from her bones and skin, far from her clothing and the air of this still dank bathroom, away from Allison, away from her wailing kid.

The girl's hand with the pipe dropped down to her side.

Allison reached out, took the pipe and brought it to her own lips.

And later, first back in the motel room and then at a couple of parties in New York City, when she wanted to charm Grey and their friends with her seamy little story—"Did I ever tell you about the time I smoked crack with a cracker in a public restroom?"—she would hesitate for a moment, remembering the instant before she'd dared to take her first inhalation; which by the way did the trick, hitting her like bolt lightning, shooting her pain out through the tips of her toes and her fingers. Allison had caught a good look into that girl's eyes then; they were dazed and vacant and lost; they were deadened. And even though she thought it might amuse her friends, Allison always left out the part where palm open and reaching, she had begged her: *Girlfriend, please. Take me where you are.*

Marilyn Stablein

The Rat Caterer

Everyone from a lowly street urinal sweeper to a high society lady enjoyed the rat massacres. Hands down people believed rats were the most odious members of the animal kingdom. To see one or a dozen rats viciously and quickly killed had an appeal that the dog or bear matches lacked.

Predictably as the spectator sport of ratting grew in popularity, the demand for live rats increased. And as any market analyst or broker will testify, when and where a demand arises, suppliers soon step forward to profit in the trade. Men who had as much cunning and diligence as the original destroyers of rats, turned their attentions to catching, harboring and breeding the rodents. Men like Charlie Doyle—a stalwart sort who exhibited the gall and stamina necessary to enter into a verminous trade—soon enjoyed the rewards of a lucrative livelihood.

Charlie raised fighting rats in cages located behind his house. A few favorite rats lived in fancier cages in his parlor. Within two months after he placed a male and three female rats in a breeding pen, he counted 2,000 rats which ate through, burlap and all, a hefty 200 pound sack of barley meal each week. He raised both Norwegian rats and black harbor rats. Like any professional breeder, Charlie sorted his animals, keeping healthy brown and black rats in separate cages.

"Rats of one species do not belong with those from another," Charlie claimed. "If I don't separate them, they'll tear one another to pieces. Barn rats, ship rats or sewer rats never get along."

Charlie let visitors into his home to tour the caged rats he kept in his parlor: specimens of albino rats and piebald rats. In one cage a black rat and a white rat, potential parents to a new generation of rats Charlie hoped, slept at opposite ends. The caged rats accepted their life of confinement and did not attempt to escape or to bite their owner. Parlor rats exhibited no anger, as if they lost the notion of freedom long ago. They appeared blind when Charlie pulled them out of their cages. But when he finished showing them to his visitors and went to return them, as soon as the rats neared the cages, they anxiously struggled to be set free again, to the freedom they knew, the freedom of confinement.

Every week Charlie delivered a batch of fighting rats to each of the eight arenas. Although there were others who supplied fighting rats for the public matches, only six months after he started his outdoor rat farm Charlie boasted he was the largest rat caterer in the city.

The rat entrants in the sporting events were not pampered like the caged rats in Charlie's parlor. The sponsors crushed them into small baskets without a drop of water to drink or a crust of toast to eat. Dozens of rats squeezed into the same type of basket that poultry farmers carried their chickens to the market in. Rats swarmed over rats in a mass of panting, squirming, squealing bodies. When each starving rat bounded into the fighting pit, their viciousness excited the crowds.

A rat breeder's job was not easy. Dozens of rat-bite scars mared Charlie's fingers and wrists. One friend scolded him: "Charlie, for God's sake! Rub caraway on your fingertips, mate, to discourage a bite. Or camphor. You can't let them eat you alive."

"Smear dung," his wife suggested. "Rats hate the smell of dung."

"I've rubbed my hands a dozen times," Charlie said, "nothing works. If a rat wants to bite, he'll bite no matter what balm or repellent I use."

"A rat's bite," Charlie said, "is a three cornered one, like a leech's, only deeper, of course, and it bleeds for ever such a time."

Sometimes a finger blackened and swelled from a nasty bite. Only once did a finger turn putrid; then the doctor amputated.

No one said the rat trade was without risk.

Once Charlie attained a modest success in the breeding business, he planned to hire young boys to pull the rats out of the cage for him and drop them into the fighting pit or ring. Let the boys rub their hands with oils and potions, he mused, maybe the rats won't bite them.

Eugene Stein

The Barn Fire

Eight cottages, pre-fabs bought in Macy's, looped around the shallow end of the pond. On the far end, bushes and willows hid the dirt road that ambled up to Route 42. Behind the road, resting on the crest of a small hill, sat a low, heavy, weatherbeaten barn, its paint peeling away in thin, irregular pancakes of skin, like a moulting reptile or a sun-burned child. Nancy Lerner had found the bungalow colony by answering an advertisement in *The New York Times*. "Children's paradise," the ad proclaimed.

The squat green barn, with its farm implements lashed to the walls and the dungy smell of cows in its basement stalls, was the only evidence that the property had once been a dairy farm. Although a practical, temperate woman, Nancy never felt entirely comfortable inside the wood building. The air was thick and dusty, the tools on the walls looked vaguely like torture devices, and the floorboards creaked; cobwebs appeared almost daily behind an old freezer and underneath a sagging ping-pong table stored in the back room. But she was grateful for the barn, because all that wet first summer, when one rain storm dissolved into the next and the pond water rose and they all wore boots—when even the dry barn became damp, and the sun came out shyly, if at all—her three daughters played there with the other children. A transistor radio crackled from morning to night, accompanying their endless games of Parcheesi and ping-pong. The girls sang along to "Band on the Run" and "The Night Chicago Died," ignoring the interruptions of the Watergate hearings and then Nixon's resignation.

Susan and Wendy, high-strung and athletic girls who often fought with each other, felt cooped up in the barn. Laura, younger than her sisters, moodier and more eccentric, enjoyed the summer, becoming fast friends with a girl at the colony named Danielle Rifkin.

Nancy befriended Danielle's mother, Myra, a frank, robust woman who was married to the owner of a string of successful gas stations. The bungalow colony was located in a small town ninety minutes north of Manhattan, and their husbands, working in the city, came up only on weekends. Summer widows, Nancy and Myra were thrown together for companionship. Myra had grown up in Brooklyn, like Nancy, but in a much poorer family. Now well-off, she could afford a chic resort but confessed to Nancy that she felt ill-at-ease among chic resorters.

The two women went shopping together at the stores along Route 42, walking into town on dry days to buy milk at the tiny Grand Union or mail a letter at the tinier post office. The storekeepers remained standoffish to the summer residents, and beneath the town's glacial politeness, Nancy and Myra and even their children could detect the faint glow of anti-Semitism. Laura, counting her change once at the general store, heard the cashier mutter to her husband, "They start early."

Myra liked to play softball with the boys at the colony, to mix cocktails, to tell dirty jokes in Yiddish. Nancy did none of these things, but there was something infectious about Myra's enthusiasm and laughter, something wonderful about her biting sarcasm, something moving and at times almost frightening about her fierce devotion to Danielle, her only child. During the whole first summer, there had been only one—not even squabble, but moment of discomfort between the two women. At the beginning of August, the bungalow colony hosted a "barn sale"— a tag sale inside the barn, although every year at least one disgruntled customer expressed regret that the barn itself wasn't for sale. Nancy and Myra sat together for hours, selling clothes their children had outgrown, costume jewelry, paperbacks, and old china. Myra enjoyed the sale thoroughly, taking on bargaining duties for both of them. Nancy laughed at one especially gruesome piece of jewelry Myra was selling, a thick necklace with fake pearls the size of peanuts. "Who on earth gave you that?"

Myra confessed that she had bought it for herself. "You should see some of the things I've bought," Nancy said quickly.

But Nancy's solicitousness only made Myra angry. "It doesn't matter. Now I can afford the real thing."

Nancy looked down at the floor. Her husband, Stanley, worked for the city; they didn't have much money and had to save all year to pay for the summer at the bungalow colony.

"Let's just forget about it," Myra said.

"Let's," Nancy said, looking up. And the two women smiled at each other, relieved.

"Moo-vie!" Danielle hollered. "Moo-vie," Laura called after her. They circled around the bungalow colony, herding everyone toward the barn. Danielle's father had bought an old sixteen millimeter projector and brought it up to the colony. Each weekend a local film rental company supplied a feature, usually a movie two or three years old. Tonight was the last film of the season. Nancy and the other women brought folding chairs to the barn and arranged them in neat rows, while Myra tacked a king-sized bed sheet—a makeshift screen—to an inside wall of the building. Laura and Danielle tested a dozen chairs before they found ones to their satisfaction.

The girls were now ten and had spent their second summer together. Like her mother, Danielle Rifkin was vivacious, a plain, extroverted, stocky child who got her pretty clothes and expensive sneakers dirty and never seemed to mind. Impulsive and bold, she saw *Jaws* twice that August and wanted to see it a third time. Laura, bookish and tentative, had to shut her eyes during the shark attacks. During the school year, they had seen each other only two or three times. They both lived in Queens, but almost at opposite ends, Laura in Jackson Heights, Danielle in far-off, princely Jamaica Estates. As soon as the summer began, their friendship had bloomed again. The summer had been wonderful, drier and warmer than the last.

Whenever the two mothers and two daughters got together for lunch on one of their porches, eating tuna fish sandwiches with sliced tomatoes from Laura's garden, the conversation bubbled up from the Rifkins and was eagerly swallowed by the Lerners. She and her mother were like her garden, Laura thought, carefully weeded but always in danger of drying out.

Her sisters, twelve and thirteen, spent most of the summer in the general store on Route 42, flirting with the local boys and even, Laura suspected, making out with them. Susan and Wendy had asked two boys to come to the movie tonight and sat with them in the back row. Around their necks the boys wore gold chains, and small crosses rested on their thin, hard chests. They were polite but Stanley was convinced they were "using" his daughters.

Midway through the movie, Stanley strode to the back and ordered the girls to disentangle themselves from the boys. Laura and Danielle turned around to see what was happening. Laura was close to her middle sister, Wendy, but Susan was often cruel to her and she hoped Susan would be punished. Her father separated the girls from their dates and sat with them in the back row.

After the movie, Laura and Danielle stayed behind, helping their mothers take down the sheet, folding it and the chairs, eager to catch their mothers' analysis of the necking incident.

"That's why I like an all-girls school," Nancy said. "Then there are no distractions." Hunter Junior High School, a prestigious school in Manhattan that Susan and Wendy attended, had recently started accepting boys, to Nancy's regret.

Next year, Nancy went on, Laura would be taking the test to get into Hunter. Hunter didn't charge tuition, and public junior high schools had become dangerous, so the competition was fierce. But Nancy was sure Laura would pass, like her sisters before her. "You're probably sending Danielle to private school."

"You don't think she could get in to Hunter?"

The girls looked at each other and then quickly away.

"I just meant you could, could probably afford a private school," Nancy said. "That's all."

"That's not what you meant."

"Yes it is. Really. And you live so far from Manhattan…"

The air in the barn, always close, had become even heavier, and now threatened to choke the girls. They couldn't look at each other or at their mothers.

"You're a snob," Myra said.

"How can you say that?" cried Nancy.

Myra took her sheet and left the barn. Danielle followed after her.

The following June, the Lerners and the Rifkins both returned to the bungalow colony. Nancy and Myra hadn't seen each other at all during the year, although they had exchanged polite, formal New Year's greetings at Rosh Hashanah and then again in January. The distance and time had only hardened the two women's feelings, but the girls, reunited, were intimate as ever and delighted that they were now allowed to bicycle by themselves to the general store, where they eyed boys but didn't dare to speak to them.

On July 4th, the tall ships were sailing into New York harbor for the bicentennial celebration. Myra and Alan had been invited to a rooftop party on Riverside Drive; the view would be ideal. Danielle asked Laura to come back to New York with them for the weekend and then, crestfallen, informed Laura that the party was going to be too crowded and that she wouldn't be able to take her after all. Nancy fumed. Myra was angry at her, all right, she could accept that. But Myra didn't have to punish Laura.

When Danielle returned from New York, she brought back with her a new CB radio. The girls used the radio every day, holing up in the barn for privacy, and speaking with a boy on Shaker Road, two miles away. They were afraid to meet him, especially when they learned he was fifteen, but they allowed themselves to flirt shamelessly with him and pretended to be experienced older women—two sisters named Lucinda and Deirdre, ages eighteen and nineteen. Removing some chopped meat from the communal freezer in the back, Nancy overheard the girls' ruttish conversation.

Nancy told Myra that she didn't want Laura using the CB radio anymore and that obviously Danielle was a good deal more experienced than Laura.

"Experienced?" Myra asked.

"With boys," Nancy said, trying carefully to keep her voice neutral, so that she wouldn't appear to be insulting Danielle.

"She can't be any more experienced than Susan," Myra said. Susan was dating a local boy. "The last time I saw her, she had her tongue down that *shaygetz's* throat."

"Fine," said Nancy, burning up. She stalked off.

The following weekend, Myra and Alan went out to dinner with another couple from the colony, sweeping ostentatiously across the lawn, Nancy observed, toward their car. Nancy was certain that Myra wanted everyone, especially the Lerners, to see her. The next day, while Myra and Danielle were out shopping, Nancy invited a few children to join Laura and her for ice cream at the Tastee Delight stand on Route 42—her treat.

"This is ridiculous," Stanley said.

"I know." Nancy, watching Myra through the shutters, jerked the shutters closed. "I know it's ridiculous."

Their mothers weren't speaking, and the girls were inseparable. Laura and Danielle played croquet on the lawn—Laura always choosing the green mallet, Danielle the blue—loafed for hours on the raft in the middle of the pond, and after Danielle's CB radio was taken away, hid in the dark eerie barn at night and spelled out on their Ouija board the names of the boys in town they had crushes on. They had lunch with each other every day, and conspired, without much luck, to have their mothers meet in the laundry shed behind Danielle's cottage or at the Grand Union. They imagined one of them drowning in the pond, and the mother of the other one saving her, and their mothers bursting into tears at the irony and miracle of it all, and then their mothers embracing...

Without much warning, Myra enrolled Danielle in a local day-camp for the month of August. Laura moped around the colony all day long, waiting for

Danielle's return in the evening, occasionally playing ping-pong with her sister Wendy but conceding the games too easily, weeding her garden, and retreating to her bedroom to peruse books she had hated even when she was younger. She scoured the children's section of the one-room, stone library on Route 42 for banal, large print, early reader editions of biographies of Florence Nightingale, Henry Ford, the Wright Brothers, and George Washington Carver.

"Why can't I go to camp?" she demanded.

Nancy angrily Endust-ed the wood slats of the cabin walls. "You know we can't afford it. We spend a fortune coming up here."

One day Danielle pretended to be sick, so that she could stay home from camp. The girls, thrilled by their own audacity, got on their bikes and rode in secret to a hair salon in the next town over, where for five carefully hoarded dollars each they obtained matching Dorothy Hamill hairstyles.

Myra took one look at the haircut and arranged an appointment for Danielle with her salon in the city.

"It'll grow out," Nancy comforted herself, running her fingers through Laura's ruined hair.

At the end of the summer, during Labor Day weekend, the colony always hosted a bonfire, which was set at the foot of the hill below the barn, next to the pond. Some of the small children at the colony called the event a "barn fire" because of its location. Friends and relatives were invited up from the city; Stanley, Alan, and the other fathers barbecued hot dogs and hamburgers on small grills; potatoes and onions, wrapped in aluminum foil and easily mistaken for each other, baked in the charcoal embers. It had been another dry season and the dead limbs that had piled up all summer burned quickly. The children—and their parents—found long, thin twigs to roast marshmallows, but the heat was so intense that their sticks often caught on fire. After the meal, huge watermelons were sliced up, and sticky fingers were washed in the nearby pond.

And they drank. Stanley drank beer, Myra and Alan drank vodka. Nancy didn't drink. Before long Myra led the colony in a medley of Yiddish songs, "Tumbalalaika" and "Der Rebbe Elimelech." As the evening progressed, the songs became saucier.

"She has a good voice." Stanley, admiring Myra, opened another beer. "And a pretty good figure."

"You must be soused," Nancy said. Stanley had never been much of a drinker.

"No," Stanley said. "But I'm feeling no pain."

Alan became more boisterous, throwing twigs and then logs into the fire, making the blaze go higher and higher. He sang a dirty Yiddish limerick, and suprisingly, Stanley knew the words too. Stanley began singing with Alan, who put his arm around Stanley's shoulder.

A spirit of bacchanalia seemed to descend on them. Someone turned on a portable tape recorder and soon couples were dancing, knocking into each other and knocking over one of the barbecues. The liquor flowed. A young couple, smooching, caught the attention of the young children, who screeched with revulsion and excitement. Susan and Wendy disappeared behind the barn with two boys from town, until Nancy chased them back to the fire. Someone began singing a filthy song, in English, and Nancy realized, with horror, that it was Stanley.

The crowd hooted Stanley's performance. Myra, laughing, turned to Nancy, her face full of scorn and triumph. The light from the fire danced over her face. Her hair was loose, the new outfit she had bought in Fiorucci in Manhattan was mussed. Her mouth was angry, her eyes were wild and burning and seemed to penetrate Nancy, to singe her. Then Myra turned away, grabbing Alan and dancing away with him.

Nancy wrapped her sweater tighter around herself, and huddled in her lawn chair with Laura. She put her head against Laura's neck and her arms around her daughter, closing her eyes and trying to cover her ears, until she heard screams. "Fire!" she heard. "Fire!" Somehow a spark from the bonfire had landed on top of the barn and set the roof on fire.

Nancy ran back to her cottage, consulted an index card with emergency numbers which she had tacked to the wall next to the phone, and dialed the volunteer fire company. When she ran back, she saw the men were trying to fight the fire, but drunkenly and unsuccessfully. They had found buckets somewhere and filled them with water from the pond, but the water sloshed out of the pails onto the dirt road or slipped through their fingers as it was passed from man to man. Or the men themselves slipped on the mud they had created. The children had found a hose and a spigot behind the barn, but the hose was full of leaks.

Soon enough, the fire truck appeared, tearing down the dirt road with its siren blaring. No one was hurt and all the children were accounted for, and as the firemen knew what they were doing, the residents ceased to worry, so that the fire itself became a source of entertainment, a thrill for the small children. Nancy and Myra backed away from the blaze, until they were standing near each other, by the fire truck. They watched as the firemen put out the flames and then rolled up their hoses. The roof had burned away, but the barn was still standing. And Myra, high from the vodka, was laughing, laughing...

"Crazy fucking kikes," one of the firemen said as he hoisted himself into the truck.

Nancy heard the laugh catch in Myra's throat, and the two women looked at each other, and Nancy blushed. The fire truck drove off, kicking up dust and mud from the road which spattered their legs and shoes. The women stood there, dumb, and watched the truck disappear around a bend.

"Sometimes I forget," Myra finally said, wiping her shoes clean. It was the first time they had spoken in over a month.

"Yes." And then Nancy understood why she had blushed, why she was ashamed. She had forgotten, too.

When she was sixteen and a junior at Hunter High School, Laura attended a concert at Madison Square Garden with her boyfriend, whom she had met in her sophomore English class. Getting off one of the escalators, Laura stumbled, and as she got to her feet, she looked around, embarrassed, wondering if anyone had noticed her fall. She realized she was looking right into the eyes of Danielle. The girls had seen each other only twice in the last five years, meeting by chance in the lobby of a large catering hall when they attended separate bat mitzvah receptions and then again at a movie theater. Danielle, thin, subdued, and, as always, beautifully dressed, was accompanied to the concert by a group of her girlfriends. Laura and Danielle spoke awkwardly but fondly, and even exchanged phone numbers, which they knew they wouldn't keep. The more they talked, the smaller Danielle seemed to become. She looked down at her feet and tried to step back into the ring of her friends, while Laura, large with confidence, laughed brashly and didn't mention the huge, unmentionable Thing that had happened to the Lerners—for there had been a great misfortune in Laura's life. Somehow the tragedy had made her stronger and braver. Danielle was meek, as if she had dieted away all her confidence.

They would go on to college and Laura would move to Chicago and then San Francisco, and they would never see each other again. Laura might think about their butchered hair or their Ouija games or her garden, but only for a moment; if they shared a past, it was a narrow past, and their memories were sweet but mixed with pain. Of those full summers what she remembered best was the barn—the pitchfork on the wall and the ping pong table—the damp barn, the musty barn, the barn on fire.

Carolyn Weaver

Celia's Bridegroom

Celia's date with Ivan is the usual, a little boring and a little shocking. They go to the movies and eat dinner at the Japanese restaurant and then they have sex at her apartment. Celia's daughter is away. Ivan pays for everything unless Celia insists that it's her turn. As always, he brings his own condoms, putting them on punctiliously, absently smiling, like a father fastening his child's raincoat. Celia likes to watch him doing this. His erection never wavers. Tonight Ivan has also brought something appalling, a battery-operated dildo that looks and feels like a real penis, slithery, pink and heavy. Celia imagines it getting up and walking around the bedroom, like the hand in the *Addams Family*. A real crime against taste, if not an actual crime in the state of Virginia. She can't look at it or at Ivan.

"Aren't you ever afraid the police will stop you or you'll have an accident and they'll see that in your backpack?"

But Ivan has no sense of bad taste, of irony or of himself as ridiculous. These are all useful things not to have for good sex. He never looks at himself from the inside out. He never thinks of how he's performing. He's always totally into it. He can even ignore Celia's self-consciousness.

Ivan has his tremendous orgasm and Celia starts making conversation to fill up the 30 minutes or so before Ivan swings his legs out of bed and pulls his pants on.

Celia likes to talk to Ivan about love and Ivan likes to talk about religion.

"Could you ever marry a woman who didn't have your religious beliefs?" she asks him. Ivan is Russian Orthodox.

"It would be very difficult," he says, exhaling deeply, stroking her arm, "I could certainly never marry an atheist."

Celia rests her hand on his hairy stomach, one leg over his hips. He smells good, like a field of strange dried grasses. Ivan is from Georgia the country, where Jason found the golden fleece. They grow tea and grapes in Georgia. Ivan has told her about icy cataracts, the bears he saw climbing. He's an original Caucasian, he says. He looks it, a giant who came down from the mountains.

This is one of the things Celia likes about Ivan, he is always sunny and expansive, even when he is gloomy, even when he's a little bored.

"What about a Jew?" she asks, instantly regretting it.

"If she converted, certainly, I could marry a Jew. Many, many Jews now are converting to Christianity," Ivan launches into a familiar exposition, "Jews for Jesus—"

Celia interrupts. "Well now, what about a Catholic?" Her family used to be Catholic, not that she wants to marry Ivan.

"Yes, the Catholic Church is close to the Orthodox church. We have many of the same principles."

"Of course, I hate the Pope."

"Celia, the Pope is God's representative on earth. It's a sin to say that you hate the Pope."

"Many Catholics hate the Pope," she says, curling into his fragrant hairy chest. "Progressive Catholics." She likes listening to the rumble of his bombast.

"And they are in a state of sin," he says, his arm around her stiffening. Ivan is getting angry, though he would never admit it.

"Okay, butt out, it's not even your religion," Celia says, sniffing his armpit. He smells better than any man on earth, she decides. She doesn't care if they have to strain for things to talk about.

They've had variations of this conversation several times before over the last five years. Celia imagines she is teaching Ivan about love. She proselytizes to him after sex, until he's had enough and starts talking about the *Bible*. It's probably a waste of time, she knows, for Ivan's far too selfish and solitary to marry anyone. He likes sex but he has no need for love, and Celia wouldn't want him even if he did. He sleeps with two or three other women, she knows.

"You are all so different, I cannot compare you," he said to her at the beginning, when it still bothered her. Now Celia sees other men, looking for one she can take seriously.

Celia mentioned feminism one day.

"Celia, I hope you are not saying *you* are a feminist, are you?" Ivan asked grimly, as if he were asking her if she was a communist. "I have no doubt feminism is responsible for the ghastly state society is in today."

"Oh Ivan, all your girlfriends must be feminists. I mean, who do you think is giving you all those free blow-jobs, anyway?" Celia was never sure where her affection verged into contempt.

She wishes she could take Ivan seriously. Ivan is not exactly stupid, but he's intelligent in the wrong way. He plays rock and jazz guitar, and has good taste in music. He can talk about poetic meter, he's pro-choice and he gets jokes. But he thinks the *Bible* is literal truth, he believes in astrology, and when Celia talks politics, he brings up the prophecies of Nostradamus. Celia can't take Ivan out in public, not to parties or art openings, even though he's good-looking. God only knows what he'd wear or say. But it's nice to have a big gigolo in her pocket, so to speak. Keeps her from being a raving dried-out old maid, and who could be better than Ivan sexually? Only someone she actually loved.

Celia is thinking about this today again. It is late October, the tenth anniversary of her divorce. Ivan's sweaty arm is under her neck. He strokes her nipple idly with his thumb, sighs heavily and says, "well, you know, Celia, I'm thinking of getting married."

Celia knows this must mean that a date has been set, invitations mailed. Ivan would never mention it if he were really only considering it.

"Why?" she says, rolling over on her stomach. There's a ditch in the middle of the mattress. Her rank enseamed bed, like Hamlet's mother's. She is having an infrastructure crisis, her bed, her car, her youth, all going, and now her boyfriend, too.

She already knows *why*, she thinks, and she is not particularly interested in the specifics: the lucky or unlucky woman, what she looks like, her age and occupation. Of course Celia put the idea in his mind in the first place. She tilled the earth, planted the soil for some more suitable woman, someone who would actually want Ivan and not condescend to him. Celia has trained Ivan to want love, to yearn for it. Either that or he's being practical, marrying somebody pretty and likable who also has a little money.

"It just seems like the time," he says, running a finger down her back. She knows he's telling the truth. He's passive and fatalistic. He waits for the universe to make decisions for him. "Don't worry, it won't change anything between us."

She can't help being jealous, just a little.

"So, is she your religion," Celia asks.

"Oh, yes, certainly," Ivan says exhaling deeply. He must be relieved now that it's out. His vagueness—why "certainly?" annoys her, sounds like a lie.

Celia lies there, breathing in his sweet grassy smell. I couldn't have stood it three years ago, she thinks, but now it's okay. He keeps me alive, but I can't take much more of him than sex and a light dressing of conversation.

"Is she from your country?" Celia asks, cattily. "Does she have a job?"

"Yes to both," Ivan says, "her family is from my country, she has been here longer than I."

"So what's wrong with me?" Celia, says, pretending to be injured. "If you married me, I wouldn't even make you live with me. You could keep doing just what you want."

Ivan smiles and pats her arm. "Yes, but Celia, you know that you and I have our differences."

"Well, I have the prior claim," Celia says. "And all I need of you is this."

"That you will always have. I will always love to sleep with you," Ivan says. "Nothing's going to change."

Celia met Ivan nearly seven years ago, in the museum where they both worked, Celia as an editor and Ivan as an exhibit builder. Ivan still earns his living there; he also makes something playing music. He had faint hopes of succeeding as a musician back then, but he's 39 now, Celia's age, and his career has not progressed. When Celia saw him standing next to the African elephant, looking at her, she thought, maybe he is my destiny. She liked to kid herself that way.

Celia turned her head away when he tried to kiss her after they went out for dinner one night, when they'd argued about religion. Both of them laughed. He had bored and embarrassed her, booming at her about God. But after she finally slept with him, Celia hardly remembered the Ivan she had rejected. On his double bed, beneath a poster of John Lennon facing one of *The Last Supper*, Celia let herself be parted and turned and surrounded by Ivan. Ivan was a champion, in a sexual class she had not known existed. It was like going through a long dreamy carwash, scrubbers and jets shooting up from nowhere. They went out to a rock concert afterwards, Celia enjoying the sensation of recent occupation between her legs.

Fasting is part of Ivan's yoga and religious practice. He once fasted for twenty-seven days. Every year, he gives up sex for the Russian Lent, which is longer than regular Lent. He also gives up animal foods, sweets, movies and television. Celia likes being in the category of proscribed luxury. Love wears out, but appetite doesn't. That must be why she's never gotten sick of Ivan or he of her, because they have never really been in love.

Celia suspects that Ivan is approaching marriage the way a woman does, as a bid to remake his life. In the last year and a half, his grandmother, mother, niece and uncle have all immigrated to the United States and moved into Ivan's efficiency.

Ivan's tired, balding mother sleeps on the prickly narrow couch. His grandmother and niece are in Ivan's bed, and the uncle bunks down on the floor.

Ivan sleeps on the balcony in an all-weather sleeping bag. In the summer his face is sunburned and in December he wakes up under a fall of snow. He laughs about it. "Oh, life on the balcony is good," he jokes, when Celia asks him how he is. The truth is, he won't get his act together to find them all a house. He has enough money, but he doesn't want to commit to living with them forever.

Ivan calls on the Saturday before Thanksgiving. Celia is in bed with a cold, helping her daughter decide what to wear to the movies. Becca regards herself gravely in the full-length mirror as she tucks in her shirt. She is neat and precise in her dress like her father.

"Well, I got married a couple of weeks ago," Ivan says into Celia's ear.

"Damn!" she cries, half-serious. "Why'd you do that?"

"Now, Celia, I told you I was thinking about it. I promised I would tell you about it first."

"I thought you were going to tell me *before* you did it," Celia replies. Becca is turning to look at the profile of her body. There is something about her unsmiling self-regard that irks Celia.

"Have you moved out of your apartment?" she asks Ivan, "Becca, can you get ready in your room?"

"Is that Ivan?" Becca whispers. "Who did he get to marry him?" She shudders.

"Not for the moment," Ivan is saying. "I will be moving into the house—" It is the wife's house, Celia supposes.

"Nothing is going to change," he says. "I will always love to sleep with you."

But of course, even if their sexual relationship is unchanged, it means they will never be able to go out to a movie or dinner together. He'll have the wife and Celia and whatever other old girlfriend still wants him.

Death is a spy who falls in love with the man on whom she is spying. Celia can't remember where she read that, but she identifies with it. At the beginning, she was in love with Ivan, or could have been. Who wouldn't be? She was so afraid he'd drop her. Once she thought he was, and she couldn't move, it hurt so much that the pain wasn't even in her, it was around her. But he hadn't. Ivan never hurt women, never positively refused them. He waited for relationships to decay. He was intuitive. He could wait a woman's love out.

It was like having fallen in love with a bear, that was how foreign he was.

For the first few weeks, she does not think about his marriage. But imperceptibly her nonchalance slips away. She wouldn't give him a thought if there were any other tall, sweet-smelling, virile man to replace him. But even the gay men she knows are more interested in their careers than sex. And Celia's getting to the end of her reproductive years, she's getting to be a woman who's no longer a woman.

She dreams about Ivan's new wife: young and pleased with herself, stupid. She positively stinks of estrogen, that heavy rubbery scent that Celia can smell now that she no longer has so much of it herself. Like all young women, Celia mistook it as her essence. Or perhaps it had been her essence.

Ivan is packing his wife's candy-pink, shag-haired suitcase at the end of the dream. Celia is nauseated again by his bad taste, even in the language of her dreams.

Celia wonders, is it wrong to commit adultery if you are not the married one? And if the sex is completely meaningless to both parties?

Ivan once said he thought his religion would require him to be faithful if he married. But Celia knows Ivan's inconsistencies. He likes to please himself. He will do what he feels like doing unless he gets some gross sign that he can interpret as indicating God's will. He compartmentalizes his whole life. He never thinks about two girlfriends facing off. They never enter his frame of vision together.

The first week in December, Celia's neighbor Lawrence asks her out. Lawrence is a lawyer, not bad-looking, but shrimpy. Celia thinks he would not feel good in her arms after Ivan.

They eat at an Indian restaurant in Georgetown that's been there forever. Looking at the menu, Celia feels suddenly nauseated. It feels a little like the nausea of pregnancy.

"A panda goes into a restaurant," Lawrence is telling a joke. He often tells jokes. "The waiters are polite and give him good service, even though they're surprised to be waiting on a panda. After he eats, he gets up, takes out a gun, and shoots everybody in the place. He gets arrested, and the police say, why would you do that, you got good service, they treated you well. And he says, 'Because I'm a panda, dummy, look it up in the dictionary.' So they do, and it says, 'Panda: eats shoots and leaves.'"

Of course, Celia is thinking, she could not accuse Ivan of negligence. He is irritatingly prudent about using a condom, like someone who always has his umbrella. But they had fooled around for a few minutes without it the last time, in October.

Ivan would make gorgeous sunny giant-children, Celia's often thought. Girls and boys built like little gods, with strong legs. Champion fencers, dancers, jugglers, maybe. Opera singers. She could start a traveling circus.

Celia wonders, though, would the child be obstinate and superstitious and vulgar, even if he had no part in raising it? No matter, it's *his* beautiful child I want, she thinks. The sunny, big-nosed, placid-natured, sweet-smelling boy or girl. When he or she grows up, we will visit Ivan and then giggle together later about his obtuseness. We will feel poignant regret that we could not take him more seriously as a husband or father.

Celia and Lawrence go to see the movie *Crumb*. The movie seems to disturb Lawrence. He shifts around in his seat and sighs heavily.

"Pretty dysfunctional family, eh?" he says at the movie's end.

Ivan wouldn't have said anything so trite, Celia thinks. He would have been dazed by the tragedy of the family and he would be laughing, too. Ivan's got brains, Celia thinks, they're just not in his brains. They're in his legs, in his jaw, in the back of his head. Ivan's children would be far more intelligent than Lawrence's.

After the movie, Lawrence and Celia are walking down M street heading to his car. It's stunningly cold, a January night, and they have their heads down against the wind. Celia looks up and 20 feet away, heading straight at them are Ivan and the woman who must be his new wife.

They don't see her yet. They are walking fast and laughing gaily like people in love. She has her arm tucked into his, for warmth, and he's pulling her along, racing her through the chill. Ivan looks happy and surprised to be happy. Celia was always too short for him, but his wife's the perfect height, goddess to his god. She's looking down at the sidewalk, laughing, as he tugs her along. She has shiny black hair parted in the middle and a pale oval lovely face. She looks like Snow White.

When Ivan glances ahead and his eyes meet Celia's, his sunniness fades. He looks at her with grim surprise, suspicion even.

"Hi," she says to Ivan, as they pass, and he nods. She guesses that they are hurrying because they are late for a movie. But for Ivan, there is no such thing as coincidence. Celia realizes that now they will never commit adultery together. It is the sign from God she never wanted and Ivan never asked for. It almost makes her wonder if God really does discourage adultery. After all, she has never run into anyone else so meaningfully, so pointedly. He has seen them together now, Celia and his wife.

Ivan nods to her, but he still looks worried, looks at Celia a little grimly, as if she might blow his cover. He has not looked at her so directly ever before. His eyes are urgent, telling her things he never would say, things he doesn't even know he feels, things like you are a mean person, and yes, all your little arrows stuck, and that's why I did not love you. It's so damn cold out, though, they just pass with that nod, and Lawrence doesn't notice, he's wondering where they left the car.

Curtis White

from *America's Magic Mountain*

Reverend Phenues Boyle Tells the Sad Story of the Big Dog of Despair

Not all of Jesus' wisdom is in the *Bible*, friends. Not by a long shot. Some stories that aren't in the *Bible* are also Jesus' stories.

For, lo, it is said:

Within each person live two dogs. Both dogs are strong and fight for a person's heart, one to go west, and the other to go east. The person chooses which dog will be the bigger by deciding which dog to feed.

For, verily, although you think your Father's heart to be stone, or empty, or an empty stone, in fact his heart is the stage for this strange drama.

One of the dogs is called the Dog of Despair. The other is called I'm Happy. Your Father-who-art-on-the-couch is constantly throwing the dog called Despair large chunks of raw meat. Hog corpses. Jowls. Shanks. I'm Happy, on the other hand, is on a starvation diet. When I'm Happy tries to walk, he can only move a front paw and whimper. He's so weak. But he takes it well, he's smiling, because he's The Dog of I'm Happy. The idea that the dog I'm Happy could ever be as big as the Dog of Despair makes the Dog of Despair laugh in doggy mirth. He rolls over on his doggy back and kicks out his cruel legs and roars with the impossibility of it. Still, just the idea that I'm Happy wants to be fed, and could be fed, might still have the strength to eat, makes him nervous. For until the Dog of I'm Happy is just completely gone, there will always be the possibility that our Father-who-art-in-possession-of-the-remote-control-television-device could theoretically feed him and stay within the stretchy laws of dharmic possibility. So he takes a long, serious, sidelong, hungry look at the weak puddle that is the body of the Dog of I'm Happy. A formerly dim doggy corpuscle flashes into fire. The Dog of Despair should just go eat the Dog of I'm Happy. And be done with it. Then I'm Happy would not only not be a threat to the food that the Dog of Despair receives by the wheelbarrow load, he would become the food itself. He would be the food that he doesn't get! Funny! Funny! The Dog of Despair thought this was unbelievably funny and poetic and in dog terms totally brilliant! The Dog of I'm Happy would itself become part of the food that makes the Dog of Despair "bigger." Get it? The multiple ironies came at him in large numbers. He turned them this way and that like multifaceted Milkbones. Then he rolled over and laughed, twitching his doggy legs in the air like a comical Hindu dog god. Then he rolled back to his feet and looked blackly dead ahead. He focused on nothing except this serious intent. He was going to do it. Now. Strike while the iron is hot and the hour is at hand. Or, as his dog-buddies said, "pounce while the bunny is lame." He just hoped that the crunching of the larger bones wouldn't wake Our Father. He rose. He took the first momentous step. He would be the All Dog now. The Everything Dog. The Dog of Ubiquity. Yes. But then another thought came to him. "I will be Big and I will be Bigger? But Big as compared to what? Bigger than what?" That was his awful, chilling thought. "If I eat the Dog of I'm Happy, I will be bigger but bigger than what since there will be no other dogs happy or otherwise to compare himself to?" Was there a dog of Mediocre Feelings around? A Dog of *Más y Menos*? Or a dog of Comic Coups, perhaps? Or Painful Fuckups? Anything would do. But he thought not. He sat down and stared off into a bizarre canine space and became absorbed in a despairing meditation on his impossible quandary. He was beginning to understand why they called him the Dog of Despair. This was some sad shit. It was impossible to avoid a simple conclusion: he, the big strong Dog of Despair, was dependent on the puny little bitch kitty Dog of I'm Happy. The thought disgusted him.

Then the most deeply disturbing thought: the arrival of the *thought* of dependency is not dependency itself, for he has always been dependent without knowing it. No, the arrival of the Understanding of his dependency is, in fact, the arrival of his failure! His defeat! Which has been sleeping in him stupidly the whole time! And he could not see it because he was the stupid, beer drinking, frisbee playing, jingle-ball chasing Dog of Despair. His "brilliant idea" of what would make him superlative, fully realized, has in fact made him fully realized: he is the DOG OF DESPAIR.

He lies down as if for the last time.

At some later point—he doesn't really much feel it but it is enough to make him lift his ponderous dog skull and look back—he feels a slight, painful, nibbling sort of feeling in his hind legs. He sees that the Dog of I'm Happy has somehow managed to drag his lax corpse over and is beginning to chew on his hind feet. Dog teeth are sharp, their jaws are strong, so already there is a gloss of blood on his black dog-lips. The Dog of Despair thinks that the blood looks like lipstick and that's just perfect for that little pussy bitch kitty Dog of I'm Happy. He laughs. Fuckin' perfect, man! I'm Happy, seeing Despair's look, grins sickly and shrugs his shoulders as if to say, "What am I supposed to do? I'm hungry."

The Dog of Despair puts his dog skull back down on the ground and groans. Then he has his last thought before he bleeds to death through his now chewed off hind-foot: "It's a dog eat dog world, man." And he makes one of those little laughs dogs make while dreaming.

Later, the Dog of I'm Happy sits at Our Father's side watching boxing on T.V. on a Saturday afternoon. It's daytime but the blinds are closed. There is dust on a plate of fudge. I'm Happy has been licking the plate of fudge all afternoon. The fudge is so old and hard that it has actually cut his tongue. Dogs do not know how to stop the bleeding when their tongues bleed. They also do not know how to stop licking fudge once they have started. But he enjoyed the taste of the salty blood mixed with the sweet of the candy and imagined in some dim way that it might actually be nutritious for him. I'm Happy has been watching on T.V. a frequently repeated commercial for a beer called Hamms. Hamms beer. It is from the Land of Sky Blue Water. It is the "beer refreshing." Hamms the beer refreshing. I'm Happy is confused. A bear paddles a canoe. There is a beaver. Smoke signals. What does it mean? It is all very confusing in his doggy brain. How does this commercial make people drink beer? Then the boxing comes back and the black and white humans are hitting each other then the beer commercial with the bear in the canoe again. The same one. Same words. Land of sky blue water. Huh. Huh. He meditates on it, continuing to lick the fudge with his bleeding tongue.

Our Father loves I'm Happy. He says, "I have a surprise for you, buddy. Come on!" And he leads the dog, who is barely able to move, so contentedly fat has he become, to a large cardboard box back in the pantry. He lifts I'm Happy up to look over the edge. There is a puppy. The puppy gets up on his little weak puppy legs and whines and wags his tiny puppy tail. "I thought you might be lonesome since you lost your pal. So I got you a new friend. He's little now, but we'll feed him and pretty soon he'll be big like you." I'm Happy feels a sinking feeling. He's beginning to wonder if this sinking feeling is what is meant by the word "happy."

Contributor's Notes

Nonfiction

Jennifer Egan was born in Chicago and grew up in San Francisco. Her short stories have appeared in *The New Yorker, GQ, Mademoiselle, Ploughshares,* and elsewhere, and she is the author of a short story collection entitled *Emerald City* (Doubleday, 1992) and a novel, *The Invisible Circus* (Doubleday, 1995). Jennifer has won an NEA and an O. Henry Award.

Amy Halloran's writing has appeared in many small publications, including letterpress projects and zines of her own making. She performs her work at a variety of venues and for broadcast on National Public Radio. She lives in Seattle.

Anne LeBaron is currently teaching in the music department at the University of Pittsburgh. She lived in WDC for part of the 90s and participated in a residency program called Meet the Composer. The excerpt in this issue is from *Croak* a musical account of the last frog on earth, which LeBaron composed and produced at George Washington University last year. She is best known for her electronic blues opera, *The E & O Line,* and her 1992 CD, *Anne LeBaron Quintet.* She won a Fulbright to study in Germany under Gyorgy Ligeti, and she's also won a Guggenheim.

Steven Moore is the author/editor of five books—three on William Gaddis, one on Ronald Firbank, and an anthology of vampire poetry—and numerous articles on modern literature. He lives in suburban Denver and works at a Borders book store.

David L. Ulin is the author of *Cape Cod Blues* (Red Dust), a chapbook of poems. His fiction and poetry have appeared in *Exquisite Corpse, Bakunin, The Brooklyn Review, B City, New Observations,* and *Rampike*; his essays and criticism in the *Los Angeles Times, Newsday, the Chicago Tribune, LA Weekly,* and *Salon.* Currently, he is writing a book about Jack Kerouac for the University of California Press.

Poetry

Jamika Ajalon was born in St. Louis in 1968. She left home at seventeen, received a BA in Film and an MA in Cultural Theory & Media. Her work has appeared in various publications, including the *Black Book Review* and *BFI Black Film Bulletin,* as well as *Afrakete: An Anthology of Black Women Writers.* She has made several short films, notably *Blood Poem, Intro to Cultural Skitzofrenia, Shades* and *Memory Tracks,* which have been shown in Europe and the States. She is currently at work on a novel, a feature-length screenplay, and a collection of short stories.

Elizabeth W. Andrews lives in Brooklyn, NY with her husband, artist Tony Geiger. For the past two years, Elizabeth has been a volunteer in the NYU Creative Writing Program directed by Sharon Olds at Goldwater Memorial Hospital on Roosevelt Island. Her poems have appeared in *Mudfish* and *Zone 3*. She is a recipient of the New Voice Award in poetry for 1995 and read at the Writer's Voice in May 1996.

Joe Asser is an artist who lives in London.

Steve Aylett's book *Slaughtermatic* is being published by Four Walls Eight Windows in New York and Orion in the UK. His first two books, *The Crime Studio* and *Bigot Hall*, are published by Serif, London. Aylett was born in Bromley, England, in 1967.

Francesca Beard grew up in Malaysia and lives in London. She started performing poetry in 1997 and since then has had work published in numerous 'zines. In February 1998 she toured in the USA with the "Heart of Darkness" slam team. She is currently working on a new project, combining music with spoken word.

Elsa Biagini was born in Florence, Italy in 1970 and is actually teaching Italian at Rutgers, the State University of New Jersey. She is the author of a book of poetry called *Questi Nodi* (Florence, 1993) and has published her work in several Italian literary magazines.

Paul Birtill was born in Walton, Liverpool in 1960. He moved to London in his early twenties, and apart from a brief period in Glasgow has lived there ever since. He has been published widely and his first full collection *Terrifying Ordeal* has just been published in London by Hearing Eye. He also writes plays, one of which was short-listed for the Verity Bargate Award.

Eugénie Bisulco was born in New Jersey, grew up in rural Arkansas, and received her undergraduate degree in English and Studio Art from Wellesley College in Massachusetts. She has a Master's in Writing from Johns Hopkins University. Her poems have been published in *WordWrights!*, and are forthcoming in a book on young women and body image. She works at the White House and lives in Arlington, Virginia with her husband.

Nicole Blackman has appeared on albums by the Golden Palominos, performed at Lollapalooza, on Spin Radio, MTV Radio, been published in *Aloud: Voices from the Nuyorican, Revival: Spoken Word from Lollapalooza 94, New York Quarterly, Cups, Excuses, Bust, The Fuse,* and *Carbon 14.* Her poetry chapbooks are *Pretty* (Spy Verses Spy, 1994) and *Sweet* (Spy Verses Spy, 1996). She awaits the day when poets headline Shea Stadium.

Claire Calman is a freelance writer, editor and poet. She has performed her poems live on Radio 4's *Woman's Hour,* and is one of five writer-performers creating a forthcoming radio comedy show (the first to include poems as part of its regular format), *Five Squeezy Pieces,* for Radio 4 to be broadcast in October. She lives in Kent, where she spends her time scribbling, gardening and avoiding working on her first novel.

Glenn Carmichael, ex-punk, ex-rapper, ex-heroin addict, began his performance poetry career as half of the Big City Beats. They founded the Hard Edge Club in Soho, London in September 1988. In December 1994, Glenn began the massively successful Bristol Poetry Slam, which hosted the UK Poetry Slam Championships '97. His latest book of poems *The Truth Is Optional* is published by Pimp$ of the Alphab£t Press.

John Cooper Clarke is regarded as Britian's leading rock poet. His work can be heard on the *Poetry Olympics* LP or on the pages of *Grandchildren of Albion* (New Departures).

Robert O. Costa was born in and is residing again in Washington, DC. He has worked as a writer/researcher, an organizational consultant and as an executive with a computer technology firm. To save his soul, Robert is on the board of the Washington Area Music Association, and he and Sara Levy (also a contributor to this issue) run Verse Alert! This organization sponsors a reading series, promotes poetry and poets, and seeks to expand the Washington-area venues available to them. Robert can be reached by e-mail at costar@radix.net.

Virginia Crawford earned her BFA in Creative Writing from Emerson College, and her Master of Letters from the University of St. Andrews, Scotland. She currently teaches in Baltimore, Maryland, is co-founder of WordHouse, and recently co-edited *Poetry Baltimore: poems about a city*. Her work has appeared in *Baltimore City Paper, Potomac Review, Baltimore Review*, and is forthcoming in *Black Moon*.

Tim Cumming was born in 1963, and lives in London. His work has appeared in many magazines, including *Billy Liar, Dog, The North, The Wide Skirt, The Echo Room, London Magazine, Scratch, Rebel Ink, Verse, Pearl* (USA) and others. He has two collections in print, *The Miniature Estate* (Smith/Doorstop) and *Apocalypso* (Scratch). Poems have appeared in the *Forward Book of Poetry, Fat City* (Dog Publications), *Long Pale Corridor* (Bloodaxe). He has read as part of the New Voices season at the Voice Box, and on BBC2 and Radio 4.

Denise Duhamel is the author of ten books and chapbooks of poems. Her most recent titles include *The Star-Spangled Banner* (winner of *Crab Orchard Review's* Poetry Prize, Southern Illinois University Press, 1999) and *Kinky* (Orchises Press, 1997.) In 1997 Tia Chucha Press published *Exquisite Politics*, a collection of collaborative poems by Denise Duhamel and Maureen Seaton.

Blair Ewing is Contributing Editor of the *Maryland Poetry Review*, and Associate Editor of *Articulate*. He produces *Poetry Jam*, a cable TV poetry show based in Howard County, MD. His work has appeared in the *Baltimore Review, Breakfast All Day, Cape Rock, Fodderwing, h2so4, Orbis, Sub-Terrain, Washington Review*, and *WordWrights!* Blair recently produced *Word Up Baltimore*, a special poetry CD in honor of Baltimore's 200th birthday.

Brenda Frazer was born in WDC and currently lives in Michigan. She is best known for her memior, *Troia: Mexican Memoirs* (Tompkins Press, 1969) written as Bonnie Bremser. (Published in London as *For Love of Ray* in 1971.) The book, volume two in a trilogy, is an autobiographical take on the difficult first five years of her marriage to the poet Ray Bremser, whom she married in 1959. The other two volumes of the trilogy deserve to be published.

Tina Fulker (1954-1992) was a mainstay of the British small press scene in the 1970s and 80s. She toured with the Slow Dancer performance group, published two full-length poetry books, *Jukebox* (Paycock Press, 1980) and *Gash* (Slow Dancer, 1992), and several chapbooks. Some of her fiction appeared in *Ambit*. She also recorded several tapes to instrumental backing. At her death her estranged husband destroyed all of her mss. The odd poem still surfaces. John Elsberg of *Bogg* published *Loose Change* in 1995, which includes some of Fulker's last poems and stories.

Karen Garthe's poetry has appeared several times (& will appear again) in *New American Writing* and in *No Roses Review*. It will be in this Spring's issue of *American Letters & Commentary*, has appeared in *yefief, The Brooklyn Review, Exquisite Corpse, The Painted Bride Quarterly, Global City Review, Beet,* etc. In 1991 she won the Open Voice Award (judged by James Sherry) from Writer's Voice. An early manuscript was a finalist in the 1994 National Poetry Series.

Regan Good is a poet living in Brooklyn.

John Greaves was born in North Wales in 1950. Played bass with his father's dance band during the early-mid sixties often supporting luminary groups from the burgeoning Liverpool scene (Yes, including The Fab Four). Left, much to his father's chagrin, to read English at Cambridge where he joined the nascent Henry Cow, with Fred Frith and Tim Hodgkinson. Touring and recording with this group and then National Health in the seventies gave rise to Greaves' first compositions in instrumental and song collaboration with Peter Blegvad, forays into post-modernism with Michael Nyman and David Cunningham, quasi-operatics with Michael Mantler. Greaves now lives in Normandy, France where he continues writing, composing, and recording.

Janet Hamill's fourth book, *Lost Ceilings* (a collection of poems, prose poems, and short fiction), is forthcoming in the summer of '98 from Telephone Books (Guilford, CT). Also forthcoming from W.W. Norton (date not set) is *The Eternal Cafe*, a collection of fiction co-authored with poet and recording artist, Patti Smith. Her poetry and fiction have appeared in anthologies such as *Up Late: American Poetry Since 1970, Deep Down: The New Sensual Writing by Women,* and *Living with the Animals* and numerous magazines, including *Bomb, City Lights Review,* and *Exquisite Corpse*. Ms. Hamill is a frequent performer of "spoken art" poetry with her band Moving Star. In September '97 she was the featured poet at the Liss Ard Festival, County Cork, Ireland, in the company of musicians Nick Cave, Patti Smith, and Michael Stipe.

Elizabeth Hamilton, California-born, works on semantics and cognition at a CNRS laboratory in Paris. She is currently preparing a cross-linguistic study of the "street" and its metaphors.

John Hegley has been captivating audiences for 26 years as a comedian/poet-singer-songwriter-guitarist-actor. He began his career at London's notoriously tough Comedy Store. His work includes the 1988 ep *I Saw My Dinner On TV* which features Robyn Hitchcock, the CD *Saint and Blurry*, plus the books *Glad to Wear Glasses, Can I Come Down Now, Dad?* and *Five Sugars Please*. He is currently on stage in London with his new show *John Hegley & Nigel*. As he put it in *Metro*, "It's not easy to dance with a pen."

Brian Hinton read English at Oxford, and works as Curator for the Julia Margaret Cameron Trust in the Isle of Wight. Poetry collections include *Ties* (Tears in the Fence, 1995) and *The Heart's Clockwork* (Enithareon, 1989) with illustrations by the painter Julian Bell. He has also written rock biographies of Joni Mitchell, Van Morrison and Elvis Costello, for Sanctuary, and co-edited Emily Tennyson's *Journal*. Brian Hinton appears, as a malignant variant of himself, in Iain Sinclair's novel *Radon Daughters*.

Bruce A. Jacobs, born in Rochester, NY, and educated at Harvard, is a poet and freelance writer who sometimes works on horse farms. His poems have appeared in *American*

Writing, *African-American Review, Haight Ashbury Literary Journal, Atlanta Review*, and other journals. He has work forthcoming in *Beyond the Frontier*, a new anthology edited by Ethelbert Miller. Bruce has been a resident at the MacDowell Colony, Ucross Foundation, and Chateau de Lesvault, France. He received a 1995 Individual Artists Grant from the Maryland State Arts Council. His collection of poems, *Speaking Through My Skin* won the 1996 Naomi Long Madgett Poetry Award and was published by Michigan State University Press.

Valerie Jean is a single mother who writes as much as she can while putting her daughter through college. Her poetry, fiction, essays, and reviews have been widely published, most recently in *Callaloo* and in *Spirit & Flame*, an anthology of African American writing published by Syracuse University Press.

Halvard Johnson has had four published collections of poetry—*Transparencies and Projections, The Dance of the Red Swan, Eclipse*, and *Winter Journey* (all from New Rivers Press). Recent poetry and fiction has appeared in *Puerto del Sol, Wisconsin Review, Mudfish, CrossConnect, Gulf Stream, Blue Moon Review*, and *Synaesthetic*. He has received an NEA grant in poetry (1990) and Maryland State Arts Council grants in fiction (1995) and poetry (1997). He lives in Baltimore, Maryland.

Martha Johnson is fifty-two years old, a Yuper (born and raised in Michigan's Upper Peninsula), wife, mother, itinerant teacher of anatomy and physiology to nursing and medical students (Catholic University and USUHS, respectively), former—happily—accountant, new poet, workshop junkie, also published in *Mediphors* and *AmLit*.

LuAnn Keener has an MFA in creative writing from the University of Arkansas. Her book of poems is *Color Documentary* (Calyx Books, 1994). LuAnn's work has been widely published in literary journals, including *The Greensboro Review, Northwest Review, Southern Poetry Review, Chelsea*, and *Quarterly West*. She is recipient of numerous awards, most recently the Irene Leach Poetry Prize, the Hackney Poetry Award, the Chelsea Prize for Poetry, a MacDowell Colony Creative Writing Residency, and a Writers at Work Award in Poetry. She lives in Salem, Virginia, with her son.

Mimi Khalvati, born in Tehran in 1944, grew up on the Isle of Wight and attended the Drama Centre, London. She now lives in Hackney and is a visiting lecturer at Goldsmiths College and coordinator of the Poetry School. Her Carcanet books include *In White Ink* (1991), *Mirrorwork* (1995) and *Entries on Light* (1997).

Ronald Koertge lives in South Pasadena, California, where he is a professor of English at Pasadena City College. Koertge has written a novel, *The Boogeyman*, a lot of young adult novels, including *Arizona Kid, Mariposa Blues*, and *Tiger, Tiger, Burning Bright*, as well as poetry collections like *Diary Cows, Life on the Edge of the Continent: Selected Poems*, and *Making Love to Roget's Wife* (University of Arkansas Press).

Wayne Koestenbaum is the author of *Ode to Anna Moffo and Other Poems* and *The Queen's Throat: Opera, Homosexuality, and the Mystery of Desire*, a National Book Critics Circle Award nominee. His poems and essays have appeared in *The New Yorker, Paris Review, Best American Essays*, and elsewhere. He is Associate Professor of English at Yale. His most recent book of poems is *Rhapsodies of a Repeat Offender* (Persea Books, 1994).

Avra Kouffman was born on 15th Street in Manhattan in 1967. After dabbling in arts journalism and studying cultural anthropology, she joined a PhD programme at the University of Arizona, where she taught writing and literature for five years. She has also taught in the Slovak Republic and in London language schools. In 1996, she moved to London to research her thesis, but soon got distracted by the great performance poetry/spoken word scene. Deciding the thesis could wait but the poetry couldn't, she is currently becoming super-happy as a performance poet in London.

Elizabeth Mary Larson has published fiction and poetry in *Antietam Review, Happy, The Lucid Stone, Lumpy Head, Shattered Wig Review, Rag Shock, Bridges,* and *Through the Cracks.* She has taught Freshman English at Howard University and the University of Maryland. She has received Individual Artist Awards from the Maryland State Arts Council in 1995 and 1997. Her chapbook of short stories, *Stomp and Other Stories,* won an Artscape Literary Award in 1996.

Sara Levy is a near-miss lifelong DC resident. She has worked as a bookstore clerk, bicycle courier, researcher, news editor, and is currently a law librarian. Her interests include travel, obscure pop bands, distance running and Tarheel basketball. Along with Robert Costa, she is the co-founder of Verse Alert! which promotes local poetry and poets.

Lyn Lifshin's most recent book is *Cold Comfort* from Black Sparrow Press, who will publish her next collection in 1999. In addition to many collections of poetry, including *Black Apples, Not Made of Glass, Blue Tattoo* (Holocaust poems) and *Marilyn Monroe,* she has edited four anthologies of women's writing (including *Tangled Vines*) and been the subject of a documentary film, *Not Made of Glass.* Her new web site is www.lynlifshin.com.

Julie Liu recently graduated from Malacaster College and resides in St. Paul. This is her first publication.

Roger McGough is a bestselling poet. Since the Penguin Mersey Sound of 1967 to the latest Penguin Modern Poets volume of 1996, he has gone on delivering good advice and uncomfortable perspectives. *Defying Gravity* (Penguin 1995) sparkles with verbal dexterity.

Gwyn McVay is the author of two chapbooks of poems *Brother Ikon* (Inkstone Press, 1996), and *This Natural History* (Pecan Grove Press, 1997). She is editor of *So to Speak: a feminist journal of language and art*; previously she was associate editor of the *AWP Chronicle* and worked for the *Journal of Buddhist Ethics.* Her poems have appeared in *New American Writing, Sulfur,* and *The Prose Poem,* among others, and are forthcoming in *Calyx* and *Tikkun.*

Miriam Morsel Nathan, born in the Dominican Republic of Czech parents who emigrated there in the 1940s, grew up in Richmond, Virginia. She is Director of the Washington Jewish Film Festival: An Exhibition of International Cinema. Her work has appeared in *Sojourner: The Women's Forum,* the *G.W. Forum,* and *Hayotzer.* Miriam has been a participant in the Festival of Poetry at The Frost Place for the past few years and has resided in the Washington area since 1965.

Dorothy Porter lives in Melbourne, Australia. She is the author of eight books including *The Monkey's Mask: An Erotic Murder Mystery* told in verse. Other titles include *Little*

Hoodlum, The Night Parrot, Driving Too Fast, and *Akhenaten.* Porter has also written Young Adult fiction.

Minnie Bruce Pratt's second book of poetry, *Crime Against Nature,* which was chosen as the 1989 Lamont Poetry Selection by the Academy of American Poets, was also nominated for a Pulitzer Prize, and received the American Library Association's Gay and Lesbian Book Award for Literature. Her other books include *We Say We Love Each Other, Rebellion: Essays 1980-1991,* and *S/HE,* stories about gender boundary crossing. She has recently completed a collection of long narrative poems, *Walking Back Up Depot Street,* forthcoming from the Pitt Poetry Series. She lives in Jersey City, New Jersey.

Jeremy Reed has published several volumes of poetry and eight novels. He has been a prize-winner of the National Poetry Competition and has won a major Eric Gregory Award as well as the Somerset Maugham Award. Recent titles include *Red Hot Lipstick: Erotic Stories* (Peter Own, 1996), *The Pleasure Chateau* (Velvet, 1995), *Kicks* (Creation, 1994), *Chasing Rainbows: a novel based on the life of Artaud* (Peter Owen, 1994) and *Red-Haired Android* (City Lights, 1993). Other novels tackle the lives of Rimbaud, Lautreamont, and De Sade. Jeremy is also a translator (Cocteau, Montale, and Nasrallah) a biographer (Lou Reed and Marc Almond), and the author of *Lipstick, Sex and Poetry: An Autobiographical Exploration of Sexuality.* We at *Gargoyle* are astonished that he isn't more widely known in the US.

Elizabeth Rees teaches in the Johns Hopkins Part-time Graduate Program and at the Writer's Center. Her poetry has appeared in many places including the *Agni Review, Ironwood, Kansas Quarterly, Puerto del Sol, Turnstile, Partisan Review, Kenyon Review, Northwest Review,* and the *Christian Science Monitor.*

Kim Roberts is the author of *The Wishbone Galaxy* (Washington Writer's Publishing House, 1994). Her poems have appeared widely in journals throughout the US, Canada, and Ireland. She is a recpient of grants from the DC Commission on the Arts and Humanities, the National Endowment for the Humanities, and eight writer's residencies at five artist colonies.

Natasha Sajé was born in Munich, Germany, in 1955, and grew up in New York City and northern New Jersey. She earned a B.A. from the University of Virginia, an M.A. from Johns Hopkins, and a Ph.D. from the University of Maryland. Her poems and essays have appeared in *Antaeus, Poetry, Ploughshares,* and many other journals. She has received grants from the Maryland Arts Council and from the city of Baltimore. Her first book, *Red Under the Skin,* won the 1993 Agnes Lynch Starrett Poetry Prize and was published by the University of Pittsburgh Press.

Leslie Scalapino is widely regarded as one of the best avant garde writers in America today. She has taught at Bard College and The Naropa Institute. Her many books include *Defore* (Sun & Moon, 1994) and *The Front Matter, Dead Souls* (Wesleyan, 1996).

Maureen Seaton's books of poetry are *Furious Cooking* (University of Iowa, 1996; winner of the Iowa Prize), *Fear of Subways* (winner of the 1991 Eighth Mountain Poetry Prize) and *The Sea Among the Cupboards* (New Rivers Press, winner of the 1992 Capricorn Award). In 1997 Tia Chucha Press published *Exquisite Politics,* a collection of collaborative poems by Maureen Seaton and Denise Duhamel.

Edgar Silex recently received a writing fellowship from the NEA, an Individual Arts Award from the Maryland State Council for the Arts, and four nominations for the Pushcart Prize. He is the author of *Through All the Displacements*, and *Even the Dead Have Memories* (a chapbook). His work was recently published in *America's Review*, *Callaloo*, *Maryland Poetry Review*, and *Dancing Shadow Review*.

Ifigenija Simonovic was born in Slovenia in 1953. She is a very well known and prolific poet in her native language and country, having published eight volumes by the age of forty. She has been living in London for more than 20 years, where she works as a potter—a familiar figure on Saturdays at her stall in Covent Garden. Her book of poems, *Striking Root: Fifty Poems*, was published by Menard Press of London in 1996.

Bob Slaymaker has published poetry on-line, and in print publications including *Callaloo*, *Christian Science Monitor*, *Essence*, *Exquisite Corpse*, *New York Quarterly*, *River Styx*, and *Writer's Forum*. He's taught writing at the University of California, SUNY, NYU, and the University of Alabama. Bob's work has been read over WBAI-FM in New York, and he's been a featured poet at both Borders and Barnes and Noble there.

W. Loran Smith just graduated from Vermont College and has recently published his first book, *Night Train*, with Plinth Press of West Hartford, CT.

Andrew Sofer's poems have appeared in *Poet Lore*, *The Formalist*, *Phoebe*, *Folio*, and elsewhere. He is currently completing a PhD in English at the University of Michigan, Ann Arbor.

Virgil Suarez was born in Havana, Cuba in 1962. He is the author of four published novels: *Latin Jazz*, *The Cutter*, *Havana Thursdays*, and *Going Under*, and of a collection of short stories entitled *Welcome to the Oasis*. With his wife Delia Poey he has co-edited two best-selling anthologies: *Iguana Dreams: New Latino Fiction* and *Little Havana Blues: A Contemporary Cuban-American Literature Anthology*. Most recently he has published an anthology of Latino poetry entitled *Paper Dance*, co-edited with Victor Hernandez Cruz and Leroy Quintana, and his own third collection of poetry and memoir entitled *Spared Angola: Memories from a Cuban-American Childhood*. He teaches Creative Writing and Latino/a Literature at Florida State University in Tallahassee, Florida where he lives with his family.

Peter Tatlin meditates, is meditated, can think of nothing else to say about himself. Except that he loves to give readings, and welcomes invitations to read in public from any quarter of the globe.

Alexander Theroux is the author of three highly regarded novels: *Three Wogs* (1972), *Darconville's Cat* (1981), and *An Adultery* (1987), as well as a collection of poems, *The Lollipop Trollops* (1992), several books of fables, and two collections of essays, *The Primary Colors* (1994) and *The Secondary Colors* (1996). He lives in West Barnstable, Massachusetts.

Mike Topp was born in WDC. He is currently living in New York City unless he has died or moved.

Tim Turnbull was born in rural North Yorkshire in 1960 and lived in the same village for many years. He's worked in forestry most of his adult life and for 15 years sang in a variety of punk, industrial, ska-type bands. When he finally got sick of other people, he started to write and perform his poetry, moving to London 5 years ago and taking to the city and the poetry like a rat to sewers. He's performed all over England and the United States, both on his own and with the slam-team "Heart of Darkness". He's a regular contributor to *Rising Magazine* and is this year off to the Edinburgh Festival with Big Word.

Christopher Twigg. Born October 1958 in Worcestershire, England, the son of a Priest. Cambridge English degree. Art school. Teaching in Hounslow and Granada. Stops painting; starts writing, inspired by Spanish poets (especially Antonia Machado). Learns guitar, nine years performing. ICA, West Coast of Ireland. Books: *Adventures in the West* (RMG, 1994), *In the Choir* (Alces Press, 1996). Currently recording CD of his 'lyrical ballads'.

Ruth Vaughn was born in India and spent the first twelve years of her life on the move, ending up in New Zealand via Britain. Whilst studying Art History and French at university, experimental theatre lured her back to Europe. Her performance background has led her to studying carnatic violin. Now concentrating on writing and music, she plays frequently with seminal jazz poet Michael Horovitz and Indian violinist, B. J. Chandrashekhar. She lives in London.

ruth weiss lives in Albion on the Northcoast of California with her lover, artist Paul Blake. For more information check out the 1996 Contemporary Authors Autobiography Series, volume 24 (available only in libraries) and online *Left Coast Art Magazine* www.leftcoastart.com. Her most recent book, *For These Women of the Beat*, was published by 3300 Press in 1997.

Tim Wells lives in Stamford Hill, NorthEast London. He's old enough to remember Chairman Mao and edits the Rising series of poetry zines. He remains decorus when drunk and is nice to girls (usually).

Terence Winch makes his living playing traditional Irish music in the Baltimore-Washington area with a group called Celtic Thunder. His books include *Irish Musicians/American Friends*, *The Great Indoors* (poetry), and *Ancestors* (short stories). His work has been included in *Out of This World: Poetry Project at St. Mark's: Anthology*, *Before Columbus Foundation Poetry Anthology*, and *None of the Above*.

Rose Zaeske (formerly Barger) was born in Miami, grew up in Florida, studied visual art at the Corcoran School of Art in Washington DC, then lived in Baltimore, MD for six years. She has worked to express herself creatively in a variety of mediums, two and three dimensionally as well as in words. It is in the Baltimore/DC area that she has exhibited her painting and sculpture and had some small publications of her written work. In '96 she started reading at a few Baltimore poetry readings and in '97 experimented with writing in a theater environment. Since July '97 she has been doing her best to travel the world, with current plans to settle in Ireland with her new-found life partner, and to continue writing, painting, sculpting ... and whatever else comes up.

Fiction

Kim Addonizio was born in WDC and now lives in California. She holds a master's degree from San Francisco State University. Her first poetry collection, *The Philosopher's Club* (BOA Editions) received the 1994 Great Lakes New Writers Award and a Silver Medal from the Commonwealth Club of California. Her second book of poems, *Jimmy & Rita*, was published by BOA in 1997. Kim is co-author, with Dorianne Laux, of *The Poet's Companion: A Guide to the Pleasures of Writing Poetry* (Norton, 1997), and the recipient of two fellowships from the NEA, and a Pushcart Prize. Her book of stories, *In the Box Called Pleasure*, is forthcoming from FC2.

Roberta Allen is the author of *The Traveling Woman* stories; *The Daughter*, a novella-in-stories; *Amazon Dream*, an alternative travel book; *Certain People*, a book of stories (Coffee House, 1997) and *Fast Fiction: creating Fiction in Five Minutes*, a writing guide (Story Press, 1997). Recent stories have appeard in the *American Voice* and *Bomb*. She is also a conceptual artist who has exhibited world-wide, with artwork in the collection of the Metropolitan Museum of Art. She lives in New York City.

R.R. Angell ended a high-tech career to focus on writing. "Greyhound" is a "scary little story" that grew out of the frightening undergirdings of his first novel. He has degrees from Duke University, University of Maryland Business School.

Mary Caponegro is an Associate Professor of English at Hobart and William Smith College in Geneva, NY. Her work has appeard in the *Mississippi Review, Tyuonyi*, and *Conjunctions*. She has won the General Electric Young Writers Award "for excellence of achievement in fiction," and the Prix de Rome. Her books of short stories are *Tales From The Next Village* (Lost Roads, 1985) and *The Star Cafe* (Scribner's, 1990). Her new book *Five Doubts* is due this fall from Marsilio in Italy.

Billy Childish was born in 1959 in Kent, England. A legendary figure in underground writing and music, Childish entered the Naval Dockyard at Chatham as an apprentice stonemason after completing his Secondary education at 16. After an unsatisfactory stint at art school and several years of unemployment, he started publishing his gutsy proletarian art. Childish has published 30 collections of poetry and been featured on over 70 LP's. He continues to write and paint in Chatham. His first novel, *My Fault*, was published in August 1996. He is dyslexic.

Julia Duncan lives in Alexandria, Virginia, with her spouse, two children, a familiar, a demanding muse, a killer feline (the cat formerly known as Prince), and the dark creatures in the dim recesses of her mind. "Ghost" is her first published story.

Mary Halnon is a native of the D.C. area. She received her B.A. in English from William and Mary and her M.A. in American Studies from UVA. She teaches poetry and fiction writing at the high school level and currently resides in Charlottesville, Virginia. "How It Seems in September" is her first published story.

Ken Hollings is an expert on trash culture, weird science and the forthcoming apocalypse. His writings have appeared in numerous magazines and journals, including *ZG, Impulse,*

Anime FX, Active in Air Time, NME, Wire, Neon, Ten:8 and *CTHEORY* as well as the anthologies *The Last Sex* and *Digital Delirium*, both published by St. Martin's Press.

Stokes Howell's first collection of short stories is entitled *The Sexual Life of Savages and Other Stories* (St. Martin's, 1996). His work has appeared in *Grand Street, Exquisite Corpse, Sulfur*, and an anthology called *Angle of Repose*.

Kevin Jackson's forthcoming books include a dictionary, *The Language of Cinema*, and a collection of essays, *Invisible Forms*; he's also scripting a two-part documentary about Anthony Burgess for the BBC.

Shelley Jackson holds an AB in studio art from Stanford and an MFA in creative writing from Brown. She is the author of the acclaimed hypertext novel *Patchwork Girl* (Eastgate Systems, 1995), the web-based multimedia project *My Body: a Wünderkammer* (Alt-X, 1997), and *Stitch Bitch: the Patchwork Girl*, a essay/performance about hypertext fiction presented at "Tranformations of the Book" (MIT, 1997), an international conference. Her short stories have appeared in various journals, including *Black Ice* and *Conjunctions*, and she has illustrated several children's books in addition to her own, *The Old Woman and the Wave* (DK Ink, 1998). She lives in San Francisco, and specializes in lies and digressions.

R.A. Kapler works as a technical writer and editor. His last story, "Hallowed Ground," appeared in *Gulf Stream Magazine*. His play, *Live Oak*, won first prize in 1992 at the Florida First Coast Writer's Festival. He is highly inefficient but makes a great martini. He fancies himself a boulevardier.

Gregory Maguire was born in Albany, New York, received his Ph.D. at Tufts University, and has lived in Boston and Cambridge, as well as Dublin and London. He has been a fellow at the Bread Loaf Writer's Conference and at Blue Mountain Center. He is the author of *Wicked: The Life and Times of the Wicked Witch of the West* (HarperCollins, 1995).

James Mathews grew up in El Paso, Texas and now lives in Maryland. His stories have appeared in *The Florida Review, The Pacific Review, The Wisconsin Review, Carolina Quarterly*, and others. He is currently at work on a novel.

Jeff Minerd is winner of the 1996 F. Scott Fitzgerald Short Story Competition and recipient of a 1997 grant from the Maryland State Arts Council. His stories have appeared in *The North American Review, The Crescent Review, Wordwrights!*, and other magazines. He leads fiction workshops at The Writer's Center.

Pedro Ponce has received a Tara Fellowship in Short Fiction from the Heekin Group Foundation. He lives in Baltimore.

Lou Robinson was born in Delaware, Ohio and currently lives in Ithaca, New York. Her chapbook of fiction, *Extremes of High and Low Regard*, was published by *Top Stories* and included in the *Top Top Stories* anthology published by City Lights, and her novella, *Napoleon's Mare* was published by Fiction Collective Two in 1991. Other work has appeared in *Trivia, Conditions, Quarterly, f(Lip), Epoch, Tessera, Trois*, and in three short story anthologies by Crossing Press. Lou is also co-editor of *Resurgent: New Writing by Women* (Univ. of Illinois, 1991).

Elizabeth Roca lives in Silver Spring, Maryland, and is completing an MA at Johns Hopkins University.

Helen Schulman is the author of *Not A Free Show* and *Out of Time*. Her new novel, *The Revisionist*, was excerpted in *The Paris Review* and won a Pushcart Prize.

Marilyn Stablein lives in Kingston, New York, and is co-owner of a great little bookshop, Alternative Books. Her most recent chapbook is *Vermin: A Bestiary* (Reservoir Press, 1997). Other titles include *The Census Taker: Tales of a Traveler in India and Nepal* (Black Heron Press, 1985), *Instrusions in Ice* (Wash 'n Press, 1987) and *Climate of Extremes: Landscape and Imagination* (Black Heron Press, 1995).

Eugene Stein was born in New York City, attended Yale and the Columbia University Graduate School for Journalism, and now lives in Los Angeles. His short stories have appeared in *Harper's*, the *Iowa Review*, and the *Pushcart Prize Anthology*. He is the author of the novel, *Straitjacket & Tie*, and a collection of stories, *Touch And Go* (Rob Weisbach Books, 1997). Eugene had a story in *Gargoyle* 27.

Carolyn Weaver is a writer in D.C. "Celia's Bridegroom" is her first published fiction.

Curtis White was born in 1951 in San Lorenzo, California. His fiction books include *Heretical Songs, Metaphysics in the Midwest, The Idea of Home, Anarcho-Hindu*, and he edited *An Illuminated History of the Future*. An upcoming issue of the *Review of Contemporary Fiction* will be dedicated to his work. He co-directs Fiction Collective 2 and teaches at Illinois State University.

Artists & Photographers

Andi Olsen's computer-generated collages have appeared in many journals and on many book covers, while her assemblages have been exhibited throughout the U.S. and abroad.

Cynthia Connolly grew up in Los Angeles, California, moved to DC in 1981, and graduated from the Corcoran School of Art in 1985, "which exhausted my artistic brain and I didn't do practically any art until about 1992. I booked the club d.c. space for its last 5 years, from 1986-1991. I work at dischord records, which allows me to go away to do art stuff." Her photos have been shown at the Institute of Contemporary Art in London; The Fairy Grotto, Sydney, Australia; Washington Center for Photography, WDC; "Culture is our Business," The Centre of Contemporary Photography, Melbourne, Australia; "Ascent of Western Civilization: American Independent Music 1976-1991"; Thread Waxing Space, NYC, NY; SFSU, "Fetish," San Francisco, CA; Alleged Gallery, NYC, NY; White Columns Gallery Auction, NYC, NY; and in many other locations. Cynthia published a book in 1988, *Banned in DC* that is still in print and has sold over 9,000 copies. She can be reached via email at cynthia@dischord.com or at po box 9743, Washington, DC 20016

Connie Imboden was born in El Paso, Texas. She has an MFA from the University of Delaware. Her work has been exhibited and published extensively in the US and Europe. She is represented by the Walter Gomez Gallery in Baltimore, MD.

a different beat

writings by women of the beat generation

edtied by richard peabody

"Heroic Rick Peabody helps rescue the women of the Beat Generation from the neglect accorded them as being, in Joyce Johnson's words, Minor Characters. Hardly surprising considering the position of women through the ages. Yet, the women are there, responding to and adding special qualities to 'the call' . . . . The writings are provocative in themselves; they are indispensible for a full sense of the significance of the Beats in a world of men and women." —Ted Wilentz

"It is as if we were archaeologists encountering the long lost tomb of the Beat Women of the 1950s, covered with the desert dust of misogyny, business interests and indifference. But polish off the dust of male convention and what have you and the words are beaming out strong." — Kevin Ring, Beat Scene

"This well-balanced anthology, which should focus more attention on Beat women, is recommended for all literature collections." —Library Journal

"But A Different Beat is more than gals getting back at guys. It chronicles a time of enormous change for women in America; challenging the norms of their day, with painful, sometimes tragic consequences." —The Herald (Glasgow)

"A Different Beat reveals an alternative history of Beat literature, and is a welcome insight and long-awaited addition to the Beat Canon." —The Word

"A refreshing look at the contribution of women writers to the beat generation genre so often represented by Mr. Kerouac and his boozy boys club. . . . this collection provides an informative link in feminist history as well as being a powerful collection of work in its own right." —Tour

"There are some surprising treasures here." —Publishers Weekly

"A Different Beat is a fine anthology of writing by outcasts from a previous boys' club, the Fifties beats." —GQ Magazine

"...a mature anthology documenting the life of women in the Beat Generation with humour, irony and even tenderness." —The List (Glasgow & Edinburgh)

Serpent's Tail/High Risk $13.99   paper   235pp.   ISBN: 1-85242-431-1
www.serpentstail.com   Distributed in US by Consortium

Death in Equality

by

Lucinda Ebersole

"*Lucinda Ebersole writes like Janis Joplin sings: sassy, sensual, strong, and Southern. Like Joplin, her voice is truly original, one we'll be listening to, and savoring, for a long, long time.*"　　　　　—Janice Eidus

"*If you have a flair for writing Southern Gothic stories, but are smart enough to know that that literary cottonfield has been picked clean, what do you do? If you're as smart as Lucinda Ebersole, you construct a metafictional structure that will allow you to have your grits and eat them too.*"　　　　　—Steven Moore, Rain Taxi

"*Lucinda Ebersole has a gift for fusing twisted comedy with unblinking tragedy; this passionate interweaving of tales accrues a surprising cumulative power.*"　　　　　—Jennifer Egan

"*Relentlessly, Ebersole introduces one character after another and then snatches them all away . . . . They remind us that death is the great leveler: it brings everyone, whether young, old, white, or black, into that mythical state of equality.*　　　　　—Susann Cokal, Review of Contemporary Fiction

St. Martin's Press　　　$19.95　　　cloth　　　146pp.　　　ISBN: 0-312-15106-3

EXPRESS EXCESS

**ELECTRIC
CUTTING
PERFORMANCE POETRY
WORD BENDING
OFF THE WALL
LANGUAGE SHAKING
VERB OUTLAWS**

GARGOYLE
PAST AND PRESENT
ALWAYS AVAILABLE FROM
THE BOOK BAR

EVERY WEDNESDAY 8:30p
THE ENTERPRISE
2 HAVERSTOCK HILL
LONDON NW3

Please send (enter number of copies required in box)

☐ **Grandchildren of Albion Live on Cassette** Volume One
(95 minutes – NDC 23) at £8 each incl VAT plus 75p p&p

☐ **Grandchildren of Albion Live on CD** Volume One
(78 minutes – NDCD 24) at £10.50 each incl VAT plus £1 p&p
(CD differs from cassette in that all Ifigenija Zagoricnik-Simonovic's and Adam Horovitz's sets are omitted, as are Donal Carroll's second and third poems.)

☐ **Grandchildren of Albion Anthology**
(400-page illustrated – ND17-20) at £9.99 plus £1.50 p&p

☐ **Michael Horovitz's Midsummer Morning Jog Log**
(Paperback edition) illustrated by Peter Blake, at £3.50 plus 75p p&p

☐ **Midsummer Morning Jog Log** 700-line rural rhapsody
(Clothbound edition) illustrated by Peter Blake, at £8.50 plus £1 p&p

☐ **Wordsounds and Sightlines: New and Selected Poems by Michael Horovitz**
at £6.99 plus 75p p&p

☐ **The POW! Anthology**, edited by Michael Horovitz and Inge Elsa Laird
(108-page illustrated – ND21-22) at £6.99 plus £1 p&p

The POW! Anthology
An illustrated anthology of poets, singer-songwriters, musicians and performance artists of the world – to celebrate, commemorate and consolidate the first Poetry Olympics Weekend festival

Includes –
Damon Albarn
Simon Armitage
Sujata Bhatt
Nick Cave
John Cooper Clarke
Ray Davies
Carol Ann Duffy
Paul Durcan
James Fenton
John Hegley
Miroslav Holub
Nerys Hughes
Brendan Kennelly
Hanif Kureishi
Christopher Logue
Roger McGough
Adrian Mitchell
Moondog
Grace Nichols
Patti Smith
E J Thribb
Stan Tracey
Andrei Voznesensky
Heathcote Williams
Jah Wobble

THE POW! ANTHOLOGY

Order form to:
New Departures, PO Box 9819, London W11 2GQ

Name

Address

Postcode

I enclose a crossed cheque/postal order for

£ _____ to cover the total cost of this order including postage and packing, made payable to New Departures, to the PO Box address.

If ordering outside the UK, please double the amount for postage and packing. Allow 21 days for delivery (or longer for outside the UK).

For more information about: the contents of any of these titles; back issues of New Departures and Michael and Frances Horovitz's books (including signed editions); and/or readings and events to come, please enclose extra postage and indicate particular interests.

Box 5144, Hattiesburg, MS 39406
http:\\sushi.st.usm.edu\mrw

mississippi review

What was his name? *Jonathan could no longer remember. His reverie had so absorbed him that whoever it was waiting for him had slipped his mind. Rob. Tom. John. He had thought it was the dress guy, the guy who liked to have Jonathan waiting for him, all made up, dainty, girlish. It was the crucifixion guy though. That was why Jonathan had made his dash to the can. Had to get the nails off. Had to get the dress off. Had to get his head together and reverse the whole plan...*

"Tom Woolley's *Toilet* smacks of brilliance. His sinuous, newsy, mega-refined yet weirdly aggressive voice gave me an incredible rush."

— Dennis Cooper

"Tom Woolley is the kitchen god of bathroom sex. *Toilet* is filled with the liquid writing of human fluids."

— Kathy Acker

"Both cheery and cantankerous, the stories and rantings of *Toilet* are linked by a battery-acid tone and a smart, atomic energy. Tom Woolley is a wholly engaging original, and injects his humor with equal parts horror and sad, eerie nostalgia."

— Scott Heim

Toilet
by Tom Woolley

ISBN 0-9655915-1-4
$11.95

MENACE PUBLISHING & MANUFACTURE
BOX 23151 • ALEXANDRIA VA 22304-9315
MENACE@ZIPLINK.NET • 703.567.1068
HTTP://WWW.MENACE.COM

8 | OYSTER BOY REVIEW

print & electronic magazine of fiction & poetry

"A goddam kick-ass, teeth-cracking publication." Harry Crews
"A fiercely independent literary magazine." Shelby Stephenson

Issue no. 8, January 1998, Second Poetry Annual: Scott Baker, Hannah Bonner, James Broughton, Douglas Chambers, Cid Corman, Thomas Rain Crowe, Michael Estabrook, Keith Flynn, Ricky Garni, Larry Griffin, Damion Michael Higbie, Debra Kaufman, James Koch, Kevin McGowin, Alex McCardell, Thomas Meyer, C. Earl Nelson, Jon Powell, Mark Roberts, Michael Rumaker, Laurel Speer, and Jonathan Williams.

Upcoming excerpts from Ken Wainio's Starfuck & Michael Rumaker's Pagan Days.

Subscriptions: $12.00 for 3 issues. Single copies: $4.00. Send submissions to: Oyster Boy Review, 103B Hanna Street, Carrboro NC 27510

Find OBR on the web at http://sunsite.unc.edu/ob & on sale in DC at Atticus Books.

We're interested in the underrated, the ignored, the misunderstood, and the varietal. We'll make some mistakes.

SCHNEEMANN

MORE THAN MEAT JOY :
PERFORMANCE WORKS AND
SELECTED WRITINGS : REVISED
2ND EDITION : $35 DELUXE PAPER-
BOUND : 10¼ x 8½, 292 PAGES :
DOCUMENTEXT / McPHERSON & CO
1 - 8 0 0 - 6 1 3 - 8 2 1 9

SCHNEEMANN

Piglet sidled up to Pooh from behind.

"Pooh!" he whispered.

"Yes, Piglet?"

"Nothing," said Piglet, taking Pooh's paw. "I just wanted to be sure of you."

— A.A. Milne
The House at Pooh Corner

"The writer is **afraid** of feelings that are not suited to publication; he takes **refuge** then in **irony**; all he perceives is considered from the point of view of whether it is worth describing, and he **dislikes** experiences that can never be expressed in **words**. A professional **disease** that drives many writers to **drink**."

— Max Frisch, *Montauk*